CU00825846

HOW TO CHOOSE AND USE

TAPE RECORDERS

by

H. W. HELLYER

A.M.R.T.S., A.I.P.R.E., Assoc. A.E.S., M.S.S.M.

FOUNTAIN PRESS : LONDON

First published 1970 Fountain Press Limited
46–47 Chancery Lane
London W.C.2

ISBN 0 852 42430 2

Printed in Great Britain by
Clarke, Doble & Brendon Ltd., Plymouth

CONTENTS

PREFACE

CHOICE IS AIDED BY KNOWLEDGE. When we set out to pick a tape recorder from the wide and growing range available we must be guided by (a) the depth of our pocket, (b) the purpose to which the apparatus is to be put, (c) the amount of use it is likely to get and (d) what other equipment it has to match.

To complicate matters, there is the little woman's arbiter: 'You can't put that thing there'. And as important to the technically minded is the problem of accessibility, ease of adaptation and serviceability. All these things make our choice more difficult.

The following notes are intended as a guide to prospective buyers and a reference for users of tape recorders. They are based on a number of years' experience as an audio engineer, observations of comments in the salesroom and blasphemy in the workshop, and the help of many enthusiasts and friends in the ranks of the manufacturers, the 'trade' and the esoteric world of technical journalism.

Especial thanks are due to Norman Stevens, who has nagged me into writing this book and offered encouragement and advice, to Gordon J. King for helpful guidance, to David Kirk, Deputy Editor of *Studio Sound*, for assisting in the preparation of articles on which some of this work has been based, and to the following manufacturers or their representatives who have been unusually forthcoming.

BASF Ltd.
Bang & Olufsen.
Messrs Bosch (Uher Division) Ltd.
Multicore Solders Ltd., Bib Division.
Sony (U.K.) Ltd.
A.E.G. (Telefunken) Ltd.
Grundig (Gt. Britain) Ltd.
Miniflux Electronics Ltd.
Daystrom Ltd (Heathkit).
Tandberg Ltd.

I am indebted also to R. J. Lovell, Managing Director of Tape Recorder & Hi-Fi Centres, Bristol & Cardiff, for offering full workshop facilities and unlimited encouragement.

H. W. Hellyer,
Bristol 1970.

CHAPTER ONE

BACKGROUND STORY

LIKE MANY ANOTHER INVENTION, tape recording was proposed and described long before the state of technology allowed the principles to be carried into practice. Oberlin Smith, in the American Journal *The Electrical World* described the principle of magnetic recording as long ago as 1888. Nobody took any notice: there were no laboratory facilities to carry out the experiments he outlined.

The Telephone

It was ten years later that Valdemar Poulsen, of Copenhagen, Denmark, produced the first workable idea, and named his invention the *Telegraphone*. His 1898 model recorded crosswise on steel piano wire mounted horizontally on a drum and originally this was turned by hand. Later, Poulsen added a driving motor, and the version of the recorder marketed by the American Telegraphone Company in 1920 had two spools of steel wire and a 100-volt motor to drive them.

The snag was that the wire would twist, whatever precaution the engineers took, and at a velocity of 7ft. per second a tangle or break could be positively dangerous. Tape came later, first in the form of steel tape to eliminate the twisting of steel wire, later with Fritz Pfluemer's German patent of 1928, as paper tape with pulverised iron particles capable of being magnetised.

In those early days, the recorder was an acoustic instrument. The electronic amplifier had not been invented. Lee de Forest's triode valve which made this next step possible was first combined with the *Telegraphone* in 1912, when the Doctor was experimenting in all manner of ways, and wrote: '. . . you may be interested to know that in the spring of 1912 I used the tube as an amplifier in connection with the old steel-wire Poulsen *Telegraphone*. I am sure this is the first combination of those two great inventions . . . one of the first applications of the three-electrode tube as an amplifier was in connection with the *Telegraphone*.'

Poulsen's original machine required headphones, recorded crosswise, which limited frequency response, and its dynamic range was less than 20 decibels. It could not compete with the disc recordings then being produced. Nevertheless, the *Telegraphone* fired the public imagination and

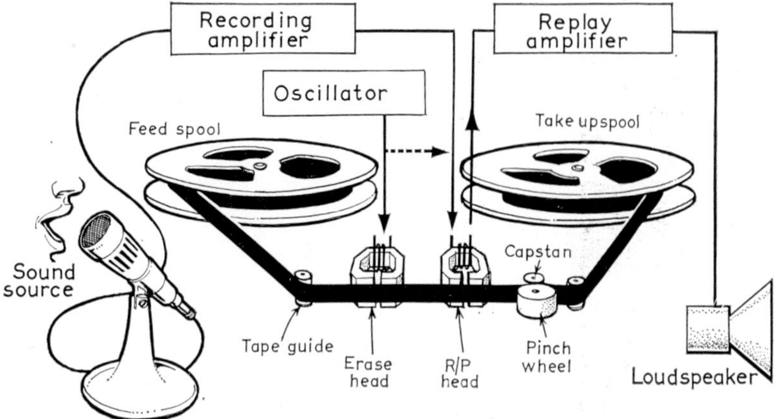

Fig. 1.1: Basic tape recording system. The tape runs from left to right, past an erase head which wipes off 'magnetically' all previous recordings, past a recording head, propelled by the pressure of a roller against the constant speed revolving capstan, to be taken up by the right-hand spool. The recording head may be separate, or may do double duty as replay head also.

The audio path is from the sound source to microphone, through the recording amplifier to the tape head, thence from the magnetised tape via the tape head to a replay amplifier and via a loudspeaker to the listener. When replaying a recorded tape, the bias derived from the oscillator is not applied to the erase head.

won the Grand Prix at the Paris Exposition of 1900. Technical journals enthused and newspapers gave it the usual seven-day-wonder treatment. In particular, the application of such a device to business was quickly realised, and where else but in America?

Poulsen raised five million dollars of capital stock at a par value of 10 dollars a share for its manufacture. His backers anticipated an office dictating machine. Even at 7ft./sec., the *Telegraphone* ran for 30 minutes. There was no rewind: one changed over the spools and started again. All seemed set for success. But in a parallel to John Logie Baird's efforts with television development years later, Poulsen's brilliance did not extend to the realm of business and the firm collapsed. A Danish firm which was organised in 1909 also failed, in 1916, without having managed to sell a single machine.

Nevertheless, what Valdemar Poulsen called his 'apparatus for electromagnetically receiving, recording, reproducing and distributing articulate speech' certainly worked, and he must be given the credit for fathering the art and science of tape recording. His brainchild simply took too long to reach maturity. Before the frequency range could be extended and the noise level reduced to manageable proportions, several more inventions were needed.

A number of companies in different parts of the world investigated the phenomenon of magnetic recording. In Germany, AEG, who later marketed the *Magnetophon* pressed ahead steadily. In the USA, individuals who were associated with large companies followed their own ideas. Leading figures in the field were Marvin Camras of the Armour Research

Fig. 1.2: Then and Now: At the top we show Valdemar Poulsen's original barrel-type wire recording machine, the 'Telegraphone', built in 1898, which is now housed at the German Museum in Munich. Although this model is operated by an electric motor, instead of by hand as first made, the fundamental design is in accordance with modern principles.

Underneath is a view of the control panel of a modern 'home studio', by no means out of the range of the keen amateur enthusiast. This one was seen on the BASF stand at the Hanover Fair in 1969. *(Photos, courtesy of BASF.)*

Foundation and Dr. W. W. Wetzel of the 3-M Company, now famous as the makers of Scotch tape. Brush Development Company, in at the beginning, continued to tinker with the new toys, under the guiding eye of S. J. Begun, while Lynn Holmes of the Stromberg-Carlson Company, the research team of Bell Telephone Laboratories and the Naval Research Laboratory went their individual ways about finding out all they could.

Significant Developments

It was from the last-named source that the most significant step was to come. Investigating the transmission of high-speed messages by wire, W. L. Carlson and G. W. Carpenter of the US Navy hit upon the technique of a.c. biasing, using high frequencies. Their patent, in 1927, described the application of high frequency bias to the steel tapes and wires that were then being used. Poulsen and his associate Pedersen had discussed the need for pre-magnetisation, but their ideas were based on d.c. bias. The effect of bias, and the various theories about it, can be found in the next chapter.

The development of the ring-type head (see Chapter 3) enabled tape speed to be reduced by the use of longitudinal recording instead of the cross-wise system that had grown up from the early days of wire magnetisation. In 1935, when the *Magnetophon* first came to the public scene, using a 'revolutionary' coated plastics tape, based on Pfluemer's patent, there were already several better quality steel tape recorders, but the plastics or paper tapes cut recording costs by 75%. They were not without their challengers.

In the twenties, Kurt Stille licensed a magnetic recorder based on the *Telegraphone*, using steel tape, and it was this machine which brought the next stage of development to Great Britain, where several films were made, using this type of machine for the sound-track. Gramophone records had been used, large discs which rotated at 33⅓r.p.m. (history repeats itself with the modern microgroove!) with the drive mechanism coupled to the projector.

Early attempts to record on the film met with little success, but in 1928 Fox Movietone brought out a motion picture which used a sound track beside the pictures, scanned by a photo-electric system. The cost of 35mm. film makes photographic recording an unlikely challenger to magnetic tape, but in the early thirties, when tapes had not been brought to their present state of advancement, and economic feasibility, James Miller, an American inventor, designed a method of mechanically recording on film.

Philips developed his system and by 1935 the Philips-Miller technique was in use in broadcasting studios. A 7mm. film strip carries a layer of gelatine and a deep black coating above this. The strip is run at constant speed past a chisel edge that is activated by electrical impulses and cuts a track in the black layer. The resulting transparent track is then scanned on playback by a photo-electric cell and the output from the latter can be amplified and replayed.

Not only was this developed to a fine degree long before magnetic tape

Fig. 1.3: The factory floor Then and Now. On the right—cottage industries for the pioneer tape recorder manufacturer, in the days when female emancipation was still but a dream. Compare this with the photograph below which shows part of the production lines of the present Bang & Olufsen factory.

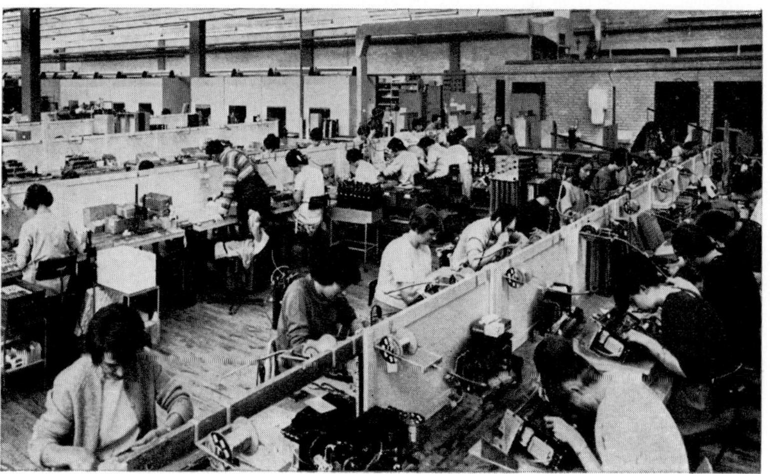

but also was it the forerunner of multitrack systems which made stereo a real possibility. As a matter of pure history, the first ever stereophonic broadcast of a concert was from the Dutch Radio Service in 1946, using the Philips-Miller system, with the transmission being sent out on two wavelengths.

Wartime Strides

Undoubtedly, the most rapid advance in tape recording techniques came during the Second World War, especially in Germany. Hitler's Nazi Party seized on the possibilities of the new medium and aided its development. Pre-war rivalry had produced such monuments as the *Blattnerphone*, the English Marconi-Stille, used by the BBC, the *Echophone* and *Textophone*, while in America, Bell Telephone Laboratories designed the *Mirrorphone*, for a while holding the field, with only the Brush Company and their *Soundmirror* to compete with.

In 1937, the Acoustic Consultants design for the steel-tape *Soundmirror* was put on the market, with Brush behind it. This was the first piece of magnetic recording equipment to be marketed commercially in the USA. In 1939, the *Mirrorphone*, Bell's speciality, caught public attention at the New York World's Fair, but few people visualised tape recording as the domestic entertainment medium it was to become.

During the 1939–1945 war, tape recording developed rapidly but unpublicised. In the USA some Defence work went on. Brush threw their large resources into magnetic recording equipment for the Forces, helping to develop coated paper tape and plated wire, while the Armour Research Foundation, hampered by limited workshop facilities but aided by a very lively knowledge of public relations which helped bring the medium to public notice, were later taken over by larger companies.

But it was in Germany that the development of the *Magnetophon*, and of oxide-coated tape, made the greatest advance in the shortest time. At the end of the war, when American technicians took over the AEG files for investigation, it was discovered that the machines then being made had a bandwidth of 10kHz, used a.c. bias and coated paper tape, suffered much less than the American machines from wow and flutter and had a very acceptable signal-to-noise ratio.

The United States Alien Property Custodian held patents on the *Magnetophon* and offered these to several large corporations, but was coolly received. It did not seem that tape recording was much of a commercial proposition. Ampex, then a very small company—as they boast, of garden-shed proportions—took an active interest. Rangercord Inc. and Magnecord Inc. also brought out professional machines.

Improving the Tape

The main drawback was still the tape itself, whose 'raven red' oxide coating tended to shed itself badly, and which lacked high frequency characteristics, so that high speed transport was still necessary for any

Right: The Bang & Olufsen 2400 is the latest addition to a long line of Danish models with many facilities.

Left: The Uher *Variocord* 23 couples a good specification with a reduction of frills to offer high quality at modest cost.

Below: The Brenell ST200/400 is a straightforward no-nonsense British machine built to high standards.

Fig. 1.4: Table models both attractive and professionally styled are exemplified by this group of contrasting models.

quality of programme. The relatively low output also impaired the dynamic range; poor signal-to-noise ratio could not be overcome entirely by the circuits then in use, although valved designs had reached a high stage of development.

To improve the coercivity (ability of the tape to take and retain a recording) Brush Development Company tried new kinds of magnetic oxide, but there were difficulties in erasure and it was left to Minnesota Mining and Manufacturing Company (3-M Co. Ltd.) to bring tape to something like the present day standards. The joke is that Dr. Wetzel and C. Hegdal, physicist and chemist respectively, were employed by 3-M to investigate packing and wrapping materials and their development of magnetic tape was in an attempt to improve the methods of adhesive wrapping then available. Modern tape recording was born when a Minneapolis radio dealer acquired a Brush machine and the enquiring scientists tried out the product they had invented but which had until then not been put to use.

As a matter of historical note, the first demonstration given by Dr. Wetzel featured not some world-shaking musical epic but a piece entitled: 'Who put the overalls in Mrs. Murphy's chowder?' From such trifles as this, and Thomas Edison's 'Mary had a little lamb', is the fabric of electronics history woven.

Although the Magnetophone had been the first machine to use coated magnetic tape, we can say that it took parallel developments by 3-M and BASF (formerly IG Industries) in Ludwigshaven in the use of new oxides and plastics tapes, with the important additional research into backing and bonding materials which allowed the use of finer oxides, to bring tape recording within the reach of the domestic market. In 1944 BASF began to use Luvitherm, an unplasticised polyvinyl chloride (PVC) foil and by 1950 tape recorders had found their way into many homes.

This small view of history cannot be left without a mention of another 'first' in which Britain played a part. In 1936, magnetic recording made its musical debut (according to the information presented by BASF) with the first 'serious' recording of the London Philharmonic Orchestra, conducted by Sir Thomas Beecham, made at Ludwigshaven.

Fig. 1.5: An eight-foot long console with tape recorder, record player, radio tuner and integrated amplifier, plus preamplified mixing unit, may not be an easy fit in the average living room, but this Telefunken assembly is produced from a number of separate standard units all in the high fidelity bracket. The heart of the ensemble is the Magnetophon 250 tape recorder.

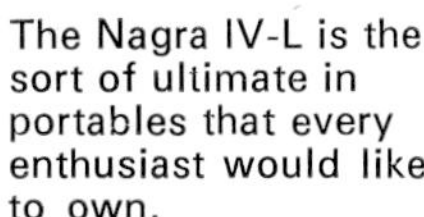

The Nagra IV-L is the sort of ultimate in portables that every enthusiast would like to own.

The Uher 4000L offers the most facilities in a compact package for its price in the world.

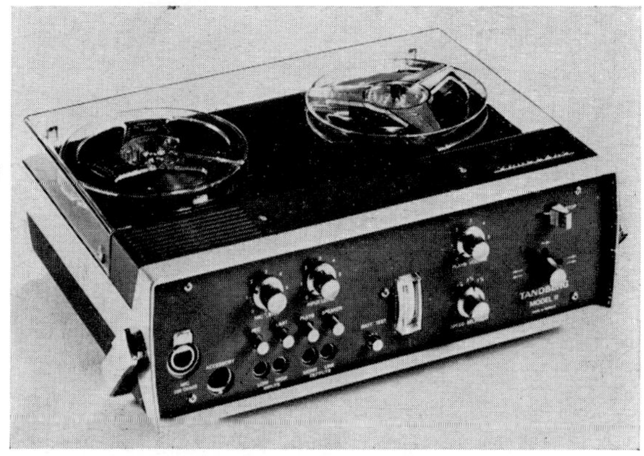

Special feature of the Tandberg 11 is its servo-controlled motor system.

Fig. 1.6: Portables-plus. This selection of high class and high priced reel-to-reel portables features specifications that make no compromises.

Computers awaited tape for their development, although the origin of the computer principle goes back to the Chinese abacus! First practical proposition we are able to note is the seventeenth-century 'Napier's Bones', a kind of slide-rule analogue computer. In the nineteenth century, Charles Babbage, widely regarded as the father of computers, put together some ingenious mechanical counting machines and Charles Xavier Thomas (France) invented a multiplying machine which led to comptometers. These entered the stage in 1885, in America, sponsored by a gentleman by the name of Felt.

But computers, as we think of them, had to wait until the late forties. The first electronic computer, the ENIAC, was introduced in 1947, had eighteen thousand valve circuits and a failure rate that was something like thirty per cent. In 1951, Remington Rand brought out a commercial model and from then onwards computers have not looked back. The development has owed much to magnetic tape (as compared with punched tape and other media still widely used) in conjunction with transistorised circuitry.

Fig. 1.7: Queen Anne never knew what tape recording was, but this Dynatron Hambledon audio furniture unit follows the style named after that monarch, thus neatly combining ancient and modern.

Enter the Transistor

The transistor made its debut in 1948, when Bell Telephone Laboratories in the USA published their researches, carried out a year earlier by Bardeen and Brattain. But semiconductors, of which family of devices the transistor is just one type, had been around for a long time. Dad's early tickling of his cat's-whisker to receive 2LO depended on the semiconductor.

Much the same principles on which the Bell researches were based had been accomplished by Lossev, a Russian scientist, with semiconductor diodes twenty years before, according to Victor Gabel's account in *Wire-*

Fig. 1.8: Tape in the office has advanced from the bulky dictaphones to the type of transcription machine that the boss can take home to use for pleasure. Here we see the Philips Model 86, complete with headset and foot control.

less World of October 1924. The use of the semiconductor crystal diode as an oscillator goes back even farther, to 1909, and Eccles—the man, not the place.

Modern tape recording equipment owes much to the development of the transistor. Ease of construction, greater reliability, reduction of power supplies, more sophisticated circuitry; all contribute to the portable machines at which we shall be looking a little more closely in Chapter Five.

Crolyn Tape

At the time of writing, great strides are being made in tape recording. Chromium Dioxide tape for instance. In 1968, at the converted hotel room which the Audio Engineering Society in New York have converted to a recording studio, the DuPont Company gave a demonstration of a new tape which they called *Crolyn*. CrO_2 seems likely to be the next significant breakthrough in tape recording, making the present cassette revolution a valid exercise in terms of quality as well as cost.

The basic material is derived at high temperatures (more than 375°C) from chromium trioxide, at a pressure of 3,000 atmospheres of oxygen. The oxide has a higher magnetic moment per unit of volume than gamma iron oxide normally used as tape coating. Signal-to-noise ratio is said to be 8dB better and frequency response extended by half as much bandwidth again. Even at the original demonstration a bandwidth of 20kHz at the low speed of 4·75cm/sec was claimed.

The main advantages are at the higher end of the frequency band, where more can be gained at lower speed by the use of improved tape. Extra cost of the tape is then offset by economies in tape length. Drawbacks at present are the differences in bias and recording levels for saturation, which prevent complete compatibility and mean that the new tape is suitable only for machines designed to use it.

And the factor of abrasion, though not stated in figures in any of the literature I have yet seen, is significant, especially when some of the domestic machines cannot guarantee a head life of anything approaching 1,000 hours. Latest news, which will certainly be outdated by the time this appears in print, is that the Philips Co. in Holland are beginning to produce CrO_2 coated tape.

The Compact Cassette

As Philips are also the prime movers in the cassette revolution, we can expect a good deal of development on this front. At present the limitation to cassette usage is the restricted frequency response that the slow speed of 4·75cm/sec imposes. Low-noise tape, a Philips and EMI innovation, has made a great difference to amateur recording enthusiasts. This has inspired the other tape makers such as 3-M, Ampex and BASF to market very much superior brands than were available a year ago and at reasonable prices. Here is one of the advances that has made cassettes a tenable proposition. The library of pre-recorded cassettes is already quite wide and rapidly enlarging.

Towards the end of 1963, Philips introduced a 'Pocket Recorder' which operated from an enclosed cassette, where the tape was spooled on plastics hubs and presented the oxide facing to heads which moved to meet the

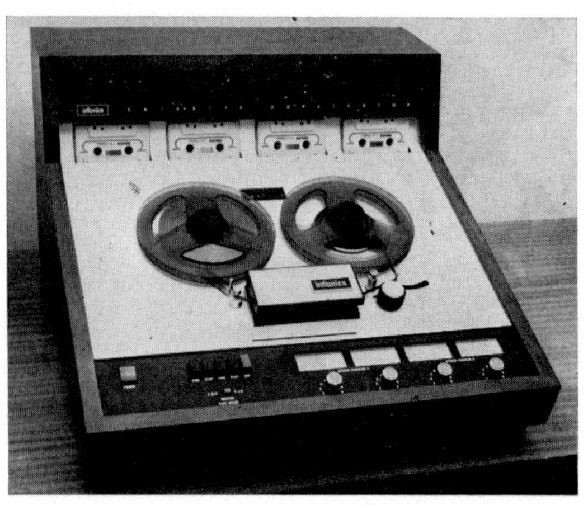

Fig. 1.9: The advantages of cassette recording are being rapidly exploited. This high-speed tape duplicating machine from Infonics will make four one-hour programmes (i.e. C60 cassettes both sides) in four minutes.

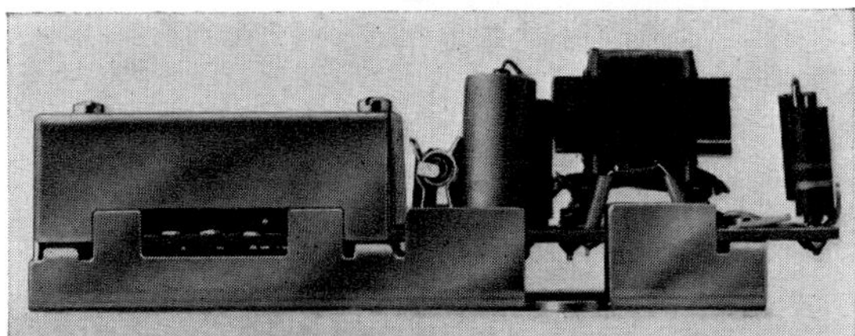

Fig. 1.10: Preamplifiers are neat, unobtrusive and necessary for the matching of low signal pickups to many tape recorders. This Goldring-Lenco unit matches a magnetic cartridge to a 'flat' input, applying the necessary RIAA equalisation. It can be mounted on the underside of the record player deck.

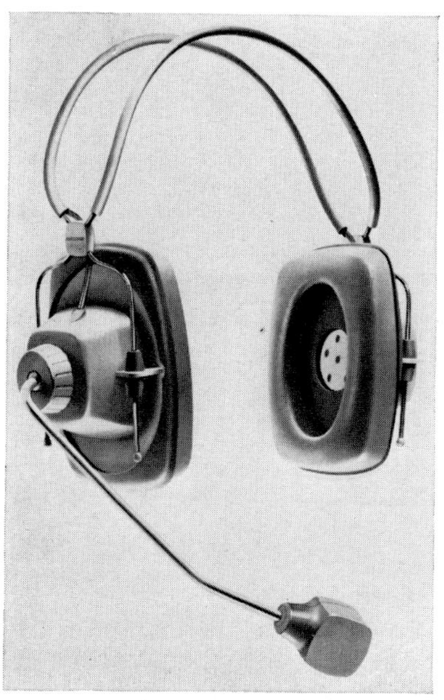

Fig. 1.11: Headphone listening is achieving a well deserved increase in popularity as stereo recording becomes more widespread. It will probably need a nationwide stereo radio coverage before the headphone boom really gets under way. On the right are shown typical modern headphones, made by Amplivox, a far cry from the bulky and uncomfortable pieces of ironmongery used to hear 2LO on a crystal set.

insertion point when the controls were operated. Space was saved by dispensing with spool flanges and allowing the tape spooled on one side to occupy the space vacated by the unspooled tape. Tape width, although nominally an eighth-inch, or half the width of the conventional tape used on flanged spools, is nearer 0·15in. (3·8mm.).

Playing time of the Philips Compact Cassettes was originally 45 minutes for the C60 cassette, playing at its only speed of 4·75cm./S., ($1\frac{7}{8}$in./S.) C90 (2 × 45mins.) and C120 (2 × 60mins.). Cassettes soon followed the expansion of the market and most cassette tape recorders in use at present employ a mechanism derived from the original Philips design. (See Chapter Five for further details.)

DC-International System

Challenging Philips for a couple of years (1965–67) was the DC-International cassette system, based on a design by the Grundig-Telefunken consortium. This used a slightly larger cassette, a tape speed of 2in./S. and contained enough tape for an hour's recording. Despite the advantages of a more rugged mechanism, a better cassette and, in the earlier models, a good performance, the DC-International cassette systems have not caught on.

There are a number of machines around with the larger cassettes in use, and to judge by their superior construction these should be in action for a number of years, but the pre-recorded library for these machines was never very enterprising. Famous names have to be added to the library list before public attention can be aroused sufficiently to make any such enterprise a commercial proposition. Philips were successful in doing this and the bulk of cassette recorders are, and are likely to stay, based on the Philips design.

Other Systems

There are alternative cassette and cartridge designs. The Grundig pocket notebook, and the cartridge systems which employ a single spool design where the tape is wound in a Mobius loop, are examples. Cartridge loading has proved popular in America, especially for use in the car, where

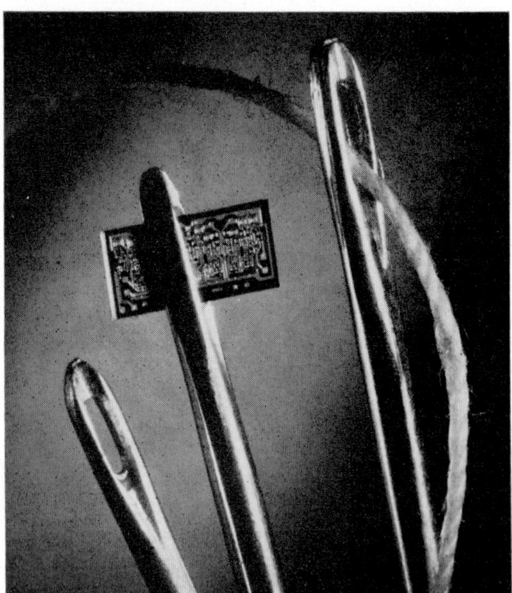

Fig. 1.12: In keeping with the trend of electronics, modern tape recorders are beginning to employ integrated circuits. A single IC can take the place of several stages in a circuit. This dramatic picture from Mullard, one of the leading manufacturers of ICs, highlights the smallness of the silicon chip on which the circuit elements are etched by showing it passing through the eye of a No. 5 sewing needle. The 'rope' going through the right hand needle is ordinary 40 gauge sewing cotton. The IC chip contains over 120 components!

Fig. 1.13: The BBC Radiophonic Workshop is justly famous. Creating special sound effects for countless programmes, it has been a great stimulus to tape recording enthusiasts. Here, Delia Derbyshire edits the tape while Organiser Desmond Briscoe stands by with the score. Below is shown the mixing console at the Radiophonic Workshop, a necessarily complicated piece of engineering, custom built.

one-handed operation is essential, and where the insertion of the cartridge starts the mechanism. A wider tape is used in this kind of cartridge system, with several tracks recorded.

A development of this technique is now being predicted for 8-track cartridge styling, using the endless loop. Both the cartridge and cassette makers, fighting a hard commercial battle in the United States, offer full recording and replay facilities and multiple loading. The size of cartridges, necessarily thicker than the cassette because of the $\frac{1}{4}$-in. tape that is used, has been whittled down to nearly the dimensions of the Compact Cassette.

Both groups of manufacturers have a long and growing list of recording personalities, and both can now add inserted radio modules which convert the tape recorders into a.m. and f.m. receivers. But the prime advantage of the cassette remains—at present—the ability to search and locate any part of the programme. The difficulty in achieving reversal of endless loop tapes has to some extent been overcome by the bi-directional design of Michigan Magnetics Inc. At the moment, the K-Set System operates on a double-four-channel technique, with shifting cassette heads.

Fig. 1.14: From the icy wastes in the picture above, to the torrid heat of the locale of Fig. 3.29, portable tape recorders have to stand up to a lot of hard use.

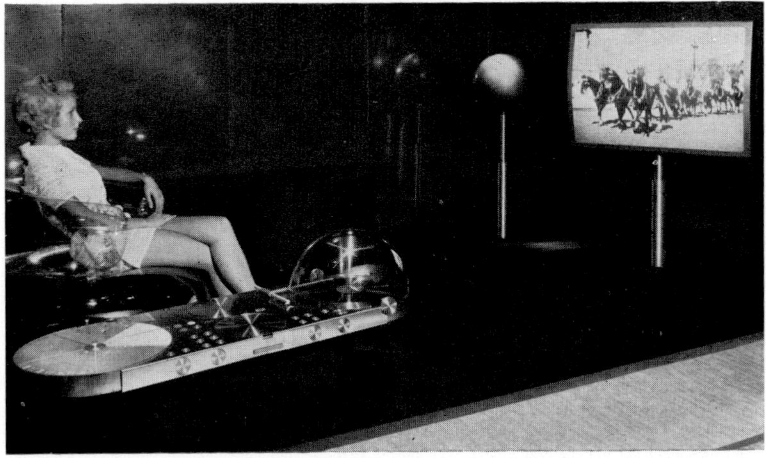

Fig. 1.15: Eric Marshall dreamed up this look of home entertainment for the 1980s for a British Radio Corporation trade exhibition in 1969. It is described as representing 'a threshold to reality', based on current trends in environmental engineering. We are reluctant to believe that the 7-inch tape spools (in the centre of the equipment console) will still be with us when that date comes round, but no doubt the ladies will still be the same shape!

Videotape

In the lucrative, competitive, expanding field of videotape, the war between systems is even more intense. There are basically three different ways to employ a videotape recording system. First, direct recording from a television receiver, to be replayed on the same receiver, or any other with a similar video acceptance. Signals are taken off at video level and used to modulate the VTR circuits. Secondly, by incorporating a camera. This is not an insignificant cost factor if any reasonable compatibility with off-air pictures is desired. Programmes can then be made and replayed at will.

Thirdly, programmes especially recorded for videotape (as distinct from those taken down and stored off-air) are replayed on special machines which can be added to the normal television receiver, simply plugging into its aerial socket. There is already a very large market in the USA for this last facility, and one Californian manufacturer is making four million cassettes a month.

Colour television has intensified the competition, and at the time of writing there is a great struggle to bring a colour TV tape player onto the market before the rival threat of EVR (a method of recording on film) which already has a library of 3,000 titles in its programme, and has issued licences to firms in Italy and Germany, and, for the player only, to Rank in this country.

Education and commerce already make wide use of tape recorders in all their forms and the near future is likely to see a growth of automation, especially in video tape recorders. Already, a Philips model which operates on mains and battery and is not much larger than a semi-professional audio machine is being used in classrooms and is offering a challenge to other systems, such as Sony, for domestic and business use.

What of the Future?

Any attempt to predict the future of tape recording must be subject to chance. Developments are coming along at a rapidly accelerating pace, on several fronts. We shall certainly see a growth of cassette (and/or cartridge) loading as tape quality allows a wider frequency response at slower speed, and it is to be hoped that mechanical design will improve to reduce the wow and flutter figure which, in this observer's opinion, is an even greater drawback than the restricted frequency response.

Automatic recording level systems require a lot of work before they can be as good as is needed for any type of quality recording. Some method of dynamic compression and expansion, similar to the rather expensive Dolby system used for good quality disc recording, may evolve in conjunction with alternative methods of level control.

Also destined, and again in the trend to automation, is a decided increase in servo-control. Details of this method of tape speed regulation are given later, but it is significant to note that servo control in quite complicated forms is already incorporated in domestic portables to overcome the effects of varying supply as batteries discharge. For videotape machines, this method of drive regulation is imperative.

The other type of regulation, i.e. voltage control, is an accepted part of hi-fi design, and most good amplifiers have some form of control and protection of vulnerable power amplifier transistors. We shall certainly see more of these protection circuits incorporated, plus various refinements that use sophisticated circuitry, currently restricted to professional machines, for tape position sensing and drive control and halting.

Some of these circuits we shall deal with in the appropriate section. At the moment, the aim is to lay the ground, standing back and taking a broad view of tape recording before looking a little closer into its principles, applications, design and maintenance, the subjects of the chapters that follow. To this end, I have included illustrations to this chapter which show the various aspects of the art and science of tape recording.

Choosing and using a tape recorder depends as much on one's appreciation of the scope of the instrument one is aiming to buy as on one's knowledge of its cost and relative performance. Too many tape recorders have suffered the unkind fate of having been used briefly, then consigned to some dark corner to gather the dust of neglect. The tape recorder is a versatile piece of electro-mechanical machinery. We shall be better able to choose what we want, and subsequently use it to its best advantage, if we know a little more about how it is made and what it will do.

Fig. 1.16: Tape recording is part and parcel of the space age. Even so, we were not sure which way up to print the picture above of the Apollo astronauts using a Sony TC50 portable tape recorder during their historic 'first man on the moon' journey.

The picture on the right shows the instrumentation tape recorder that travelled to Mars—350 million miles in 228 days—to record taped photographs on its 330-foot banked spools. *(Photo courtesy 3M Ltd.)*

CHAPTER TWO

BASIC PRINCIPLES

ANY DISCUSSION AIMED AT helping the prospective user to choose wisely and learn what goes on under the decorative covers of his tape recorder must begin with the theory of magnetic recording. There is no need for abstruse mathematics for the phenomenon of magnetism is familiar to all of us.

All we should require is a brief description of the process of transferring sound to the tape in the form of magnetic patterns, then replaying these patterns so that what we hear is near as we can afford to make it to the original sound—'. . . as we can afford . . .' because the quality of the eventual sound depends on the sophistication of the circuits, the mechanical accuracy of the moving parts and the most important of all, the magnetic 'truth' of the heads and the tape. So let's begin with a quick run through the machine, followed by a more concentrated view of this curious business of magnetism.

Basic System

Starting at the microphone (see Chapter 7) we get sound, which is basically air vibrations, changed into very small electric currents. These are amplified and processed to be applied to the recording head. Processed, because the magnetic system, as we shall see in a moment, is not linear. There are some losses which must be compensated before the signal can be passed to the coils of the recording head in the form of an energising current.

To overcome some of this non-linearity in the process, which would distort the signal, a high frequency bias is also fed to the recording head and the signal 'rides' on this to produce a varying magnetic flux at the point where the tape passes across the front of the head. The tape is coated with an oxide which will retain magnetism, and this flux imposes a pattern in the oxide. When replayed, the pattern sets up tiny currents in the coils of the replay head (often the same head as was used for recording, but see Chapter 3).

The currents can now be amplified and after correction again to allow for the non-linearity of the transfer process they are applied to an output amplifier which powers a loudspeaker and produces a replica of the original sound. The faithfulness of the copy depends on all links of this chain, but on none more so than the magnetic links of heads and tape.

Remanence and Coercivity

Two important properties stand out: the remanence of a magnetic material and its coercivity. Remanence is the ability to retain a magnetic 'pattern' after the field which caused the pattern is removed. This is the basis of the tape magnetisation function. The field is caused by the varying current through the recording head, and variation, in this case, is rather like a flux which comes and goes.

The tape is moving past the head at a constant speed (see Fig. 2.4) and virtual 'magnets' are produced in the tape oxide. These must remain, without self-demagnetisation or a tendency to 'fade' and the efficiency with which the tape can accept and retain the flux is a measure of its remanence. The magnetic conductivity of a material is called its permeability. Cores of recording heads or mumetal screens around the heads, for example, have a high permeability. This is tied up with remanence, as is coercivity, the magnetic 'hardness' or resistance to self-demagnetisation.

Thus, recording tapes have to be hard, retaining the induced pattern, and have a high coercivity, while recording heads must reflect the changes of current that produce the magnetic flux and change their magnetic force concentration in time with the alterations of current, so have to have a low coercivity. Remanence is measured in gauss, and coercivity in oersteds.

Process of Magnetisation

Much of the complicated physical jargon of magnetic laws can be left to the boffins, but even we humble users will benefit from a little fundamental knowledge of what is happening when the tape passes the head and is magnetised. Fig. 2.1 illustrates the process of magnetisation, where the cycle of growing and collapsing magnetisation is shown. The horizontal axis of the graph represents a magnetic force, H, and the vertical axis, B, is the magnetic flux induced in a material by that force.

If we imagine a completely neutral piece of material as a start, at O, and apply the magnetising force, the flux rises until at point A the material saturates. This means that it will not take any more magnetising force; no increase of flux is noted. But if the force is then removed slowly until it again reaches zero, it is noted that the flux does not retrace its path, but instead follows the curve from A to B. This value OB is the residual magnetism or remanence of the material being tested.

If the force H is now reversed in direction, the flux continues to drop from its remanent point to zero, but at this stage it needs a certain value of reverse force to have been reduced along the path BC. This reverse force OC is called the coercive force. Continuing to apply a reverse force makes the flux grow in the opposite direction until again a saturation point is reached at D, when a change in the direction of applied force will again produce a reduction of the flux to zero and eventually through F to A, but not via the original path OA. To revert completely to zero, we shall need to demagnetise the material.

Some of the preceding remarks about non-linearity become evident when we study this drawing. If we refine it a little and include the applied signal which has to produce the magnetic flux, we can immediately see that any attempt to make the induction curve a replica of the signal curve is spoiled by the kink at the middle of the transfer characteristic. Fig. 2.2 shows this clearly, and shows, moreover, that the form of the non-linearity is a severe third harmonic distortion. A little more study of the transfer characteristic shows that there are two fairly straight portions, where any change of input should give a reasonably linear change of output.

Recording Bias

Two ways of shifting the operating point onto this linear portion are open to us. The first is a simple application of d.c. bias, moving the horizontal and vertical axes of the operating point to the middle of the transfer characteristic straight arm (positive or negative), so that the input swing again causes a linear output swing.

The system works, but because the amount of the swing now available to us is drastically curtailed, the distortion danger at larger amplitudes is very real, any move in the basic bias voltage is immediately followed by a growth of distortion, and in practical terms a residual magnetism of the material is very troublesome, with attendant noise problems, d.c. bias is very seldom used.

The other method is an application of a high frequency signal, of con-

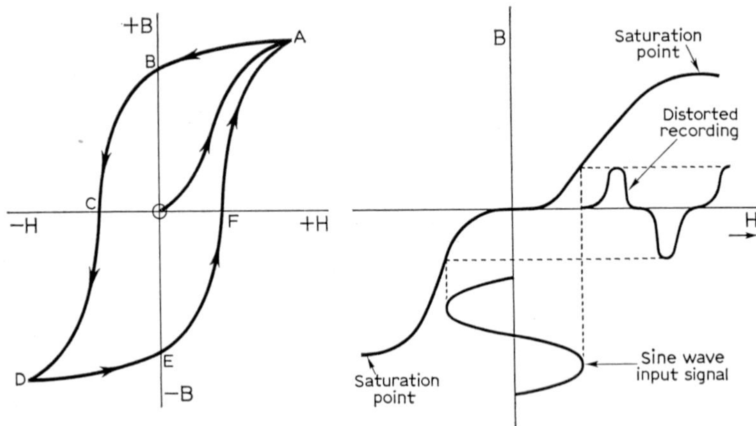

Fig. 2.1 (left): Cycle of magnetism, showing the relation of the magnetic flux (B-axis) to the magnetising force (H-axis) which produces it.

Fig. 2.2 (right): Non-linear transfer characteristic causes distortion if a sinewave signal is applied with the operating point at zero.

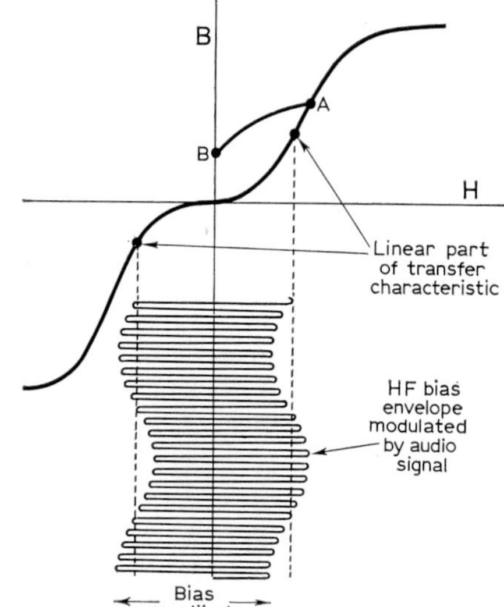

Fig. 2.3: The technique of h.f. biasing allows the reasonably straight parts of the transfer characteristic to be used, if the operating point is chosen correctly and bias amplitude carefully controlled.

stant amplitude, constant frequency and undistorted sinusoidal waveform. This has the effect shown in Fig. 2.3. As with d.c. bias, the operating point is moved to the linear portion of the curve. But now there are two operating points and the whole waveform is balanced. The result, when all is in order, can be a non-distorted transfer. But the choice of oscillator frequency and the preservation of waveform shape and amplitude are all critical factors in tape recorder design.

Action of Bias

To understand the action of bias fully it is necessary to look more closely at the way tape flux is caused and the way the magnetic field is distributed. On the tape there is a layer of ferrous oxide with the elongated particles orientated along the length of the tape (for longitudinal tape recording, as is used with domestic and professional audio machines: transverse orientation is employed with many videotape systems and with some computer tape; this is one reason why the purchase of 'job lot' cheap tape that may have been ideal for another application may not be such a bargain for your ordinary tape recorder).

The purpose of the orientation is to achieve a full density of the oxide layer. Random orientation would leave more space between particles. Each particle consists of a number of oxide molecules, and each can be regarded, for the purpose of our argument, as a tiny magnet. An unrecorded tape has these virtual magnets in random fashion, with no prevailing polarity, and if this is replayed the only result is noise. The tape is neutral.

In fact, a brand new tape may have a little higher noise level than one which has just been demagnetised by passing it through the changing field of a bulk eraser. The bulk eraser will also produce a lower noise level than erasure carried out by the circuits of the tape recorder, as more erase power can be developed—plus, of course, the bonus that the operation can be done in a few minutes.

When a field is applied to the tape, as when a signal energises the coils, these magnets are orientated in a common direction, the number of magnets that are thus forced into their new position (not physically, but as regards polarity) depending on the strength of the field, and the direction of polarity depending on the direction of current flow. So that a steadily changing current flow, as from a sinewave signal, produces a series of 'bars' of concentrated polarity in the oxide, across the track width.

This pattern can be viewed by developing the tape, and special instruments have been made for the purpose. (See Fig. 9.9). The higher the recorded frequency, the greater the number of polarity reversals and the closer spaced are these vertical bars. There is a limit to the concentration, i.e. to the strength of signal that can be applied, set by the magnetic 'saturation' level of the tape oxide. Tape flux curves and a more technical explanation of magnetising phenomena are given in Chapter 10.

Bias Level

At this stage we shall only need to note that it is important to choose both the bias signal and the applied audio signal very carefully to suit both the recording head and the tape. Any change of tape—even some changes within the batch of a similar brand and type of tape—should mean a resetting of the bias level for best possible recording conditions. See Chapter 10 for the details of these settings.

Unless the bias is reset to suit the tape, a tape recorder will only give of its best with the tape for which is is adjusted on leaving the factory. On many—indeed most—domestic machines, the user has little or no control over bias amplitude, and very seldom over frequency, so should accept the advice of the manufacturer when purchasing new tape.

In this observer's view, such a restriction becomes inconvenient now that so many good brands of tape are available to the enthusiast, and the one or two semi-professional machines that not only allow the adjustment of bias but also switch the meter to make such settings easy cannot be praised too highly for having incorporated this facility. On most machines, the settings are preset, by a variable resistor or capacitor, and it may be possible to make bulk changes to suit batches of tape, but this is all that is practicable with the average machine.

Bias Frequency

The frequency of the bias oscillator is important, and is seldom adjustable. The waveform must be undistorted and should be at least five or six times the frequency of the highest audio frequency to be recorded. Thus, for a tape recorder capable of recording 15kHz we would expect the bias

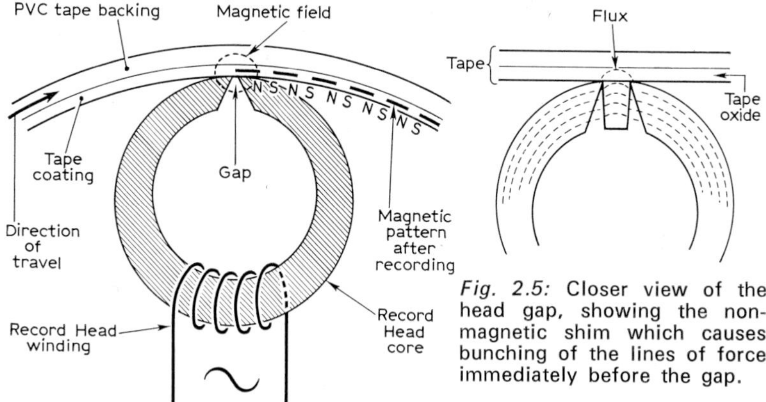

Fig. 2.5: Closer view of the head gap, showing the non-magnetic shim which causes bunching of the lines of force immediately before the gap.

Fig. 2.4: Recording methods produce a series of short magnets (actual length dependent on tape speed and signal duration—i.e. wavelength) in the oxide coating of the tape. Flux is produced by magnetic fields caused by signal currents in the head winding concentrating in front of the gap.

oscillator frequency to be between 75 and 90kHz. This is to allow sufficient reversals of bias field to occur in the short time of the flux reversal for the highest frequency being recorded.

For quite modest head dimensions, at normal recording speeds, the time any spot takes to pass the recording gap may be as little as a tenth of a millisecond. So any bias frequency of as low as 10kHz, for example, would distort the audio signal, preventing parts of it from reaching the straight portions of the transfer characteristic. Fig. 2.4 illustrates the principle of virtual magnet formation in the tape oxide and it will be noted that this magnetisation at precisely the spot it is wanted is achieved by bunching the lines of force from the gap of the recording head in such a way that a concentrated field is produced in front of the gap. This is explained in greater detail in Chapter 3.

Head construction has advanced to a high degree, and the precision of modern engineering plus the benefit of some latterly developed materials has enabled recordings of quite superlative quality to be made. The fineness of the gap, the shape and smoothness of the head facing and the magnetic properties of the head are all important factors in recording. It follows that such precise limitations must be conserved: a regular regime of cleaning, demagnetisation and an avoidance of such magnetising effects as rapid current changes or physical shock should be part of the enthusiast's routine. (See Chapter 9.)

Print Through

Having recorded the signal onto the tape, with the aid of a supersonic bias which preserves the shape of the audio waveform, we can now store our programme in the form of a reel of tape on which magnetic patterns can be retained (see note on 'remanence'). Poor storage, under adverse conditions of heat and humidity, will cause some of the surface magnetism to become blurred and there will also be a tendency for strongly magnetised portions of the tape (loud signals) to affect adjacent layers of the tightly wound reel.

Print through can be severe when tape is tightly spooled and stored for any length of time. For this reason, professional users will reverse and rewind a tape, spooling it for storage 'inside out and backwards'. This

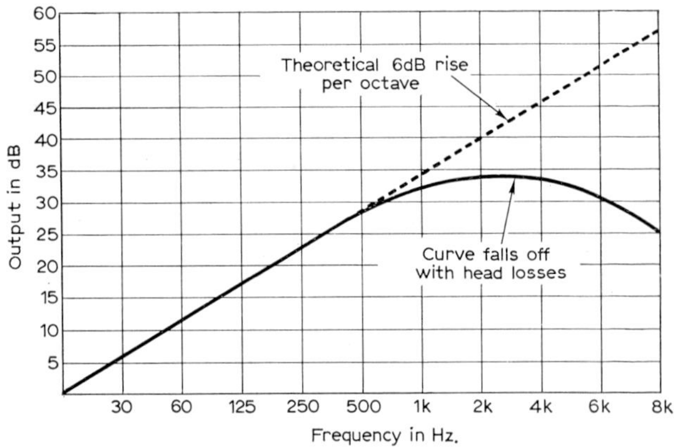

Fig. 2.6: The output from a perfect head would rise 6dB per octave on replay, but various losses modify the curve as shown.

means that each spool has to be rewound before use, but to the professional recordist, this is no problem. His equipment rewinds very quickly and under strictly controlled conditions.

The argument is that print through becomes most troublesome when the sounds are identifiable: they become a pre- and post-echo. By reversing the tape, the extraneous sound, if it occurs, has no connection with the immediately heard recording and is less subjectively bothersome. The ideal, of course, is to avoid print-through altogether, and one way of conserving tapes is to run them through the machine, rewinding at fast speed, so that no regular parts of the music are adjacent for long periods during storage.

For the recording buff with a reasonably sized library, this should be a regular routine, like changing around the wheels on his car to regularise tyre wear. (What do you mean, you don't do that, either?)

Limitations in Playback

When this series of magnetic patterns is passed across the face of a replay head, the very small magnetic flux on the tape is 'collected' by the head gap and produces current changes in the coils of the head, which can then be amplified by the succeeding circuits to produce an eventual replica of the original sound. But there are several limiting factors.

Firstly, the head gap, which is really not a gap at all, but a space that is filled with a diamagnetic shim, has to be smaller than the shortest wavelength to be reproduced. The polepieces have a lower magnetic resistance than the gap, which thus samples the density of the flux as the tape passes, but it is the change in flux which is doing the work, and if the change came within the width of the gap it would have no effect on the current through the windings and would thus be lost.

So, all other things being equal, the narrower the gap of a replay head, the higher the recorded frequency it can handle. Recording heads are not quite so severely limited and where there is a separate recording and replay head, the latter will have a narrower gap. As we shall note in the next chapter, there are also some other considerations.

The next limitation is that all frequencies are not reproduced with an equal efficiency. Non-linearity has been mentioned before: the replay characteristic, to which we shall have occasion to return in some detail, is a fine example. Instead of the signals recorded on the tape all producing the same effect, we find that for a given constant speed of tape travel, the higher frequencies produce a much higher output than the lower.

This is because the effective 'change' mentioned above takes place more often as shorter wavelengths (higher frequencies) pass the head gap. The current is theoretically proportional to frequency and rises at a rate of 6dB per octave. In practice, this figure is modified, and some of the head

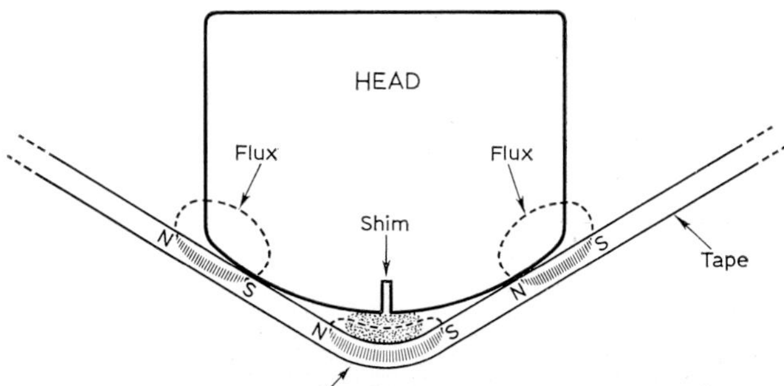

Fig. 2.7: Impurities at the head facing cause a loss of intimate contact of tape with head, and loss of response, more noticeable at the higher frequencies (shorter wavelengths).

losses mentioned in the next chapter cause the curve to droop at the higher frequency end in the way shown in Fig. 2.6.

One very obvious cause of loss, easily demonstrated by decreasing the pressure of the contact of the tape with the head, is the spacing effect illustrated in Fig. 2.7. Dirt, impurity, and a build-up of oxide particles will contribute to high frequency losses from this source. Again, regular cleaning cannot be stressed too highly as a recommended regular procedure. Chapter 9 treats this subject in greater detail.

Another cause of loss not so often taken into account is self-demagnetisation. The higher the frequency and the slower the tape speed, the nearer together are the poles of the virtual magnets recorded on the tape. Referring back to Fig. 2.4 we see that this can result in the magnetic flux flowing inside the surface layer of the oxide of the tape rather than from pole to pole of the head face. So again we find high frequency losses, and again we note that the slower the tape speed the greater effect of these losses.

Fig. 2.8 shows the frequency response curves for both record and playback amplifiers of a normal tape recorder, where compensation has to be made in the amplifier for the non-linearity of the recording medium. Taking this subject a little farther, we note that this compensation (called equalisation) has to be adapted to the tape speed. Fig. 2.9 shows the combined curves and in Fig. 2.10 we see a section of circuitry which enables these curve modifications to be carried out by switching.

Fig. 2.11 shows one type of specially constructed preamplifier designed to produce any shape of curve required during the replay process. More

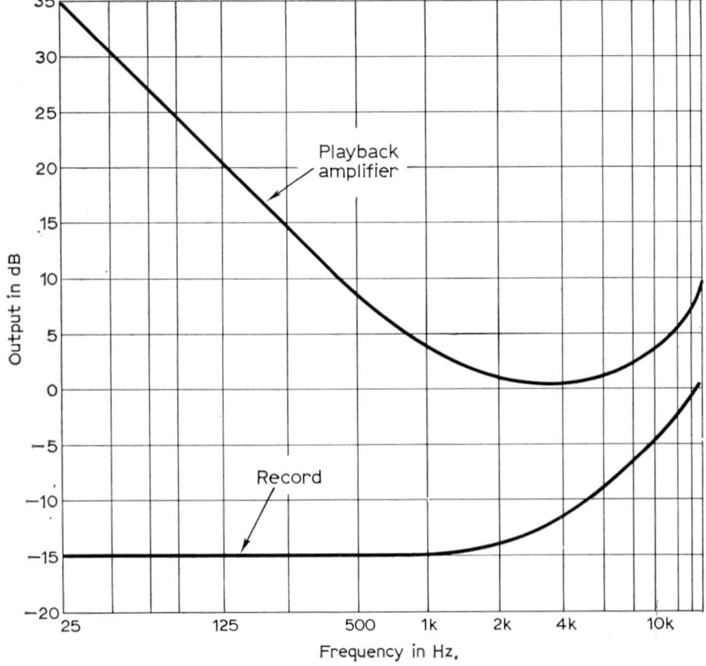

Fig. 2.8: Frequency response curves for both Play and Record amplifiers.

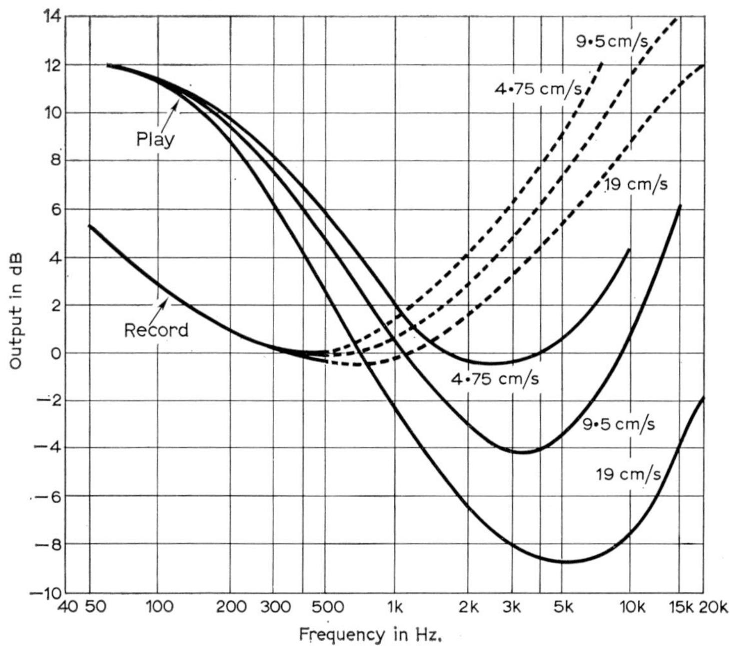

Fig. 2.9: Combined Playback and Recording frequency response curves, showing the equalising effect at different speeds.

Fig. 2.10: (a) record and *(b)* playback schematic circuits of typical 'signal-shaping' stages. (Ferrograph Series 6.)

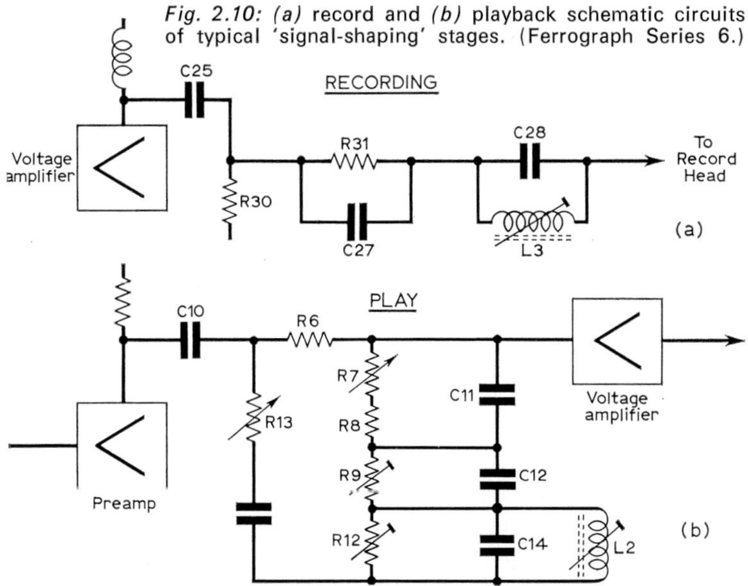

relevant illustrations and a greater detail of information on the subject of frequency correction will be found in Chapter 10.

Referring to these curves, we can see how the networks of Fig. 2.10 operates. During recording, the parallel combination of R31 and C27 (these are the maker's numbers) presents high frequencies with an easy, low impedance path. While middle and low frequencies are passed to the recording head by R31 and little affected by C27, at higher frequencies the capacitor comes more and more into use, and the result is a rising frequency characteristic. In other words, some treble boost. This helps avoid noise, giving the recorded signal a bit of a fillip in the direction where we know the most losses are going to occur.

During replay, R7 and R8 in conjunction with C11 and then R9 and C12 give some bass boost by shunting the higher mid-frequencies. But there has to be some limit otherwise all the treble would be lost, so L2, which is tuned by C14, acts as a rejector circuit to maintain the level of the higher frequencies. Because of the action of the boost control, R7 can be used as a bass control while the preceding series network contains a variable shunt of the higher frequencies, with R13 as treble control.

Speed Variation

We have seen that speed and close tolerance of head and tape contact contribute greatly to the correct operation of a tape recorder. The accuracy of the speed, as well as its mean value, is of extreme importance. Variation in speed results in a change in the wavelength of the magnet length recorded on the tape, or the virtual length replayed, and this causes a change of pitch.

Wow is the expressive term used for this phenomenon, and for a good machine the combined wow and flutter at 19cm./S should be well below ±0·2%. Short-term speed variations of between four and six times a second are most noticeable to the human ear, due to our physical structure. At this repetition rate, we can be aware of 0·2%. A good semi-professional machine could have a specification of better than ±0·01% at 19cm./S. For obvious reasons, the slower speed of operation will result in greater mechanical variations and we should take care when choosing that the specification includes a wow and flutter figure at the lower speeds. With the good noise figures we can now obtain by using modern tapes, and the fairly wide frequency range that even quite modest tape recorders can handle, it is imperative that we should not suffer in exchange from the annoying pitch changes caused by wow, or the harshness that flutter can inflict by rapid amplitude variations. There are a number of reasons for these phenomena, and ways in which they can be avoided are discussed in later chapters on design of the mechanism and its maintenance.

Of the tape recorders available to the man in the street, the most popular for many years was the single speed, half-track semi-portable, usually with 12·7 or 14·6cm. spools. More ambitious machines sported three speeds, 4·75 and 19cm./S as well as the 9·5cm./S into which convention had settled. Professional users insisted on retaining 38cm./S for the sake of its

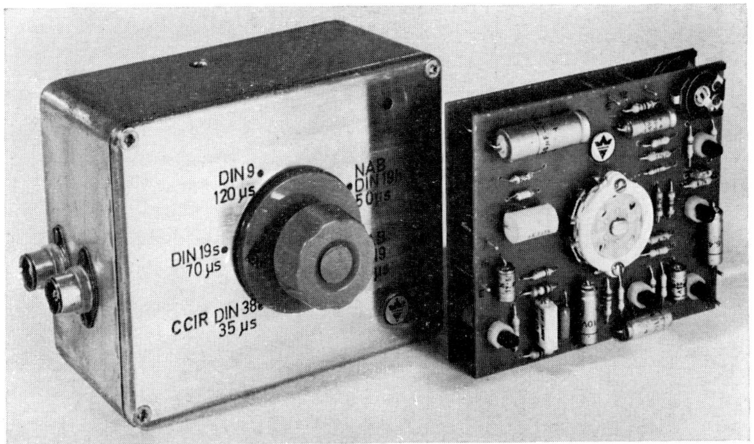

Fig. 2.11: Preamplifier by Miniflux Ltd. that can be switched for the equalisation curve that is required. An example of neat and efficient construction coupled with proven good design. The preamplifier shown is one of a family of alternatives, the Meg 3. Latest types employ integrated circuits.

better frequency response, noise ratio and stability characteristics, and suffered stoically the high cost of tape. Whereas the better domestic machines used 17·7cm. spools, professional users required 26·7cm.—no doubt one factor was that many programmes could not be taped without the use of the larger spool.

Today, we already have recordings adequate for home entertainment on cassetted machines running at 4·75cm./S. With low-noise tape which most makers produce, and a mid-price machine running at 9·5cm./S, it should be possible to approach what five years ago would have been regarded as professional standards. What the future brings, time alone will tell, but all the portents augur well.

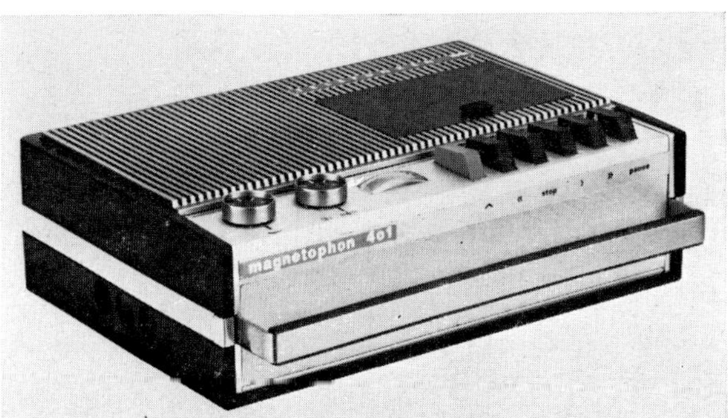

Fig. 2.12: Simplicity and ease of operation were two of the prime factors in the design of this Telefunken cassette tape recorder.

CHAPTER THREE

HEADS AND GAPS

IT MAY BE AN ANATOMICAL ABSURDITY, but to the tape recording buff the statement 'the head is the heart of a tape recorder' begins to make some sense. All depends on it: the highest frequency you are going to be able to record, the amount of signal you are going to be able to handle, the noise level that will affect the dynamic range of playback—all require that the record, replay and erase heads shall fulfil certain physical and electrical characteristics. In the last chapter we touched briefly on some of these. Now is the time for us to look a little more closely into the subject.

To recap: A three-head tape recorder will have first the erase head, which removes previous recordings by dispersing the pattern of recorded magnetism into a random form; a recording head, which produces a magnetic flux at the point where the tape passes the gap in the front facing, and a replay head which reads off the magnetic pattern on the tape, made by the recording head, to convert this to electrical signals for amplification.

In addition to this, we may find a head especially designed to apply the bias waveform separately, using the so-called cross-field system. Each of these heads has different design parameters according to its function. For the purposes of explanation it is easier to start with the recording head.

Filling the Gap

In Chapter 2 we showed how the magnetic flux was formed and the resultant 'magnets' in the tape oxide. Fig. 3.1 shows the flux lines in the structure of the head itself and the effect of putting a diamagnetic shim in the airgap between the poles, forcing the flux outwards in a concentrated field. Although our drawing shows a sizeable shim, and some of the older heads did indeed have shims that were plainly visible, modern techniques consist of butting the edges of poles together with only a very thin film of sprayed paramagnetic material. Where shims are washer-like, the material used is often gold or phosphor bronze. In principle, these shims only aid the mechanical function, filling what would electrically have to be an air gap—which is a physical impossibility, for an actual gap would very quickly get filled with tape oxide and dirt.

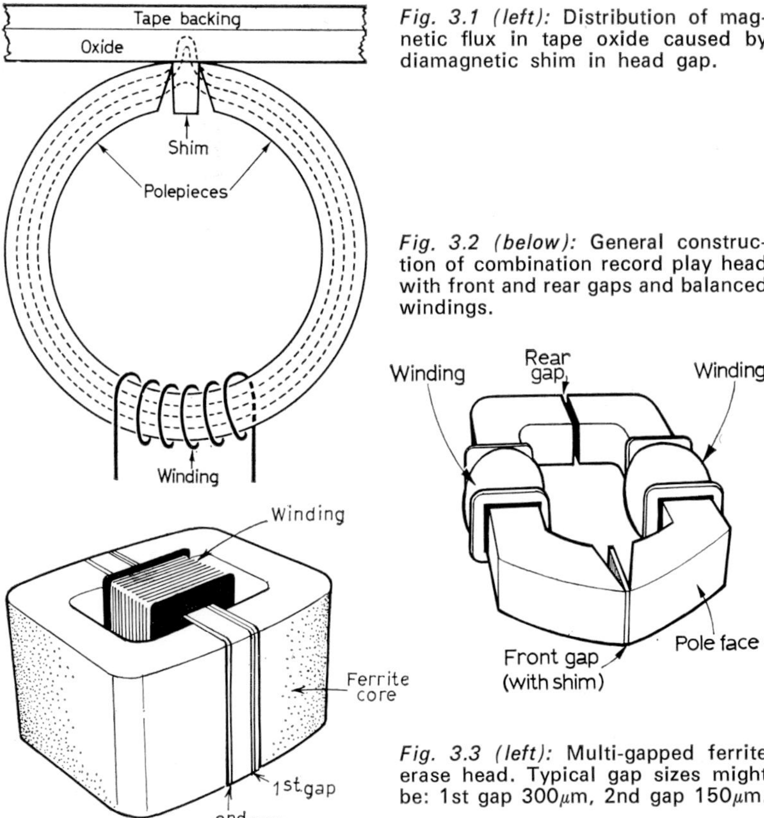

Fig. 3.1 (left): Distribution of magnetic flux in tape oxide caused by diamagnetic shim in head gap.

Fig. 3.2 (below): General construction of combination record play head with front and rear gaps and balanced windings.

Fig. 3.3 (left): Multi-gapped ferrite erase head. Typical gap sizes might be: 1st gap 300μm, 2nd gap 150μm.

The head is made from pole pieces which may be laminations or in some special cases a solid block. Mass production of heads demands a solid frontal portion, and this has become common practice. When a stack of laminations is built up to give a determined track width the irregularities at the edge of the lamination can distort the shim, which is very thin. In poor cases, increases of the effective gap length by a factor of 2 or 3 have been noted, even though all dimensions appeared to be accurate.

In making the edges of the pole-pieces mate, some very precise machining is required, and it is as much this factor as any other which puts up the price of a good head. You can buy a replay head from a 'spare parts' store for as little as a pound, but any pretension to quality will multiply the price by ten at least. Not only do the precisely vertical edges have to mate accurately, but when more than one track is used, and a stacked construction is necessary, the gaps must be exactly in line—another engineering feat.

Head Construction

Ten years ago a typical head construction specification would have been for a stack of ring-shaped laminations, each 5-thousandths of an inch thick. The thinner the lamination, the better the protection against eddy-currents, but the more difficult the maintenance of its proportions. Material of the laminations is often of Mumetal or Permalloy or some other high permeability nickel-iron alloy. This is necessary to obtain the flux concentration of high definition, and all is aimed at a reduction of reluctance.

In the older heads, the non-magnetic shim between 1 and $1\frac{1}{2}$ thousandth of an inch thick was often made from beryllium copper because of its relative hardness, which is greater than that of the polepieces. As the tape is in contact with the polepieces for a few millimetres on each side of the gap spacer, wear will tend to be uneven and some quite curious results could be seen when older heads became abraded.

The rear gap is often introduced in the ring-core to aid the concentration of the magnetic field. By separating the poles at the rear by another non-magnetic shim, perhaps ten times as wide as that of the important front gap, the relationship between the current in the energising coils and the flux at the gap is kept more nearly linear. One factor that limits the recording current is the saturation specification of the head, which is determined by the material and construction of the polepieces, and, to some extent, by their screening.

Coils are wound around the arms of the pole-pieces (not necessarily circular in plan, though still theoretically a ring-core construction, but with straight sidearms to facilitate construction). The winding must be carefully balanced to reduce hum and if the impedance of the whole head is low the current should be fairly independent of signal frequency. Low impedance heads will also have a resonant frequency, determined by the self-inductance and distributed capacitance, higher than the bias frequency, which helps prevent some losses.

Replay Heads

Basic construction of magnetic heads has not changed much since tape recordings began—and even the older machines that used steel wire as their medium employed similar heads. The basic requirements for a playback head are much as for a recording head, except that the gap dimensions must be smaller for a standard of efficiency that is similar, but as the signals that the playback head must handle are smaller, all the design factors that needed such care in the making of a recording head need even more attention when a replay head is being made.

Polepiece construction may be slightly different, so that the height of the gap is as small as possible, allowing for some spread of flux linkages to read off the track width accurately. Impedance may be high to obtain the maximum output voltage, but modern trends are for low impedance heads to be used, both because they have the advantages previously outlined and because they can be matched very accurately for low-noise performance

Fig. 3.4: A head block containing erase head and combination record/play head, with stacked windings.

Fig. 3.5: Ring-type mumetal heads (Revox style) with the mounting plate used as a datum. Note the precise adjustments and the rugged construction.

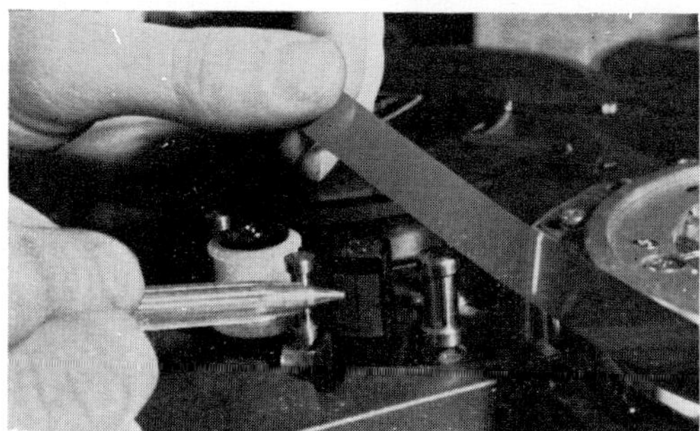

Fig. 3.6: The front gap is very evident in this study of a full-track erase head ($\frac{1}{2}$-inch tape) on the Sony CV2000B video tape recorder.

by transistorised input circuits. For many years, some better class manufacturers employed low impedance heads matched into step-up transformers and are now enjoying the advantage of a direct match to later types of circuitry by dispensing with this matching device.

Modern replay heads are made from alloys with permeability figures of hundreds of thousands, such as Alphenol. This allows the free field in a recorded signal to seek the easy path, the tape head, which is in the ratio of several thousand to one better than air. In practice, by the time the polepieces have been machined, ground, polished and fitted, this ratio is reduced by four or five times. There is little we can do about this, but mention of the fact should help stress that the greatest possible care should be taken with treatment of heads. They are delicate pieces of equipment for all their seeming ruggedness.

Effective Gap

Once or twice the term 'effective gap' has crept into the text, and the implication that this differs from the actual physical dimensions needs

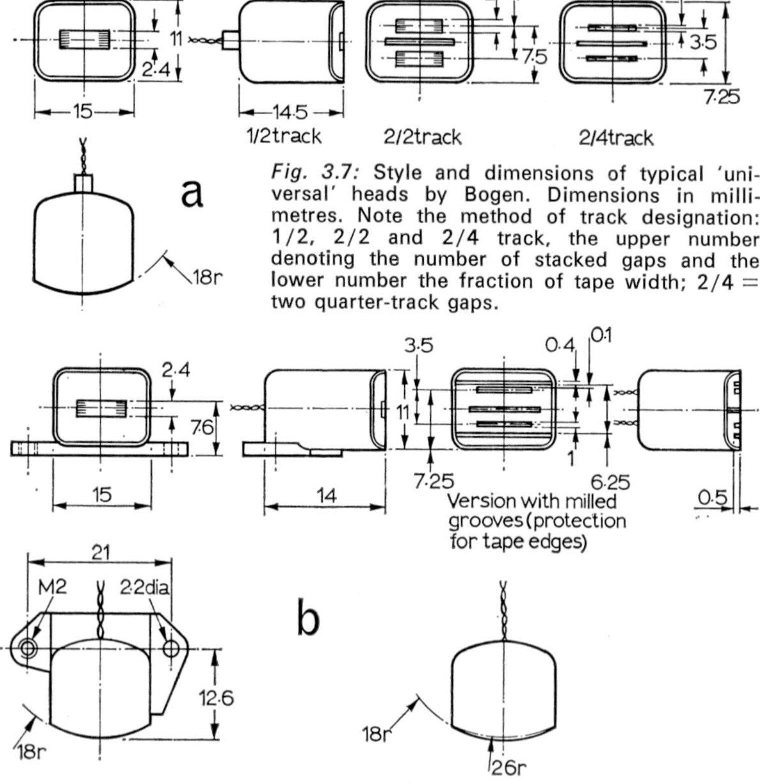

Fig. 3.7: Style and dimensions of typical 'universal' heads by Bogen. Dimensions in millimetres. Note the method of track designation: 1/2, 2/2 and 2/4 track, the upper number denoting the number of stacked gaps and the lower number the fraction of tape width; 2/4 = two quarter-track gaps.

Fig. 3.8: Quarter-track stereo heads on the Sony TC250 tape deck.

to be explained. The physical gap length is determined by the thickness of the shim or sprayed layer of filler between the polepieces. The effective gap length is a modification of the actual length due to construction, material and design, and may be twice the physical gap length. This figure will not be seen on specifications, but is important. Reputable makers will supply sufficient correlating data for the effective gap to be calculated.

When the effective gap equals the tape wavelength (determined by signal frequency and rate of tape movement) there will be no flux linkage with the core (for a playback head). The replay process depends on flux change. The greater the rate of change of flux lines, the larger the output from the replay head. Flux lines change polarity when the sinewave crosses the zero line.

The higher the recorded frequency, the more often this change occurs and the greater the output: basically, this is the reason for the 6dB per octave slope we have already noted as a tape recording replay characteristic. If the wavelength of the recorded frequency is too short, this flux change cannot produce a magnetic effect at the gap, and the windings will not register the change as a resultant current. So frequencies higher than those with a wavelength equal to the gap length will not be reproduced—in theory.

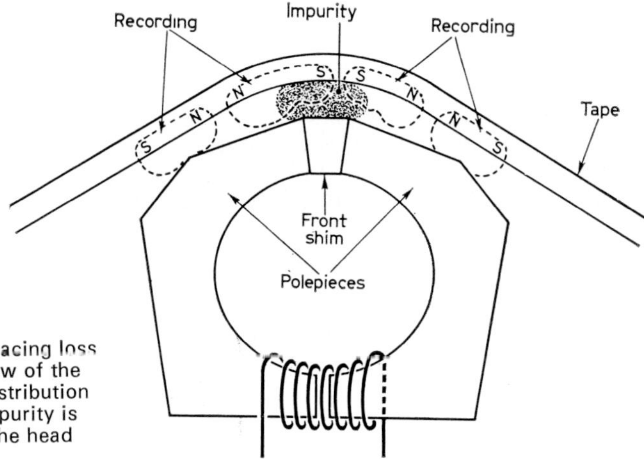

Fig. 3.9: Spacing loss Stylised view of the tape flux distribution when an impurity is present at the head gap.

In practice, the situation is not even as good as this: frequencies with a wavelength shorter than three times the true gap length are seldom recorded and reproduced with any guarantee of fidelity. To record higher frequencies than can usefully be handled by the head/amplifier system means that an excessive correction is needed, and the noise problem again rears its ugly head.

The foregoing underlines the absolute necessity to reduce the replay

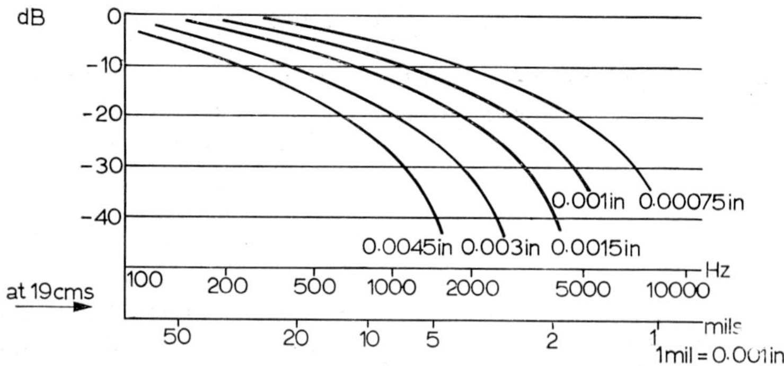

Fig. 3.10: Spacing loss. Showing the attenuation at the higher frequencies caused by impurities of varying depth, with the relationship with signal wavelength shown by the lower line, where wavelength is plotted in mils.

head gap to the smallest possible dimensions. Unfortunately, there comes a limit when the efficiency of such a narrow gap is impaired. When there is no flux linkage with the head core because the effective gap equals a recorded wavelength, and then the poles are brought closer together by whatever means, there can be a shunting effect of the flux lines both across the back of the gap, from pole to pole, and across the depth of the gap.

To circumvent this, some makers reduce the depth by angling the pole edge to produce a knife or wedge-like approach towards the gap, but this only results in a more rapid collapse of the head facing when abrasion occurs—a characteristic of some imported tape recorders. To overcome this one or two designers have employed angled poles that present a fairly

Fig. 3.11 (top right): Bosch employ a fixed head positioning in their Uher *Variocord* designs, with diecast assemblies containing alternative heads and track switching.

Fig. 3.12 (centre right): No complaints about accessibility here. The only bother—if you look really closely—is that length of stop foil that has jammed across the head facing. Infinite spacing loss?

Fig. 3.13 (bottom right): Relatively fine dimensions are employed on helical scan video tape recorders, where the heads rotate within a drum in which a slot is cut. These Sony heads are quartz, turning 25 times a second while the tape moves past at 19cm/S.

full mechanical face to the tape, but a sharp magnetic angle. These have necessarily a rounded contour and the depth between the tape contact area and the rear of the gap (i.e. depth) is reduced. This increases efficiency, but costs more to produce.

Gap fillers for such heads may be as small as 0·0001 inches and at this fineness it does not really matter whether metallic fillers or glass, mica or other substances with a good coefficient of friction, are used. Very thin metal foil would not have the eddy current features that cause such trouble at replay frequencies, anyway, so various ruses are employed, including a material such as bismuth at the rear of the gap, which has a negative magnetic figure and which tends again to concentrate the flux.

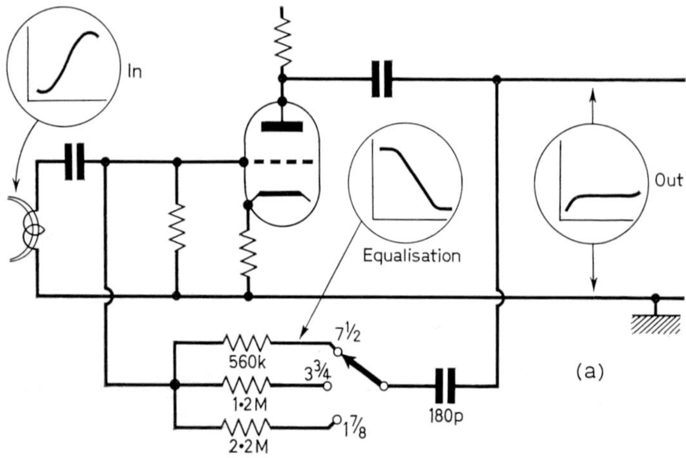

Fig. 3.14: (a) equalising circuit of a valved preamplifier, *(b)* simple matching with R1 stabilising the input stage is sometimes sufficient with low impedance transistor circuits, but *(c)* a direct-coupled design with stablisation and adjustment of bypass capacitor for the required turnover frequency may be used.

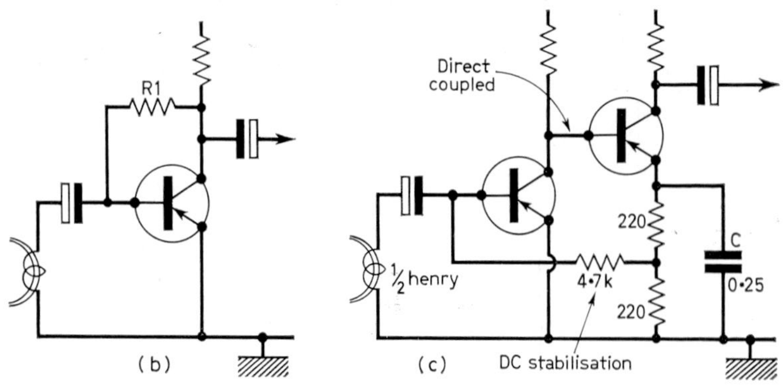

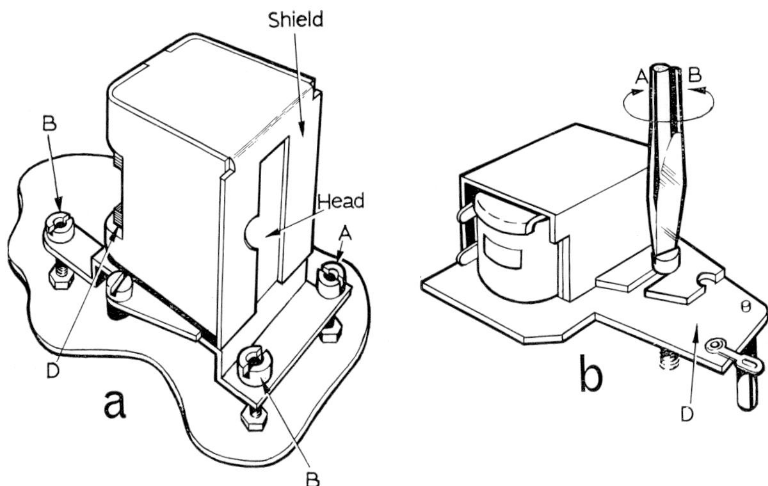

Fig. 3.15: Two methods of head mounting, used by Philips. Details of adjustment are given in the text.

Erase Heads

Many of the things that restricted the design of replay and recording heads to a definite pattern also apply to erase heads, with some important differences. These are that the gap need not be so fine, and indeed must be of sufficient dimensions to produce the varying field (see previous notes on random magnetisation) over the magnetic reversals of the highest frequency at the highest speed (i.e. the shortest wavelength) that the record and replay system with which it is associated has to handle.

Each point in the recorded tape has to receive as many reversals of flux as possible to achieve a deep erase. Depth of erase can be judged by listening to a new tape, or a bulk-erased tape, then recording this with no signal and listening to the difference in noise level. With a good machine,

Fig. 3.16: Incorrect azimuth adjustment results in an increase in the effective gap width and consequently losses more marked at higher frequencies. The effect is less with a quarter-track head.

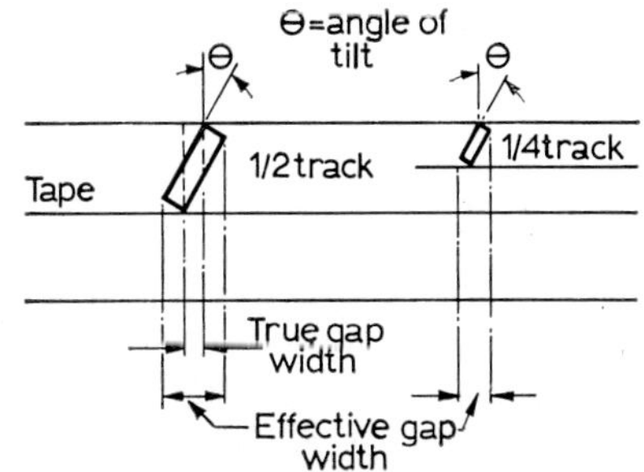

it should be quite inaudible. Too often, there is a discernible rise in the 3–5kHz region, resulting in hiss.

Gap widths may be as much as $1\frac{1}{2}$ thou' for normal erase heads, and it is not uncommon to see double-gapped erase heads, such as in Fig. 3.3, where the first gap is quite large and the second more concentrated, to obtain the necessary depth of erasure. It can be shown in the laboratory that shortly after leaving an erasing alternating field, the original recording tends to recover, and the second gap effectively obliterates this 'ghost' recording.

Because of the high reluctance of the wide front gap it is not normally necessary to have a rear gap as well in the ring-type heads now used for erasure, but what the future will bring, this prophet would be loath to predict. In the hi-fi field, at the time of writing, all the emphasis is on the reduction of noise and decrease of distortion, so we may yet see precisely engineered, multigapped, erase heads.

Pole pieces at present are mainly ferrite, with beryllium copper shims, and choice of material may be dictated as much by heat considerations as any other. With the large currents required for erasure, at the frequencies employed (remember that the oscillator supplying both bias and erase has to be several times the frequency of the highest note we want to be able to record) r.f. heating is a real problem for the designer. The worst possible

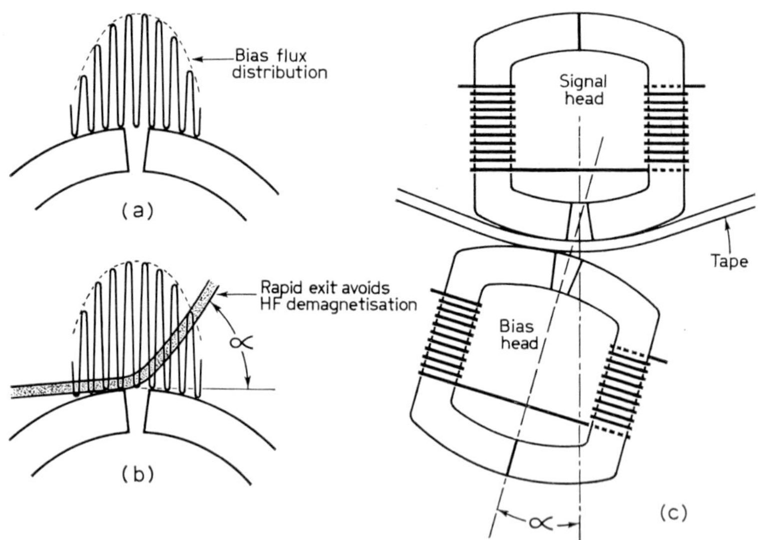

Fig. 3.17: Basic reason for a crossfield bias head. *(a)* normal bias flux distribution, cone-shaped in front of gap, tends to self-erase higher frequencies as the recorded portion of the tape leaves the trailing edge of the gap, *(b)* a rapid tape exit would avoid h.f. demagnetisation, but is impractical, *(c)* accurate placing of the bias head, with separate construction, concentrates magnetic field exactly where it is wanted.

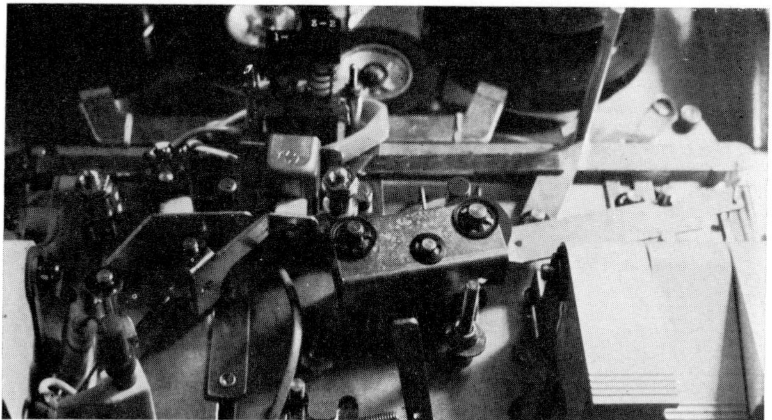

Fig. 3.18: Pressure pads like this may look crude, but unless correctly set, and sufficiently resilient, they will swiftly aggravate head wear.

condition, against which it is necessary to guard in practice, is a stationary tape with erase current applied, which can result in irrevocable damage. This is a factor seldom mentioned in the literature on practical tape recording, which the enthusiast would do well to bear in mind.

Factors of Erasure

D.C. erasure has not been mentioned because in this writer's opinion it has no place in any serious work on tape recording. It can never be as effective as we would wish. Taking the tape flux into one set saturation level is no solution to the erase problem: residual noise is quite intolerable, no matter how many reversals of field by repeat magnets can be provided. Some small machines, conserving space and oscillator power, use permanent magnet erase. Shun them!

For adequate erasure, a reversing field, with as many changing flux linkages as can be arranged, is desirable. The choice of energising frequency is made with the considerations that the number of hysteresis loops possible at the given gap width and speed shall be realised and that eddy current losses causing core heating shall be kept to a minimum. Even so, erase heads tend to run hot, and it is sometimes this tendency that damages a halted tape!

To get the high erase current we need, the head inductance is often tuned, and the erase head is such an important part of the oscillator circuit that any trouble in this department can affect recording seriously. Series tuning capacitance will often be found as a device to make the head resonate in the required frequency region.

In addition to this, pure waveform is striven for, and push-pull circuits which reduce unwanted harmonics are the order of the day. Any distortion in the erasing waveform will cause lack of symmetry and this leaves a 'pattern' of residual magnetism which comes out as noise—quite apart from the lack of symmetry that spoils the recording, as previously outlined.

Erase level, a subject that has already been mentioned and will occupy us again later, is important to reduce noise level. If no bulk eraser is available and time is favourable, it is often better to pass the tape across the head several times to achieve a deep erasure. Normally, it is the first few cycles of erasing frequency that saturate the magnetic material of the tape. But a heavily modulated tape can defeat all but the best erase heads and circuits.

Fig. 3.19 (above): A number of machines favour the tilting of a pressure pad mounted on a shield, as in the Sony example, see also Fig. 3.8.

Fig. 3.20 (below): Grundig with their pressure band system and Truvox with the single pressure strip on a swivel arm as shown, are examples of departure from the simple pressure pad concept.

Switching and Combined Heads

Mention of erasure brings up the point of erase and bias switching, which again will occupy us later, but needs our attention briefly at this

Fig. 3.21: The head assembly of the Uher 4000L.

Fig. 3.22: Head assembly, pressure arm, fixed and sprung guides of the Revox 736.

point. Combination record-play heads are in wide use, saving costs considerably by the double-purpose use of an amplifier, switched for its particular function. When such switching takes place, an impulse of bias through the combination head can cause some magnetisation, and this is a cumulative effect. Noise level grows and more frequent demagnetisation needs to be carried out.

To prevent this build-up of magnetisation, efforts are made to allow the oscillator energy to die away gradually when the recording function ceases. Various clever devices have been developed to allow a slow discharge of the oscillator supply, but nothing can effectively supersede the unswitched head that is used only for its determined function. One designer, so keen to prevent his heads suffering switching pulses, even allowed his tape recorders to be marketed with an unbearable hum when the head shields were retracted during a ‘pause’ or ‘edit’ operation, arguing that even this was better than suffering a magnetised head.

One advantage of the combination head that is sometimes overlooked is the ease of alignment. When a head is out of line, vertically, the effective gap widens. This results in an upper-frequency loss and a loss in overall output. With a combination Record/Play head, the problem does not have such a bad effect. Alignment for recording ensures accurate setting for replay. More often, the head is set for replay of a standard test tape and is then in the correct azimuth setting for recording.

Combination record/erase heads are not so frequently encountered, but deserve a mention. Very often, these have been produced so that the leakage current from erasure provides a bias field, but this is a very hit-or-miss method. More realistic, and nowadays a bone of contention between various patentees, is the crossfield bias design.

Crossfield Bias

The orginal idea of crossfield bias was to obtain a tape flux that acted transversely while the signal flux acted longitudinally, but the designs now in use, and, let us add, with some success, have an auxiliary head that carries the bias waveform and, by applying this as near the trailing edge of the head gap as possible, ensures that there is the minimum of self-demagnetisation due to the bell-shape of the recording flux.

To be brief and to save a lot of mathematics, the tape effectively shoots away from the gap at as sharp an angle as possible when the recording process is over, thus reducing self-magnetisation as much as possible. Fig. 3.17 shows this effect and demonstrates (*c*) that a correctly placed bias field can reduce the deleterious effects to a large extent. The ideal is for the bias field to decay sharply. By applying a bias field from the back of the tape at the right amplitude, and at a high enough frequency, and then allowing the tape to make a fairly sharp angle around the recording head so as to produce a falling-away action, the primary conditions can be met.

A subsidiary advantage is that application through the 'back' of the tape saturates the oxide coating with a bias waveform in a fairly even distribution, not entirely dependent on signal level, where normally the depth of penetration is more significant with ordinary bias systems. The coating nearer the recording head receives lesser bias signal, so, as long wavelengths penetrate more, they receive more bias. This is the condition we need. Higher recording frequencies can be attained. The exact position of the bias head is critical and has led to some argument among enthusiasts—which need not concern us here.

Fig. 3.23: Guides may be spring-loaded and adjustable, as with this Philips design.

Fig. 3.24: Another Philips technique, the insulated pin used as a shorting contact of the autostop, but acting also as an auxiliary guide.

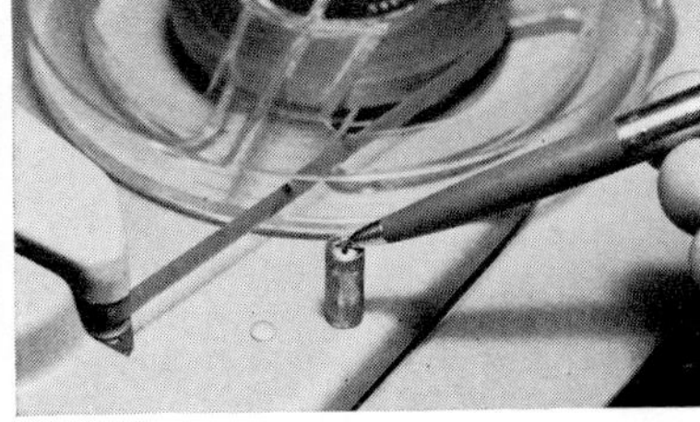

Fig. 3.25: Not a guide, although it is often wrongly used as such. Magnavox Studio deck; next to the BSR, perhaps the most popular with home constructors, but no longer available.

Fig. 3.26: Taking great care with head alignment and guide height is a wasted exercise if the accuracy does not extend also to the pressure roller and capstan relationship.

Replay Losses

Losses do concern us, very much indeed, and we need to know their causes before we can choose a tape recorder with any hope of successful results. As has already been noted, the 6dB per octave slope of a replay head output is something of a fairy story. Various losses modify the slope and must be taken into account in the amplifier design. Spacing loss is the most obvious, caused by foreign matter—or, to drop the euphemism, dirt—and the build-up of tape oxide in front of the head gap.

Its onset can be insidious: the user is not always aware of a loss during replay, and may automatically set his gain control to compensate. But recording enhances the losses: strength of flux is proportional to the square of the distance so a removal of the tape from the head by twice a given figure reduces the previous field strength four times! Add to this the tendency on replay for short magnets (high frequencies) to find an alternative flux path to the gap-pole path, via the impurity and to the opposite pole, and we have a serious loss effect more evident at the high frequencies. Fig. 3.10 shows this in some detail, and illustrates the relationship with frequency.

Spacing formulae can be worked out, and if a curve is drawn as shown we find that the attenuation A depends on the spacing d and the wavelength λ. The formula is

$$A = e^{2\pi} . \frac{d}{\lambda}$$

where e is the base of natural logarithms, 2·718, and pi can be taken as 3·142. When the spacing equals the tape wavelength d/λ is equal to unity. A = 20log $e^{2\pi}$ or 40log πe, which is 54·5dB. The figure of 55d/λ is often quoted for spacing loss calculations.

Taking an example, at 15kHz and a tape speed of 9·5cm./S, the wavelength will be 3·75/15,000 or 0·00025in. So an impurity of only a quarter of a thousandth of an inch will produce 54·5dB loss during replay. As that is a voltage ratio of about 560 : 1, the loss after recording and subsequent replay will be severe, as may be appreciated.

Head cleanliness can never be taken for granted, which is why we have devoted a full chapter to the subject later. One factor often overlooked, and relevant to the discussion of bias effects that occupied us a little while ago, is that impurities will not only cause record/play spacing losses, as described, but also a reduction of the applied bias field, and so a lower signal amplitude and an increased distortion.

Fig. 3.27: Track selection is often carried out adjacent to the heads, and switches must be treated as part of the head assembly.

Tape Guides

Tape guides need a special mention. They vary from the simple pin, deceptively innocuous, to the sprung, rotating jockey guide which may, in extreme cases, be coupled to some form of braking system. Whatever the guide structure, its main aim is to aid the travel of the tape in a true horizontal plane past the recording and replay heads. Exceptions arise:

Fig. 3.28: Even the modish styling of the Telefunken machines does not prevent their maintaining a sensible position for the track switch, right by the heads.

tapered guides are used when the angle of tape path has to be altered, as with helical scan tape recorders.

The same stricture applies to these as to all other guides: they must offer the least possible friction to the passing tape and must not cause it to deviate from its true path. This is not always such an easy task as may appear. A favourite trick of some older guides was an entrapping of oxide in the interior angles of their flanges. A frequent fault with alloy guides is a deposit of oxide which causes retardation.

Some of the guides depicted in the accompanying illustrations have peculiar tendencies to trap tape. It is imperative that correctly slit tape is used; a mistake to use cheap tape which may not be slit parallel and which, in catching in the flanges of a close-tolerance guide, can not only spoil a recording but also foul and jam mechanical drive systems, causing quite severe trouble.

Pressure Pads

The tape must move in a true horizontal plane. There will be a degree of back tension to avoid spillage. Pressure pads will be used to achieve the contact of tape with head, unless the head itself is contoured so that the tape path achieves the same effect. There are some technical arguments against contoured heads—and, it seems, as many arguments for them. Leaving the boffins to fight it out, we can say that if there are pressure pads fitted to maintain the necessary tape contact, are they effective, will they cause subsequent trouble, and how much trouble are they going to be to maintain?

An assortment of pressure pad systems from Figs. 3.18 to 3.22 show that there is no golden rule. The important thing is that the maker's original design shall be adhered to, and any adjustment or maintenance shall be towards obtaining the original pressures and tensions. It is a mistake to alter these, which have been worked out carefully to suit the head characteristics and tensions of the tape path. Where a pressure pad has hardened, some treatment to soften it is legitimate, with care taken to prevent lack of adhesion (spirits used for cleaning act as solvent to some adhesives), but such a device as the increase in pressure to achieve a little more 'top' is to be deprecated. It will only cause premature head wear.

Pressure pads are not the simple and brute force devices that they may appear. It is normal for a contact angle of between 12 and 18 degrees to be maintained as the tape passes the head, and any spread of this contact area by the action of the pressure pad can cause severe trouble. In addition, there is always a tendency of pressure pads to collect dirt and harden, thus increasing the electrostatic effect. The material of which they are made is important.

Some makers dispense with pads and use bands of flock-sprayed plastics which achieves the same general result but extends the area of pressure without extending the tape contact area. The tape runs along the band until it meets and contacts the head. These systems can be very effective, but the real enthusiast will demand a removal of pressure pads and a tape path that automatically puts the tape in contact with the head where it is wanted.

Fig. 3.29: Tape recording in the jungle—Armand and Michaela Denis and a Fi-Cord 1A portable. *(Photo by courtesy Armand Denis Productions Inc.)*

CHAPTER FOUR

THE TAPE DECK

REGULAR AND CONSTANT SPEED is the essence of good tape recording. The tape transport system must drive the tape past the head assembly at a standard velocity which should not deviate in the long or the short term from a very definite figure. A change in speed produces a change in the pitch of a note, recorded or replayed. A speed error, though the actual speed remains constant, defeats compatibility: tapes recorded on another machine cannot be replayed on the inaccurate one with true fidelity—and vice versa.

Pitch and Speed

The relationship between pitch and tape speed is a linear one. Double the speed and the pitch rises one octave. Halve it and the pitch descends by a similar amount. A semitone in music represents a change in frequency of about 6%. Most of us are well aware of such a change and would be hard put to it to distinguish a change of half that amount: i.e. a quarter-tone. But it is a peculiarity of human hearing that changes of pitch of about two per cent—less than a quarter tone—become obvious, and objectionable, if they occur in the most sensitive hearing region of from 3 to 5kHz and if they take place regularly.

Wobble

The phenomenon which most expressively describes this kind of cyclic variation is called 'wow'. Combined with a rapid variation called 'flutter', this phenomenon may be lumped under another descriptive term, 'wobble'. A combined 'wobble' of greater than 0·15% will begin to evidence itself as a roughness of the sound—depending on the programme material. The difficulty with tape deck design is that the tape itself has little mass. It depends on correct tensioning and the engineering of the surfaces over which it has to travel to achieve the minimum of unwanted friction, to reduce drag and to eliminate friction and other effects which tend to affect its passage through the head channel.

Of the components affecting this tape travel, the motor may seem the most important. In fact, modern construction has reduced its problems well below the danger level, and other parts of the system, notably the drive wheels and belts and the flywheel/pinch roller system, play a greater part in the production of short-term speed errors.

Flywheel

On some machines, the flywheel is an integral part of the capstan motor. An outer rotating cage is designed, with significant mass, which is both the rotor of a synchronous motor and the flywheel used to 'iron out' short-term changes of speed. Most tape recorders have a separate flywheel and at least one well known model employs two (see Fig. 4.18).

The capstan against which the tape is held, usually by the pressure of a rubber roller, is generally concentric with the flywheel spindle. Its speed of rotation and its diameter determine the actual speed of the tape. It may be of interest here to mention that a few tape recorders reverse the above procedure quite effectively, using neoprene coated capstan spindles and metal rollers. The end result is similar; some of the problems are different, that's all.

Because of the mass of the flywheel, its smoothing of short-term speed variations is more efficient at higher speeds of rotation. This is one of the

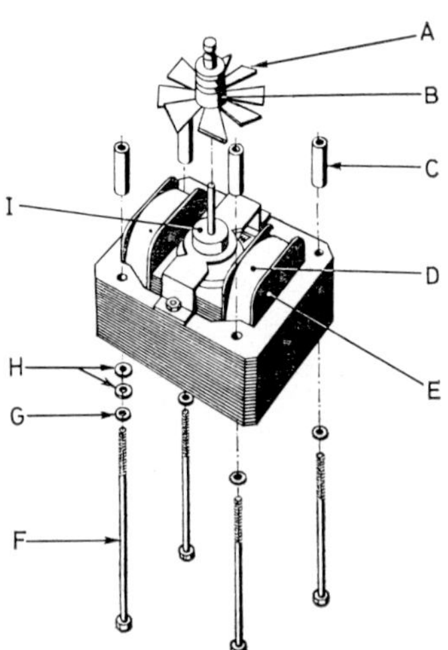

Fig. 4.1: Exploded view of typical induction motor used in an inexpensive tape recorder. A, Fan; B, motor pulley; C, distance pieces for stand-off (note that motor is often mounted on flexible suspension to eliminate vibration); D, coils; E, metal laminations; F, long fixing bolts to clamp laminations and secure motor to deck; G, thrust washer; H. main clamp washers; I, upper motor bearing.

reasons why a tape recording made at a higher speed on any given machine will be better than a similar recording made at a lower speed—but only *one* reason.

Except in the case of a badly worn capstan spindle, which would reduce the effective diameter, flywheel variations are not likely to influence the overall speed. Again, there are exceptions, notably those machines which employ a clutched flywheel and a separately clutched drive wheel, aggravated by a motor much weaker than is desirable.

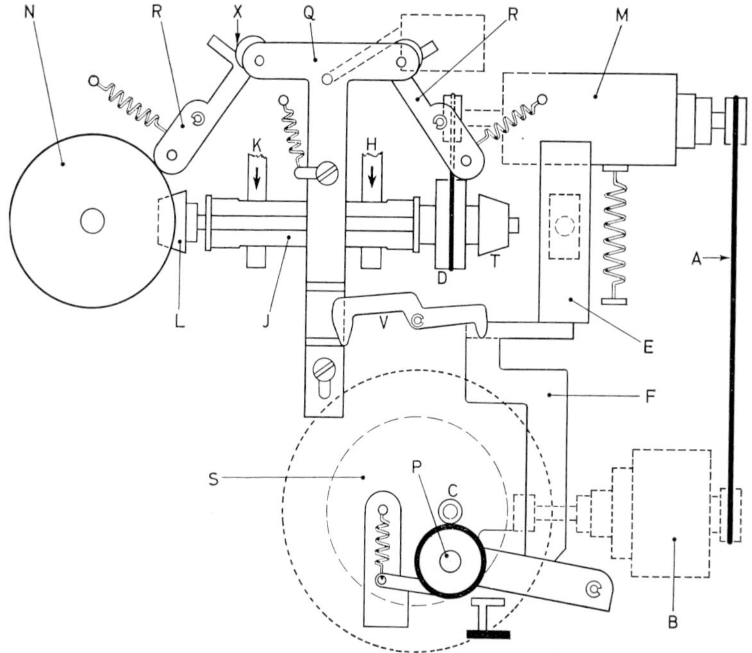

Fig. 4.2: Drive mechanism of the Akai X-IV portable. Capstan drive from the motor M is via belt A to the motor pulley, B, whose inner roller, adjustable for exact speed, contacts underside of the flywheel S on which capstan C is mounted. Pinch wheel P is held on by spring pressure.

Selection of Play impels levers F and E forward, inaugurating take-up, while V brings Q 'downwards', releasing the brake arms R and X. Drive from the inner end of the motor is now via a V-belt to the pulley D, part of a transverse arm whose ramped end pulleys L and T contact the undersides of the take-up spool and the feed spool N. Choice of drive to spools is made by levers K and H which move to lift the appropriate side of rocker bar J.

Wow and Flutter

Wow is generally considered to be speed variations below a repetition rate of about ten a second: flutter describes those speed variations above this rate. It is normal to express the lumped figure as a percentage, indicating the short-term difference from the long-term speed.

But it should always be remembered that when a recording made on a particular machine evincing 'wow' is replayed on that same machine, the effect can be either self cancelling or completely opposite in phase, with all the possible variations in between. The net result is that wow varies enormously, and the ear which may have been quite unable to detect the variation of less than ±0·2% is now very easily able to tell that there are irregular speed variations.

So, to be absolutely safe, our ideal machine must be below 0·1% W & F to be capable of claiming the label 'high fidelity'. If the threshold of perceptibility to wobble is approximately two per cent, then such a machine will never exceed the limit. To get down to this limit without having to use high basic operating speeds demands a high standard of engineering.

We can thus argue that for a long-term speed variation of two per cent —the limit we can tolerate without being aware of a pitch change—our tape recorder should not have a W & F figure greater than 0·1%.

The motor

Long-term speed regularity will depend on the motor itself. Several different kinds are used. In battery portables, the motor is a simple d.c. type with a rotating commutator and carbon brushes as contacts, except in the special case of the transistor switched brushless motor, with which we shall be concerned in the next chapter, when the specialised field of portable tape recorders is considered. Regulators and servo control will also be covered in later sections of this book and need not occupy us at this stage.

A.C. motors used in tape recorders are nearly always of the induction type. These depend on the frequency of the alternating supply for their

Fig. 4.3: Typical method of reducing torque of right-hand motor during take-up is to include a series resistance, such as the large wirewound component illustrated. (See also Fig. 4.5.)

speed of rotation. An exploded view of one such simple specimen of the popular induction motor is given in Fig. 4.1, from which it can be seen that the device is mainly a rotating barrel in a shaped electromagnet, formed by winding coils around the arms of laminated cores.

Mains voltage is applied to the coils, energising the stator section and producing a magnetic flux. This sets up a magnetic flux in the rotor by induction. There is no direct connection. The interaction of magnetic fluxes makes the rotor turn, once the motion has been started.

Fig. 4.4: Principal parts of a typical three-motor deck, the Brenell Mk5. In this view, the capstan motor assembly has been removed and swung aside for ease of demonstration.
A. Take-up motor; B. Capstan motor; C. 500Ω 10 watt resistor; D. supply motor; E. Suppressors; F. Brake; G. Drive idler; H. Speed change mechanism; J. Flywheel; K. Rewind switch; L. Record/Play switch; M. Stepped capstan pulley; N. Speed-change switch; P. Tape position indicator pulley.

Motor Speed

The speed at which it will turn depends on the number of poles formed by the windings of the stator. Poles may be regarded as magnetic 'strong-points'. The number of poles, and the frequency of the alternating flux, determines the number of revolutions.

A two-pole motor, for example, supplied from the 50Hz mains, turns at 60 × 50, or 3,000 revolutions per minute, because the alternating voltage applied to the pole faces changes their polarity with a frequency equal to the supply, i.e. fifty times a second, when there are two poles.

A four-pole motor will rotate at half that speed, i.e. 1,500 r.p.m., because the field created by the changing flux effectively rotates half a revolution for each mains cycle. The more poles the motor has, the slower it will run, but the more powerfully and regularly it will run. And, of course, the more expensive it will be to make.

Other advantages the multi-pole motor possesses are a lower external magnetic field, with a consequent reduction of screening problems, less vibration, due to the larger rotor and the more regular running, and the easier design of drive systems, which are a form of gearing and need not thus be such a high ratio as with a two-pole motor.

A little earlier, the throwaway phrase 'once the motion has been started' was slipped in. This is a vital point in tape recorder design. Induction motors will not start unaided. They need a 'shove' to get them going. As some of us have found when troubles cropped up far from the workshop, the shove could be physical—the twitch of the capstan, like starting the engine of an elderly car. But there are more sophisticated ways of achieving the same end, and two of the principal methods to be noted are the shaded pole design and the more obvious, and more expensive, capacitor start.

Shaded Pole

Shaded pole motors are fairly easy to recognise by the copper shading rings in the structure of the laminations. Some 'slip' is inherent in the design. The magnetic flux is changing at mains frequency, (50Hz), and the rotor is constantly trying to catch up with the rotating flux, never quite getting there. So although the speed is tied to the mains frequency and is independent of voltage changes within wide limits, it is not a strong electrical entity and is vulnerable to changes of load.

An increase in loading causes more slipping and more magnetic lines

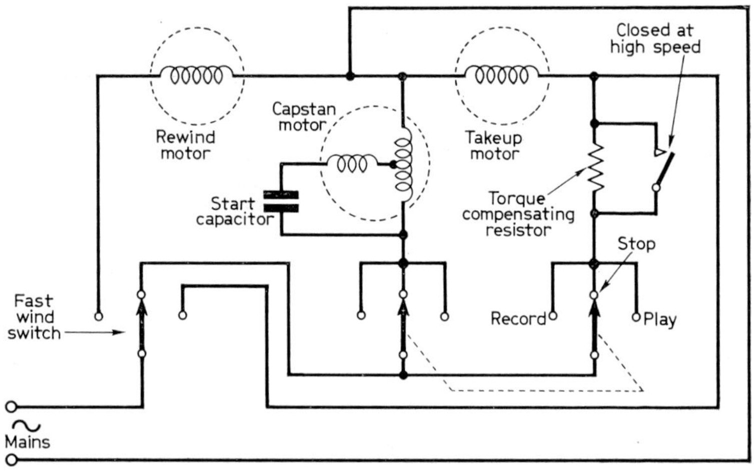

Fig. 4.5: Wiring diagram of three-motor deck (Fig. 4.4), omitting suppressor units across switch contacts.

are 'cut' which gives an increased current flow and a greater torque. This rising speed-torque curve is handy when the shaded-pole motor has to be used for fast winding, where an empty spool rotates much faster than a fully loaded one; it is not such an advantage when we come to the capstan motor, whose main requirement is regularity and whose torque can vary widely in single-motor designs, depending on the proportions of tape spooled.

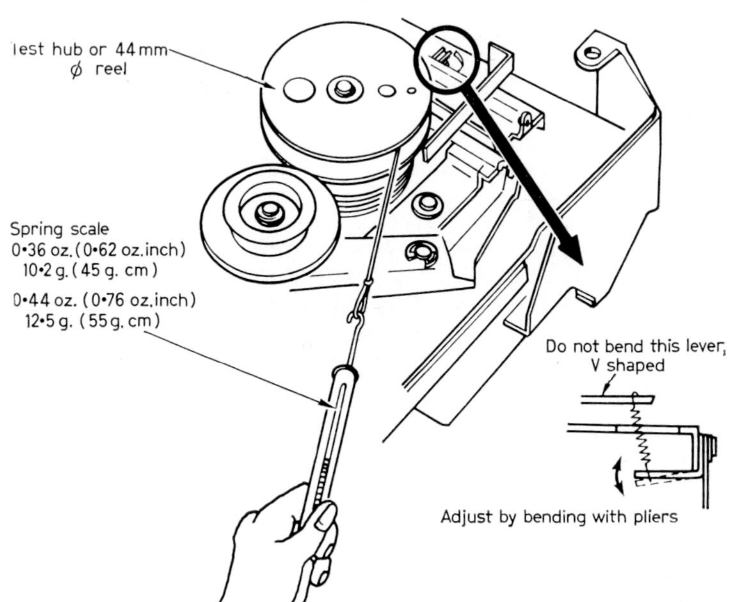

Fig. 4.6: To avoid erratic drive action, prevent tape stretching, reduce the chance of spillage, etc., careful adjustment of take-up tension is required. This method using a special test hub and spring balance, is widely employed.

Supply Voltage Variations

As we have already noted, variation of supply within fairly wide limits will not have any effect on speed or efficiency of the motor. But outside the limits a reduction in supply voltage lowers the full load torque, i.e. the full rotational force available at full load speed. So we can supply the motor with a varying voltage to a broad extent and control speed.

This method is employed in some three-motor designs, either by running the take-up and capstan motor in series for Record and Play, so that they share the supply and run at a mean half-speed, or by inserting a resistor in the circuit to reduce the applied voltage.

Figs. 4.5 and 9. show this method. It can never be as efficient as direct control. As a capstan motor, in fact, the shaded-pole motor leaves a lot to be desired. Its low wow and flutter figure (when well-constructed) can be outweighed by its tendency to vibrate.

Synchronous Motors

The type of motor we have been discussing is asynchronous. A motor which turns at the same rate as the magnetic field causing the rotor to move is termed a synchronous motor. It has some features which prove an advantage in tape recorder design. Chief among them is long-term speed stability.

Its short-term speed stability is not so good unless great care is taken in the overall design of the deck to reduce variations in tensions, etc. This is because of the tendency of a synchronous motor to 'hunt', to vary about the speed of the rotating magnetic field. Some additional precautions to obviate flutter are needed, but these are more than compensated by the improvement in speed stability.

One kind of synchronous motor, the hysteresis type, has a magnetically 'hard' outer coating to the rotor. Soft magnetic material loses its magnetism easily. Hard magnetic material possesses a high remanence. The rotor is thus aided in its natural effort to 'lock' to the strong field. Speed changing can be made more accurate, especially if the device of switching poles (twice the number of poles = half the speed of rotation) is employed to reduce mechanical inconsistencies.

This kind of speed changing is sometimes used with asynchronous motors, but those that employ capacitor starting, as in our Fig. 4.5 example, need additional capacitors for the extra speeds.

Salient Pole

Salient pole motors, which have flat spots milled in the rotor and soft iron laminations, with some advantages in conducting lines of force, also have start capacitors. These capacitors are large types with good insulation. Because of their expense, and that of the good quality contacts needed for pole switching to achieve a change of speed, mechanical methods are more often used, with the motor running at a constant speed.

This constancy is aided—it should be stated here—by the simple device of turning the motor 'inside out'. The rotor becomes the outer shell of some motors, is shaped at the bottom to achieve a fan action, thus removing the need for yet another vulnerable item, and its flywheel property helps greatly to iron out short-term variations in speed. In one or two machines, it has even taken the place of the flywheel itself, with great success.

Speed Changing

Tape recorder speeds have evolved from the early days of 30 i.p.s. to a fairly standard $3\frac{3}{4}$ i.p.s. for normal domestic use, with twice that speed, $7\frac{1}{2}$ i.p.s., used for any pretensions to quality, twice that again, 15 i.p.s., demanded still by some broadcasting organisations who are almost fanatical about their high standards and positively pachydermatous when reminded of the advances of modern techniques.

The lower speed, $1\frac{7}{8}$ i.p.s. has been used mainly for speech recording on reel-to-reel machines, where alternative speeds can usually be incorporated. But developments of tapes, heads and mechanisms have enabled this economic speed to be retained for music also. Cassettes have been pre-

Fig. 4.7: Top deck view of portable mechanism, with particular emphasis on spring operation.

Fig. 4.8: View of motor, flywheel and drive idlers of the mechanism shown in Fig. 4.7.

recorded with a very wide variety of programme content, to an extremely high standard, running at $1\frac{7}{8}$ i.p.s. With the general availability of chromium dioxide tape, as outlined in Chapter One, the frequency response of cassette-loaded and cartridge-playing tape recorders is likely to be widened, with even better results at this speed. The relationship between speed and quality has been noted in Chapter Two.

The Talking Books Society, especially in the U.S.A., have introduced a still slower standard, $\frac{15}{16}$ i.p.s. to get more material on regulation reels, but only a few machines are designed to accommodate this slow speed.

In the foregoing paragraph, deliberate reversion to the old notation of inches per second was made. At the time of writing, not all authorities, and certainly not many British tape recorder manufacturers, are facing the changing world by calling cycles per second 'Hertz' and giving their tape speeds in metric fashion. Elsewhere in this book we shall employ metric figures, and for the benefit of those who still boggle, here are the rounded off equivalents:

15 i.p.s. = 38cm./S
$7\frac{1}{2}$ i.p.s. = 19cm./S
$3\frac{3}{4}$ i.p.s. = 9·5cm./S
$1\frac{7}{8}$ i.p.s. = 4·75cm./S.

Stepped Pulley

The simplest method of changing speed is a stepped pulley on the capstan motor spindle, engaged by an intermediate or idler wheel which in turn drives the flywheel, the upper spindle of which is the driving surface for the tape. Fig. 4.9 gives one example of the way this can be done, using a ramped lever, but there are almost as many methods as there are makes.

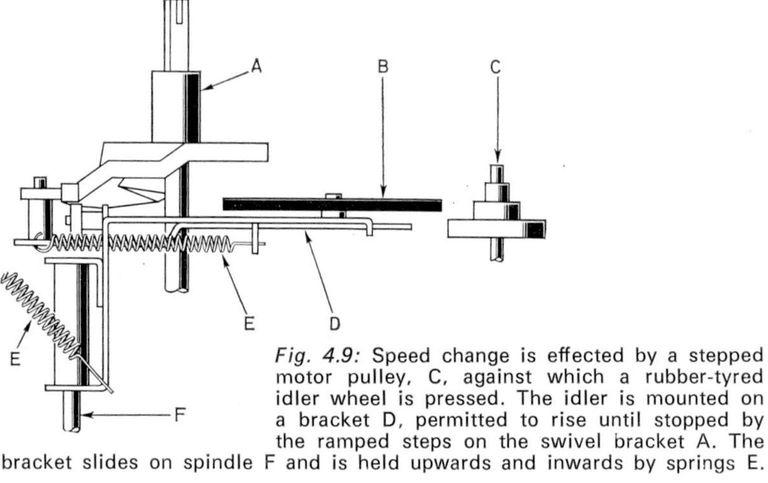

Fig. 4.9: Speed change is effected by a stepped motor pulley, C, against which a rubber-tyred idler wheel is pressed. The idler is mounted on a bracket D, permitted to rise until stopped by the ramped steps on the swivel bracket A. The bracket slides on spindle F and is held upwards and inwards by springs E.

Fig. 4.10 shows one in which the power to the machine is also switched by the speed selector. The frequency conversion method depicted in Fig. 4.11 is used also as a speed changing device, by forked levers feeding the belt to the appropriate groove in the pulley.

Ramp systems are usually moved against the pressure of a tensioning spring. In addition, a spring is needed for lateral movement, putting the idler wheel into engagement with the driving and driven surfaces. It is important that the levels of the relative members are correct and that the surfaces of peripheries are parallel and free from blemishes.

One of the prime causes of wow is an indentation in an idler wheel (or a rubber-tyred pressure roller), causing an effective elongation of the capstan path. This is generally the result of the idler having been left in engagement with the motor pulley and flywheel when the machine was not in use.

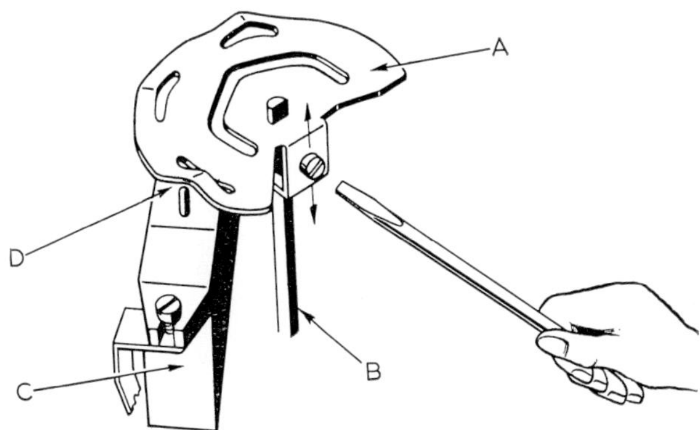

Fig. 4.10: Coupled to the speed selector action is the on/off switch operation in the design of Fig. 4.9. On main spindle B rotary bracket A with detents D actuates the pin of a microswitch, mounted on bracket C to allow some adjustment. The fixing screw on the spindle, whose adjustment is indicated, allows a setting of the switch-on time.

Fig. 4.11: Conversion to an alternative frequency, when an a.c. motor is used, may only require the refitting of the drive belt in another groove of the pulley. The grooves A and B are of different diameters.

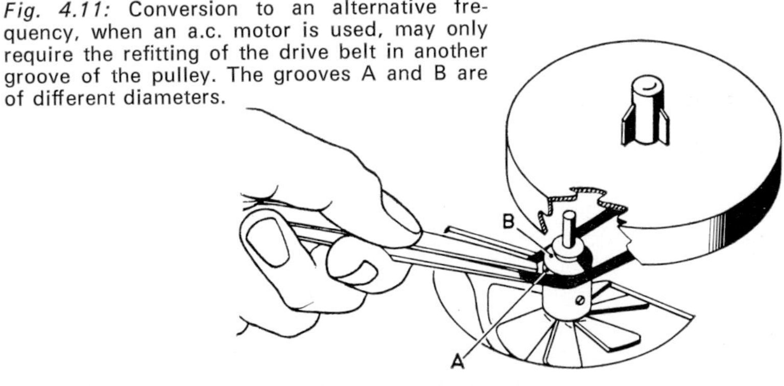

Fig. 4.12: Motor pulley of the Bang & Olufsen 2000 is a large brass cup. Note the inserted annular pad to reduce mechanical noise.

Belt Drive

Belt-driven machines are more suitable for single-speed operation, and many inexpensive designs have evolved. To change speed, mechanical complexity may be required, with its attendant risks. The fork system, already mentioned, requires also a tongue on the motor pulley. Any variation in the setting of either can easily cause damage to the belt. Normally, this is made of soft rubber, although various plastics substances have been used. In one or two earlier designs, a wire spring took the place of the conventional belt.

The difference between the speed-changing devices is that idler drives are usually required to be changed while the machine is at a standstill, to reduce the chances of 'scuffing' the rotating surfaces, whereas belt systems have to be changed during the time the motor is running. This can dictate the overall design of the machine, and the choice between belt and idler is fundamental.

Belt or Idler?

Each has certain advantages; each has disadvantages. Both have the edge over direct drive where cost is concerned—or should have, unless a designer has been led away by his own enthusiasm and finished with a mechanical system of which Emett or Heath Robinson would have been proud. There are still one or two of them about!

Quite often, a compromise has been effected, with belts and idlers sharing the honours in the same machine. The following notes are intended to explain why this apparent inconsistency should occur.

Belts or drive bands are flexible, may be made of rubber, composition with rubber base, plastics materials, rubberised fabric or coiled metal spring. All have been used with varying degrees of success. The most im-

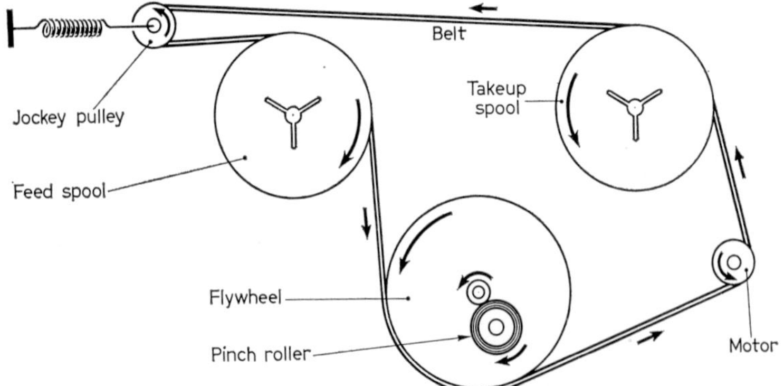

Fig. 4.13: Common belt drive relying on the wrap of the belt on the driven circumferences plus the tensioning imparted by a sprung jockey pulley. (See also Fig. 4.14.)

Fig. 4.14: Single belt drive requires some form of tensioning. In this popular Philips design a jockey pulley on a sprung bracket is employed.

Fig. 4.15: Indirect drive, via an edge-wheel impelled by belt action is a feature of this AEG design.

portant single criterion is the regularity of the cross-section. Elasticity follows a close second.

Round section belts will more often be used with a large diameter motor pulley. It is more difficult to maintain the constant diameter of a circular section belt; under tension, the belt flattens at contact points. For smaller diameter motor pulleys designers favour belts with angular cross-section, usually square or triangular, but occasionally rectangular with a longer flat side.

Shaped Belts

Shaped belts are intended to sit snugly in grooves of the pulley, although they may be allowed to find their own level on the broader flywheel surface, which can lead to 'wander' and belt slap when inconsistencies crop up during use. Flat section belts sit better on a wide running surface and flat fabricised belts can accept changes of tension, so may be used for slipping belt designs.

Some vertically mounted machines take advantage of the feature to include a 'slipping clutch' which is independent of gravity or outward spring pressure. The system demands a free-running roller mounted on a swivel arm, pivoted to increase tension for fast winding but retracting to enable the looser belt to slip for take-up. Some interesting piles of spilled tape have occurred when these systems have developed faults.

With these belts or bands and with any other type of belt drive, the great advantage over an idler system is the much larger contact area with driving and driven members that the belt can provide. The general system becomes much simpler, and can, properly designed, be less noisy.

Mechanical Noise

Perhaps the greatest drawback to the domestic tape recorder, and an argument that the gramophone record enthusiast will delight in advancing, is the mechanical noise of the deck. Even on quite expensive machines this will be found. An investigation of the design sometimes leads one to the conclusion that it evolved in a blacksmith's shop, and had never, before being marketed, been heard operating in the comparative quiet of the family drawing room.

The author's reaction to this, some time ago, was to search around until he found a really quiet model and then to overlook any other drawbacks it may have possessed—which may not have been very scientific, but has fortunately proved satisfactory.

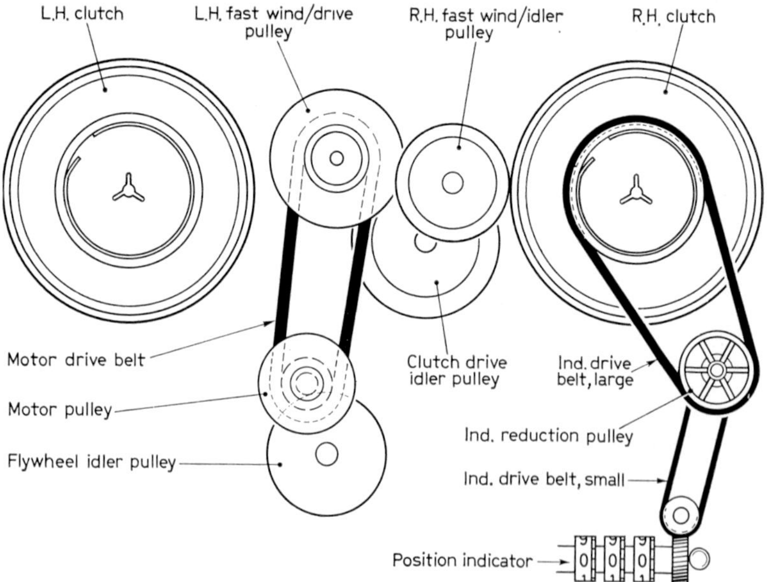

Fig. 4.16: A combination belt and idler system by Grundig, using friction clutches.

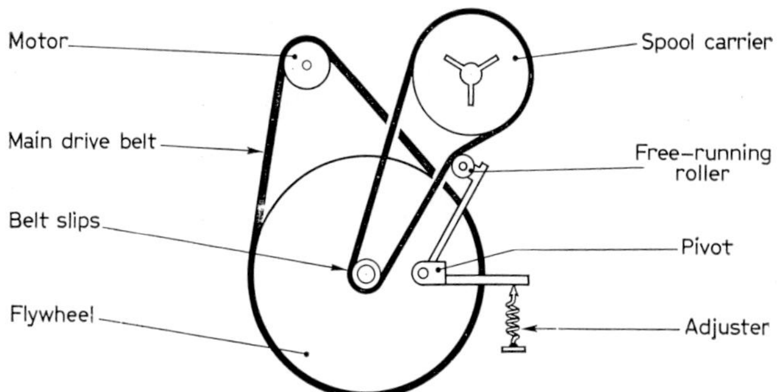

Fig. 4.17: Flat belts and a slipping drive for reduced torque are a feature of several designs.

Fig. 4.18: For more reliable regularity of transport, double flywheel designs, such as this Telefunken example, have been worked out.

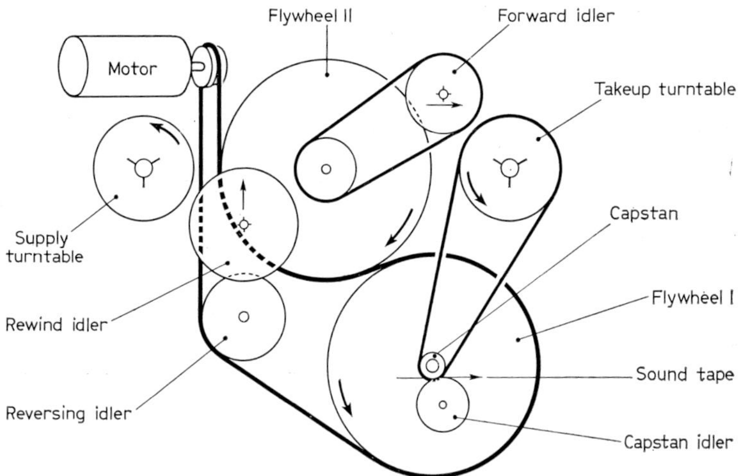

A thick belt is better than a thin one, other things being equal. It resists momentary snatch, does not stretch and contract again so easily, although adequately elastic, and can absorb the rapid change of torque when the machine changes function, as when the operator selects rewind suddenly from normal forward motion.

Ageing of thick belts is not so evident, although with some the type of ageing that ensues from their having been left unused in one position, a tendency to form into the 'shape' of the way they are routed around pulleys, can be troublesome. Luckily, this type of deformation is cured by heating and allowing the belt to run into shape and, if this is any consolation, is always the result of neglect.

Belt Thickness

Other things being equal, we said. And this argues a qualifying factor: thick belts are better, only if the motor pulley is large enough to accommodate them without adding to the power required to drive the motor. There are certain manufacturing limits.

Again we are faced with the need to compromise. The making of thick belts of regular cross-section is not a simple job, and flat section belts are easier to produce. They are also less of a contributory factor in short-term speed variations when any changing of speed by belt and pulley alteration has to be made. A flat belt can be rubbed down to an even thickness more easily than a round one.

In general it can be said that the larger the diameter of the motor pulley, the less the effect of belt variations. But to achieve the correct 'gearing' ratio between motor and flywheel, this requires a slower running motor or a larger flywheel, since speeds are in inverse proportion to diameters.

Putting this into mathematical form, taking the speed in r.p.m. of the

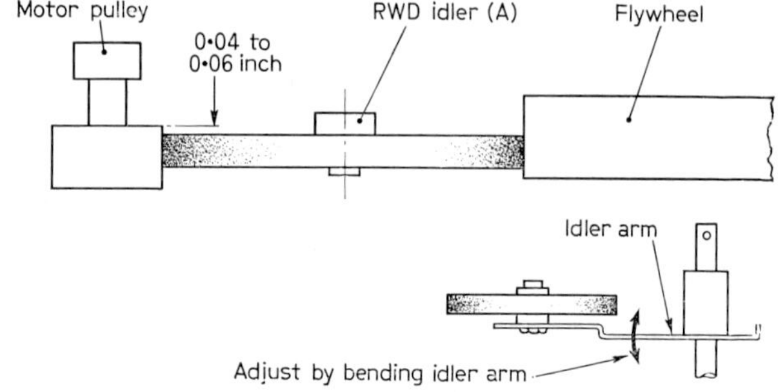

Fig. 4.19: Direct idler pulley drive requires an absolute level of the main drive members. In this example, adjustment of idler level is made by the set of the bearing bracket.

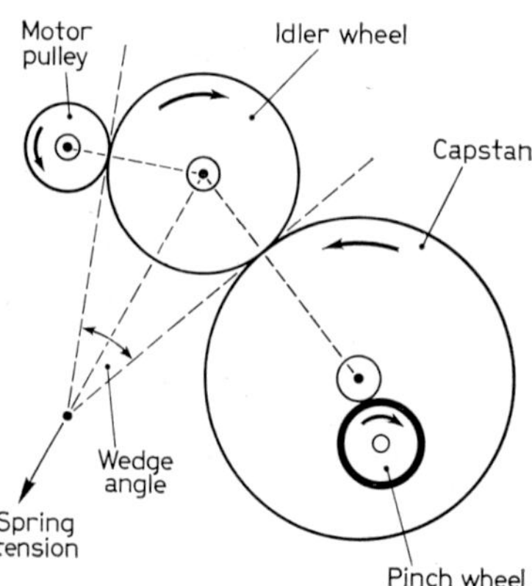

Fig. 4.20: Placing of idler wheels relative to motor pulleys and flywheels is critical. The wedge angle has to be calculated for maximum torque without slip, and for effective starting.

motor pulley to be N^1 and that of the flywheel (and its concentric tape driving spindle) to be N^2, the diameters of motor pulley and flywheel respectively to be D1 and D2 and the belt diameter or thickness to be d, then

$$\frac{N^1}{N^2} = \frac{D2 + d}{D1 + d}$$

Taking practical figures, a drive spindle 2·5mm. radius to drive the tape at 9·5cm./S needs to have an angular velocity of 362 r.p.m. If the motor is taken to revolve at 3,000 r.p.m. and the belt diameter is 3mm., with a flywheel of 100mm. diameter, the motor pulley would need to be

$$D1 = \frac{N^2(D2 + d)}{N^1} - d$$

which is

$$12{\cdot}43 - 3 \quad \text{or} \quad 9{\cdot}43\text{mm.}$$

Idler Drive

The use of intermediate wheels is well established, and many of the things remarked upon when considering belts will apply equally to idlers. Regularity of thickness equates with non-eccentricity; a steady, unimpeded run is similar to the need for a level application of forces; avoidance of stretching is almost the same as avoidance of scuffing.

With idler drive a high speed motor may be coupled to a large diameter

Fig. 4.21: Top view of idler-driven tape deck with top cover removed. This model, the Sony TC260, is one of a generation of similar designs.

capstan with greater success—but the motor will need some reserve of power to overcome the friction of the system. Because the area of contact between motor pulley and idler is small and between idler and flywheel not only small but subject to deforming forces at start or speed change times due to flywheel mass and inertia, it is very important that the wedge angle between the flywheel rim and the motor pulley is correct.

Instead of designing all out for maximum theoretical drive, the designer has to take into account all the possible frictional forces and make the motor deliver the maximum torque without stalling. The limits between which this can be done are very clearly defined for any given motor.

In the idler system, contrary to the belt, the driving medium, the idler, should not affect the ultimate speed of rotation by its size—although in practice, because of the slipping action, differences in wedge angle* from the ideal, and vagaries of spring tension holding the idler into contact, it can quite seriously affect the speed.

Slippage

Wear can cause slippage as the surface of the idler glazes with use. Regular maintenance is the answer to that problem. Replacement is the best remedy for worn idler wheels or those that have become damaged in use or by standing under pressure. The process of grinding (which can be done as an emergency repair quite effectively) is a short-term solution, as it must alter the size of the wheel and the efficiency, if not the theoretical speed, of the system.

The materials used for idler wheels have varied from pure rubber through neoprene, metal skimmed thinly with polyethylene to hard composition. All are vulnerable to the attacking force of oil, grime and heat, as are belts.

We shall consider the primary maintenance procedure in a later chapter, and need only mention here in passing, that cleanliness and just sufficient lubrication—no more—are the twin secrets of good tape recorder care.

Clutches

Smooth running of the tape deck depends on all the parts of the system operating at the correct tension, with the correct torque, turning at the right speed. Direct drive machines use the properties of the motors to maintain the correct tensions.

Reeling motors are non-synchronous induction motors, giving a smooth pull on the tape. Although they are subject to long-term speed variations when the line voltage alters or when there are changes in the load (which renders them unsuitable for capstan motor operation), they are especially suitable for the varying conditions they will meet as the tape fills or is unwound from each spool.

* *Wedge angle is normally between 35° and 40° for optimum drive with least slip.*

Fig. 4.22: Idler drive is used with some portable models to achieve a strong but compact system. Note the spring-loaded ramp in the centre.

Fig. 4.23: A common idler is used to drive the lower section of a split clutch for take-up and the fixed upper portion for fast winding. A spring blade returns the wheel to its 'normal' level.

Fig. 4.24: Part of the drive system, discussed elsewhere, depends on the accuracy of tape guides, head shields and pressure pads. In this view, the head shield indicated is on a spring swivel.

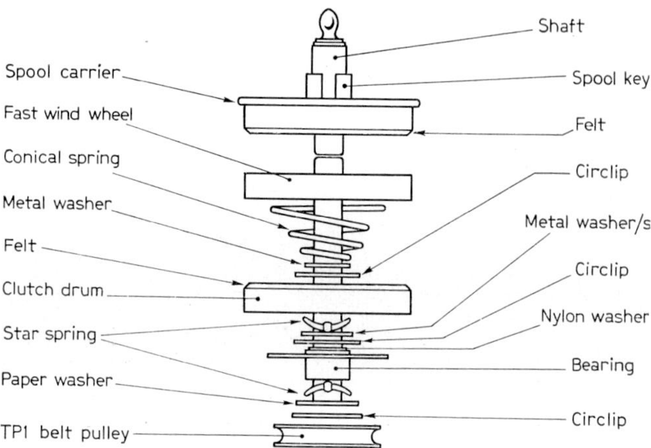

Fig. 4.25: Clutch arrangements for machines that are intended to work either horizontally or vertically tend to be complicated, as in this partly exploded version from Akai. Adjustment of tension is made by bending the legs of the star washers.

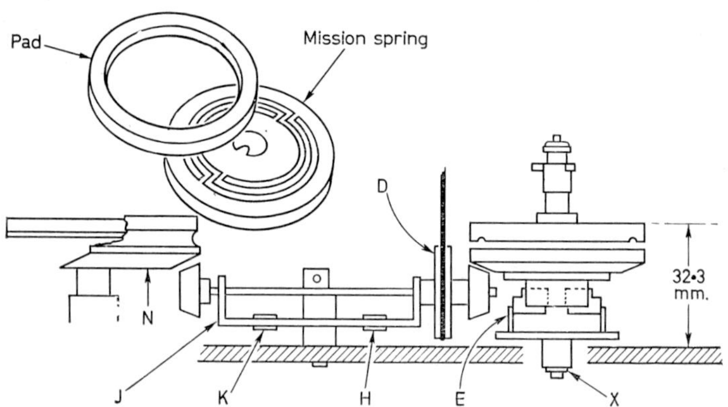

Fig. 4.26: Akai, like Uher, employ the rocker-bar system for spool drive, with the impelling force provided by a V-belt from the motor to pulley D on the take-up side of the rocker J. An alternative view of this system can be seen in Fig. 4.2.

The position of levers K and H can now be seen, as can the shaped underside of the spool carriers (see N). In addition, lever E is shown in greater detail, revealing its action on the take-up spool to provide a reduced torque. The lower bearing of this shaft can be seen at X. During forward motion, the supply reel is free, back tension for the tape being provided by pads.

To show the clutch action in greater detail, the supply spool is separated, with its torque transfer pad and the underside of the upper section, whose grip is controlled by a mission spring, drawn inverted for greater clarity.

Because the tape goes from a larger diameter (full reel) to a smaller diameter (empty reel) the speed of reel rotation changes throughout the spooling operation. But a nearly constant tension on the tape has to be retained, and this is done by keeping the take-up motor stalled, or run in a low-voltage manner.

Under these conditions, the torque that is developed increases as the load increases. The supply spool is under-run, or auxiliary braked to maintain enough back tension to obviate flutter. All this is necessary because

Fig. 4.27: Gravity clutch arrangements on the take-up side of a Philips design.

the tape is driven at a constant speed by the pressure of a roller against it, engaging it with the driving surface of the capstan spindle; in other words, by friction.

Tape recorders with no separate reeling motors have to resort to other methods to obtain the necessary variation of torque. A clutch device is needed on the take-up side and some method of maintaining back tension on the supply side.

This is never as satisfactory as the direct drive method, and the difference in torque between a full and empty spool on a machine with a gravity clutch may be such as to defeat its own object. The take-up is too weak at the beginning, too fierce at the end, and the fast winding is inadequate as the ends of a rewind are approached.

In fact, though the direct drive has the advantage of constant tension, it tends to produce a faster but tighter rewind or fast forward wind which can be a disadvantage, especially with a tape that has some tendency to stretch or suffers from print-through during storage. The clutched machine has a much softer wind, even though it will be a good deal less fast.

Gravity Clutches

Weight-dependent or gravity clutches form the largest proportion in the less expensive tape recorders. The principle is simple: the lower section of a split spool carrier is driven by belt or idler coupling to the motor—often via other drive components. Above this, the spool carrier section is allowed to rotate, with a friction disc of felt or cork between the two parts.

The weight of the spool and tape provides sufficient friction for the torque to be transferred from bottom section to top. As the weight increases, so does the friction, and more force is available to drive the heavy load.

Variations of this basic design will be encountered, with adjustable tension in many cases. In Chapter 11, dealing with the servicing and maintenance of decks, some of these variations are described in detail. Their adjustment is precise (see Fig. 4.6) and their correct operation depends —again—on cleanliness and the minimum of the right lubrication.

Vertical Mechanisms

For vertical operation of a tape deck, gravity is of little use, and instead an outward pushing force is made to maintain contact with the sections of the clutch mechanism, where split clutch methods are used. This can lead to design complications and the multi-layer, multi-sprung clutch assembly which horrifies repairmen.

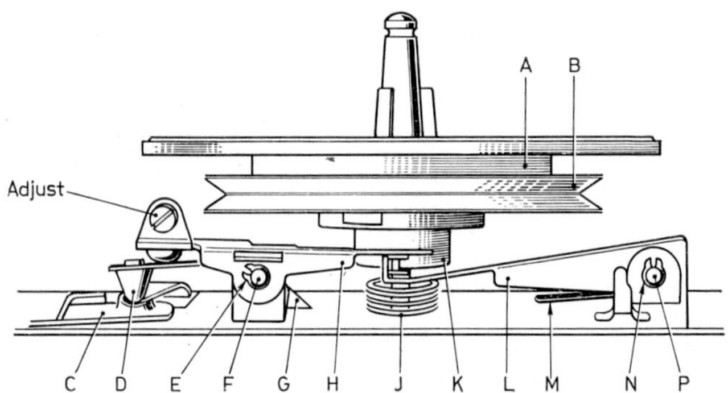

Fig. 4.28: A typical Tandberg clutch. In the position shown, suitable for take-up, turntable A has reduced friction with pulley B. The trip bar C has moved with the selector lever system, and the Delrin button D on lever H is in its middle position. Lever L is depressed against the thrust of spring J and cartridge K moves downwards. Setting adjustment is by an eccentric cam held by the screw which is indicated.

During fast rewind, lever H presses down on the lug of cartridge K, compressing J more, and thus allowing a freer rotation of A. The opposite action takes place during fast forward winding, when H is raised and L applies upward pressure, clamping the rotating parts together.

Alternatively, it can produce the flat-belt, tensioned lever assembly that is very effective when all works well, but tends to vary between extremes of stretched or broken tape and tangles all over the workshop floor when there is trouble with the tensioning. One particular design, with a com-

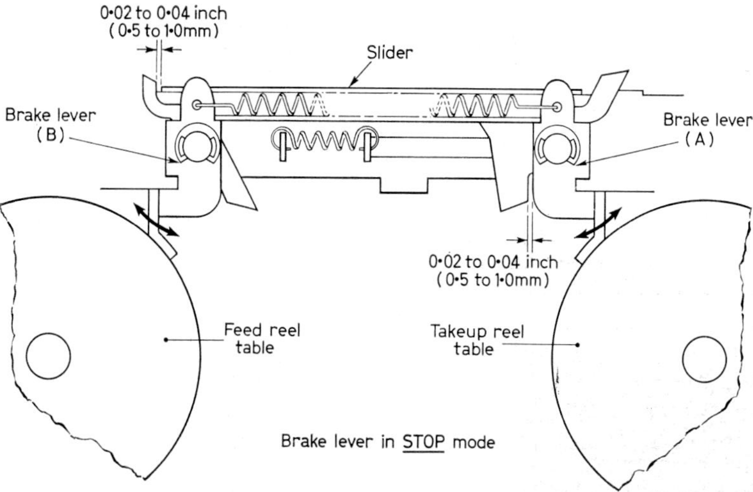

Fig. 4.29: Typical clearances and adjustments for a balanced brake system, employed by Sony.

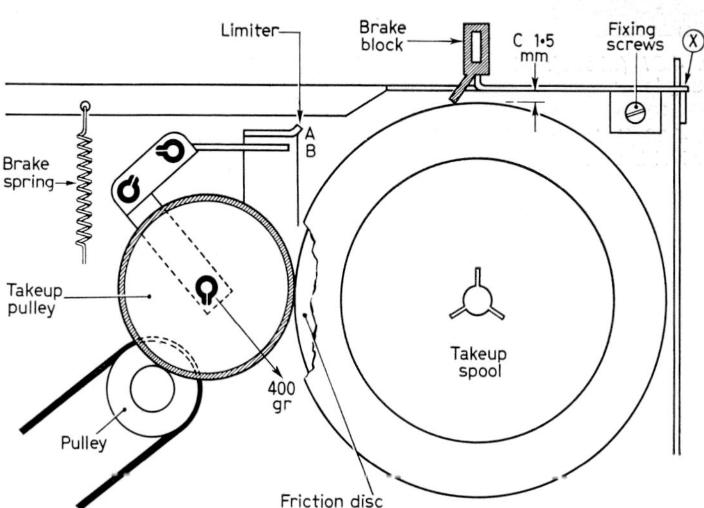

Fig. 4.30: Brake and drive system used on some Philips machines. Note shape of differential brake, action depending on the direction the spool rotates.

bination spring and gravity arrangement that relied upon a soft lead weight as a balance for the tensioning arm, has resulted in some fine examples of 'elongated music'. In general, the vertically operated machines tend to maintain a harder tension, both forward and to the reverse. For this reason, their adjustment becomes much more precise.

Other types of clutch mechanism will be met—as with drives, there are as many systems as families of tape recorder—and one of the chief examples of a controlled semi-gravity clutch that has fathered other variants is the system depicted in Fig. 4.28, by Tandberg of Oslo. Adjustment of clutches such as these will also be dealt with in Chapter Eleven.

Brakes

Many of the finer points of braking should also be left to the later chapter on servicing and maintenance methods. Like a good butler, the brake is a silent and unnoticed servant. But whereas most of us have to

Fig. 4.31 (above): Simple peripheral brake, with a cork or felt pad on a sprung lever.

Fig. 4.32 (below): Differential braking is achieved by a free rubber roller on a swivel bracket which first retards then grips the plastics spool carrier.

Fig. 4.33 (above): Auxiliary braking, operated by the pause control, consists of a peripheral felt pad.

Fig. 4.34 (below): Peripheral brake consisting of a cork pad on a swivel lever.

make do without a butler, very few rotating mechanisms can manage without some sort of brake.

The spools have to be halted at varying speeds of rotation, and halted in such a way that the tape neither stretches nor breaks, and does not spill off untidily. Not always such a simple design factor when we consider the wide variations between full and empty spools, spools of different sizes, and different hub sizes (which can be even more important) and the needs for fast winding.

The rudimentary brake system of a peripheral pad, or a pair of brake blocks on spring-loaded arms held off while the tape is running, is all very fine for the slow-running, single-speed machine. Yet even there we find the brakes slightly offset to give some priority to the take-up side, preventing snatch. The adjustment may be no more than a bend in a lever. Some further details to our illustrated brake systems will be given, described and illustrated in Chapters 11 and 12.

The subject of the tape deck mechanism in general, and braking in particular cannot be left without some reference to the operational and differential brakes. These are intended to use the changing spool diameters as guides to braking force, by sensing the amount of tape loaded or unloaded, and, in the case of the simple servo brake, to apply a braking force proportional to the speed of rotation and its direction.

The first kind require swivelled levers that allow the angle of the tape egress from the spool to be the determining factor for tension braking. The second have either bands of fabric (on metal spools) or bands of metal (on plastics spools) whose angle of wrap is important. A small variation of the pad brake that retains some differential features can be seen in Fig. 4.30.

Fig. 4.35: Truvox tape-decks using endless-loop cassettes were used in the Battle of Britain presentation at Madame Tussauds. Slide projectors were synchronised from each deck.

CHAPTER FIVE

PORTABLE TAPE RECORDERS

DESIGNING A PORTABLE tape recorder is not just a matter of whittling down a larger machine. Nor is it simply the technique of arranging a battery power supply and fitting a handle. There are a number of special circuits, some of them peculiar to portable machines, some of them used also in larger models but having a special application to the portable. Since the cassette and cartridge revolution the portable tape recorder has very much come into its own.

Now that a really good electret (capacitor) microphone can be unobtrusively fitted in the casing of a portable, and the engineering developed until the noise level of the mechanism and its electrical drive system is eradicated; now that low-noise tape can be used in the cassette and even at the low operating speed a reasonable frequency response can be obtained, we are well on the way to a situation where the only reason for not making a tape recorder portable is the need to attain a superlatively high standard, as in the studio, where the tape speed dictates the use of a larger spool.

Power Supplies

Power supply is no problem. Portable tape recorders can as easily be operated from a mains supply as from their internal batteries. The machine is basically a battery-driven design, and when used on an external a.c. supply the only addition is a voltage-dropping transformer, a rectifier to convert the applied current to d.c., and the consequent smoothing and suppression circuits. Insertion of the mains plug into a switched receptacle socket, or the movement of a mains/battery selector switch determines which type of supply comes into service. See Fig. 5.1.

Refinements of the power supply system which are particularly applicable to portability are a control of the d.c. motor for absolute speed and a regulation of the supply for maximum performance for the maximum time. The effect is to achieve a 'run-down' period between the onset of battery deterioration and the critical voltage below which performance is degraded, which is as long as possible. To this end, much research has gone into cell life and leakage, capacity and discharge rates.

Further refinements include the development of really leakproof batteries (not just those that bear the name) and various types of rechargeable cell. Working along the same lines, specialist portable tape recorders often have mains units that incorporate charging devices, with cutouts and warning systems. Some of these will be described and illustrated in this chapter.

D.C. Servo Control

Motor control varies between the simple zener diode method, which prevents the applied voltage from rising above a pre-determined amount, to the differential amplifier and sensor system that uses a number of transistors in a finely balanced circuit that continually monitors performance and corrects for errors. Specimen systems are outlined in the following notes.

It should be remembered that this type of control is by no means peculiar to portable tape recorders. More and more single-motor machines are nowadays a d.c. servo-controlled design. Of no more than historic interest are those early machines that had vibrator-operated, rotating converter or 'chopper' supplies, but reference to these is made because the basic idea of a 'chopper' has been developed for some of the later, very fine portable machines.

Supply arrangements of regulated machines are necessarily more complicated, and an example of good regulation combined with compact design and efficient operation is the Uher 4000L Report whose charger and power supply circuit is given in Fig. 5.2. See also Fig. 5.8 where the circuitry is further developed and the motor control circuit of this deservedly popular machine is given.

Storage Batteries

In this model, as in several Telefunken designs, an accumulator is used, descriptively named a 'Dryfit' battery. Unfortunately, the recovery ability of these rechargeable batteries is rather critical and there are frequent cases of wastage due to neglect. It is a very good system for the enthusiast who is going to give his machine regular use and as regular maintenance, so that the battery receives a frequent periodic recharge. Human nature being what it is, we put off the action we should be doing, and once the battery has been allowed to discharge itself too much, and is then left standing, unused, for a while, no subsequent recharging is going to remedy matters.

The author may well be challenged by some battery-maker on this score, but will defend his views on the grounds of experience: many portable tape recorders have been brought to my workshop after periods of neglect and all the ruses at our command have failed to recharge Dryfit batteries so that they will continue to hold their charge and regain the original charge/discharge cycle of which we know them to be capable.

Properly used, correctly maintained, the Dryfit battery is a fine example of value for money. It saves its cost many times over, and, of course, saves

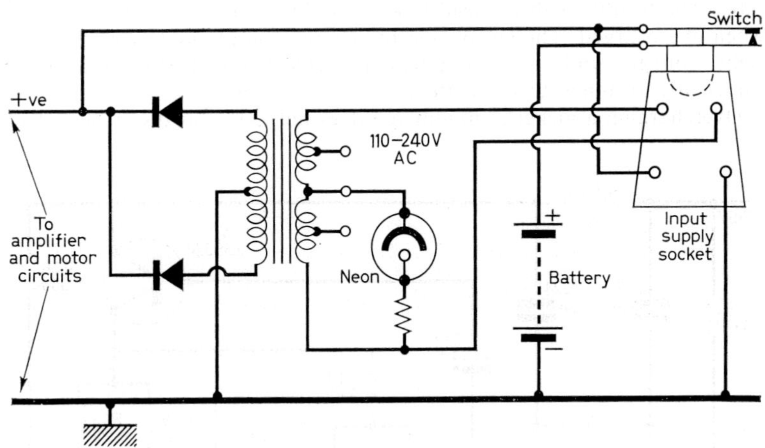

Fig. 5.1 (above): Supply arrangements, Sony TC800. Insertion of mains plug or external d.c. supply plug opens switch and isolates batteries.

Fig. 5.2 (below): Power supply and charger unit for the Uher 4000 *Report.* The unit switches off at a charging current of 30mA and the warning lamp then lights.

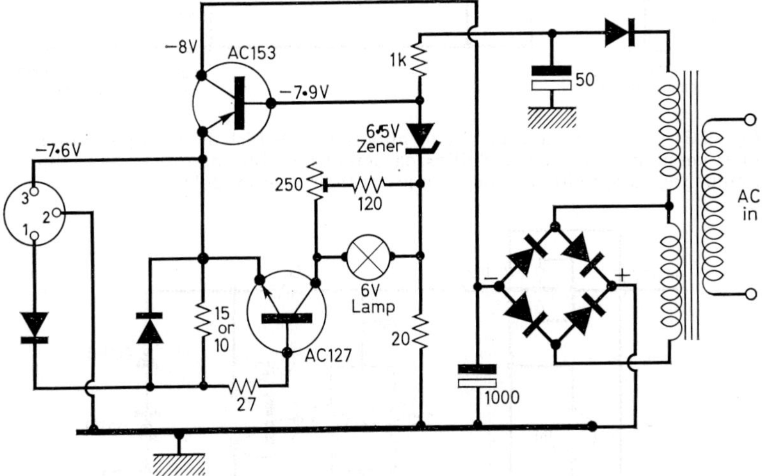

the inconvenience of having to hunt for cells (5 × 1·5V cells, U2 or equivalent) when the shops are probably closed or the piggybank is temporarily embarrassed.

Storage batteries may be lead-acid or nickel-cadmium. There is a good deal of difference, and a change from the former to the latter will mean slight alteration of the charger unit to accommodate the different charge rates. The trouble with the lead types was always that they suffered badly when overcharged. The cut-out on the charger simply *had* to work at the right voltage, and an inadvertent movement could shift the preset sufficiently to ruin a storage battery.

Overcharging a nickel-cadmium cell does not have this disastrous effect,

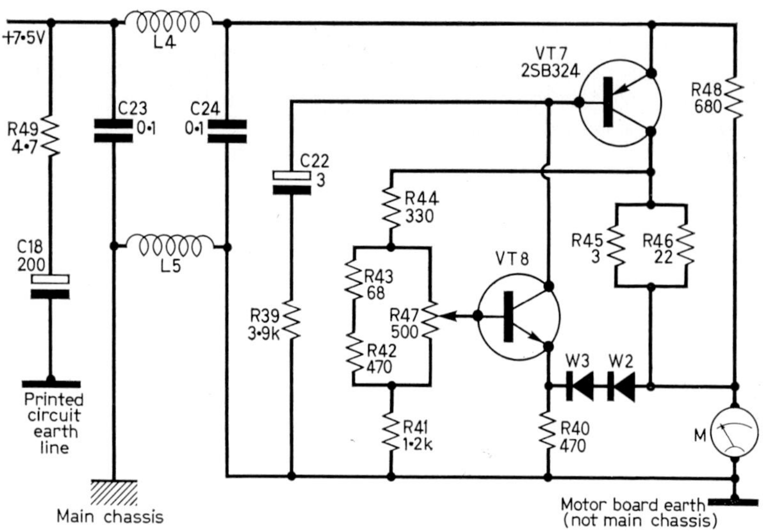

Fig. 5.3: (a) Motor control circuit adopted by British Radio Corporation for their versions of the basic Philips cassetted portable tape recorders with *(b)* Philips regulation circuit used to improve their later models.

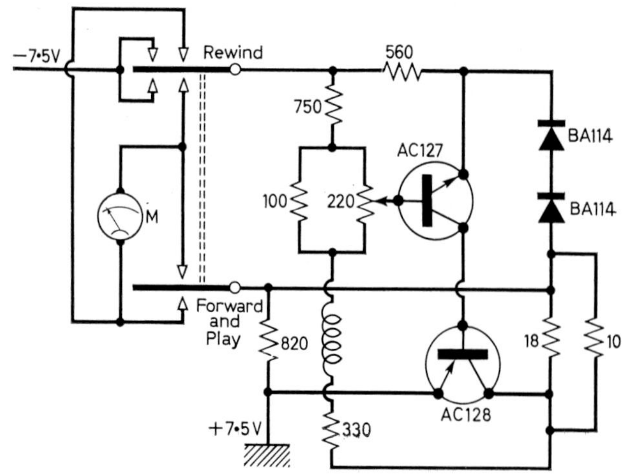

so we can safely allow a little more latitude to the charger. However, it is always desirable to do things properly, and Messrs. Bosch, who import the Uher machines to this country, have advised the alteration of the resistor that shunts the emitter diode of the AC127, from 15Ω to 10Ω. This puts the charging circuit out of action at a higher current, 30mA instead of 20mA.

Zener Diode Regulation

Note the use of a zener diode in the given circuit, and also its application in other circuits of this chapter. In this example, the diode gives 5·8 volts across the positive and negative terminals when these are bridged by an 8Ω 5-watt resistor and the mains power supply is connected. Charge current will then be 700mA. Thus from the maximum to the minimum charging current there is the wide range of 670mA but the charge voltage must remain at 7·4 volts all the time. For a nickel-cadmium battery the range is not so wide and charge currents from 300mA at the beginning to 100mA at the end of the charging process are typical.

The silicon semiconductor diode, (named the Zener diode after C. Zener who in 1934 proposed the use of what was already a well-known principle), acts as a voltage regulator diode. If any semiconductor diode is forward biased, normal current flows up to its handling capacity. Applying a reverse bias will prevent current flow, except for a very small leakage current. The zener diode exhibits similar characteristics up to a certain point, when the application of a reverse bias greater than the 'zener' figure causes a sudden increase in current flow.

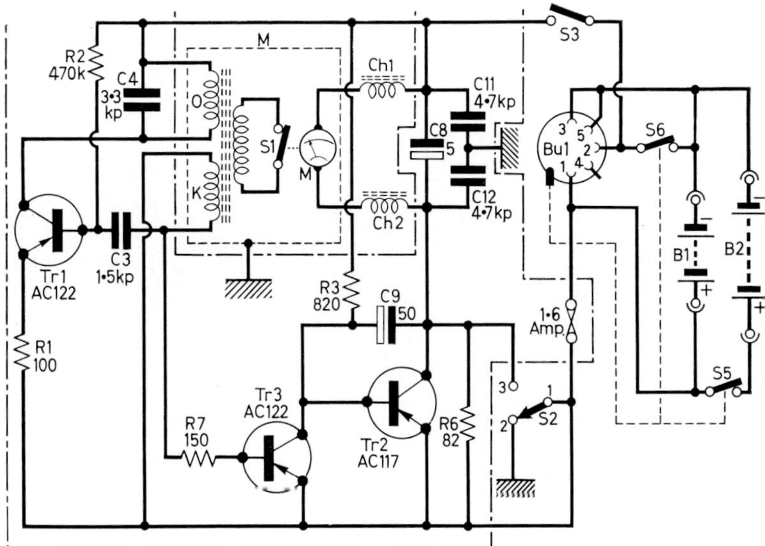

Fig. 5.4: Control circuit and motor regulator of Telefunken *Magnetophon* 300.

The voltage at which this phenomenon occurs is known as the 'breakdown voltage' and careful design is needed to prevent the diode thrusting its heart out by attempting to pass all the current that is available. So zener diodes are used to control heavy-current transistors rather than as direct shunt regulators themselves. An example of this can be seen in Figs. 5.3, 5.4 and 5.5, where the zener diode plays an important part in voltage regulation.

The circuit of Fig. 5.5 was devised by Marconi Instruments Ltd. and is intended to aid the testing of equipment with odd and unusually small batteries without calling in the big guns of stabilised and regulated bench power supply systems. By using a slightly higher battery supply and a simple series regulator with zener control, the small-current demands of such equipments can be met.

There is the absolute minimum of components and a 12 volt supply is

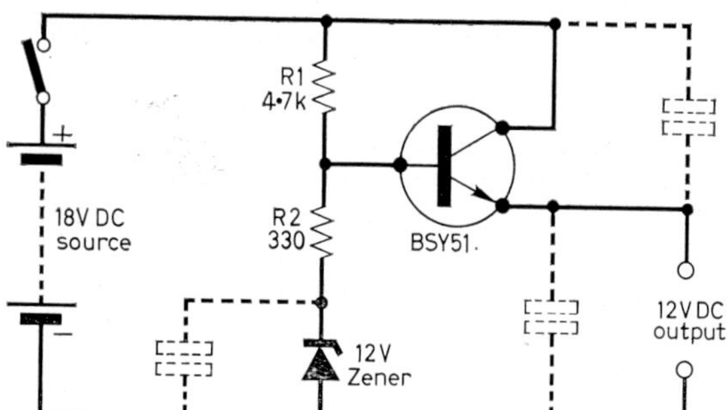

Fig. 5.5: (a) Simple Zener regulation circuit. The capacitors shown dotted are used for protection against overload.

Fig. 5.5: (c) View of the battery container and regulator panel of the Akai X-IV portable. The extremely neat printed circuit assembly is indicated.

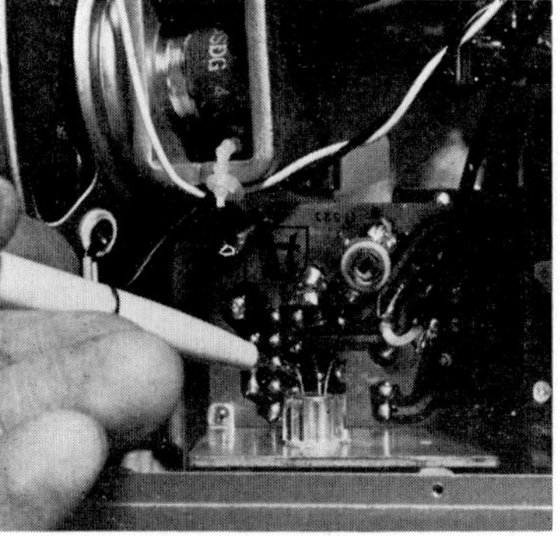

Fig. 5.5: (b) Speed change and regulator panel of the Sony TC222. There are several variations, sharing the principle of electronic control of a d.c. meter.

delivered from an 18 volt source, which is easily simulated from two 9-volt batteries in series. The output impedance is comparable to an equivalent 12-volt battery. Currents of up to 35mA can be drawn—quite sufficient for a transistor radio or a simple amplifier circuit, but not for the motor requirements of a tape recorder.

Overload Protection

Overload protection is often overlooked. In this circuit, the capacitors shown dotted are employed to protect the regulator from initial charging surge current that can occur at switch-on. This will happen if a high value of capacitance is across the resistive load. If the primary source is dry batteries, the transistor can be protected by a second capacitor, of higher value than the first, between collector and emitter. The two capacitors then charge in series without drawing a heavy current through the transistor.

There are occasions when a.c. ripple may be present. This can arise when the source is a secondary cell that is being recharged, and then a lower value of capacitor across the zener diode will help. This C discharges via the base-emitter path in series with the load when the supply is switched off. Then when it is switched on the output voltage builds up again slowly at the charging time of the second capacitor.

Protection against brief but heavy resistive loading is given by an increase in the values of the resistors R1 and R2. During the overload, the base-emitter current increases the voltage drop across R1 and the base voltage falls below zener voltage cut-off. Although the circuit ceases to regulate, collector currents that are so high as to be destructive can be prevented.

The beauty of the system is that the appropriate voltage can be obtained by simply selecting the zener diode to suit. Thus, such a circuit can be employed to run a radio that requires 9-volts supply from a car battery system that operates at 12 volts.

Operation from Car Batteries

It should be mentioned here that the problem of running the portable tape recorder from a vehicle system is not just one of voltage dropping. As the car's charging system can briefly push the supply up to 14 volts or more, and as the current demands of a tape recorder will vary according to its mode as well as the output power demands, the simple solution of a series dropping resistor is not tenable. Some form of regulation is needed, hence the apparent complication of the circuits that accompany this chapter.

One feature that appears on all these circuits and is not always evident as to its operation is the cut-out switch which prevents the inadvertent connection of the batteries (left inserted) when mains supply is being used to drive the tape recorder. Mains/battery isolation is provided on some tape recorders by simple switching, but more often the fail-safe device is a stowage plug which completes the battery circuit.

If the original design had a Continental 6-amp plug, such as in Loewe-Opta or Grundig models, then this will be used, inserted in the inbuilt stowage socket before battery operation can take place. Sony have a switch operated by the insertion of the mains plug; Uher use a rim-switch on the remote control DIN socket so that when the rechargeable accumulator is inserted (itself depressing another plunger and operating a micro-switch) it can receive the supply from the mains unit for charging, or the mains unit itself can drive the machine.

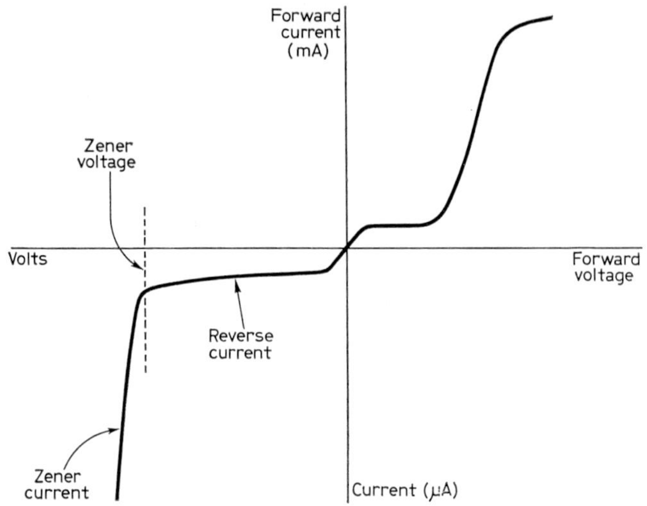

Fig. 5.6: Zener characteristics.

A brief word on the action of the zener diode may be helpful. Referring to Fig. 5.6, if we plot forward- and reverse-currents against forward- and reverse-voltages of a semiconductor diode we get the irregular curve shown. Note that the scale is not regular. It would need more paper than we have on this page to extend the vertical scale to cover the vast increase in forward current, so the lower part of the vertical scale is in micro-amps while the upper part is in milliamps and amperes.

When the reverse voltage goes past the breakdown point there is a sudden excess of reverse current. The zener diode exploits this characteristic. The voltage across the diode remains substantially constant for wide variations of current. Reverse current results from the movement of minority carriers at the semiconductor junction. These are accelerated across the junction by the reverse bias voltage. They gain more and more energy as the reverse bias increases until they eventually displace valence-bound electrons from their atoms. So at this juncture, pairs of current carriers (i.e. free electron and a hole, for those who accept the 'hole' theory) are created, thus adding up to the high zener current.

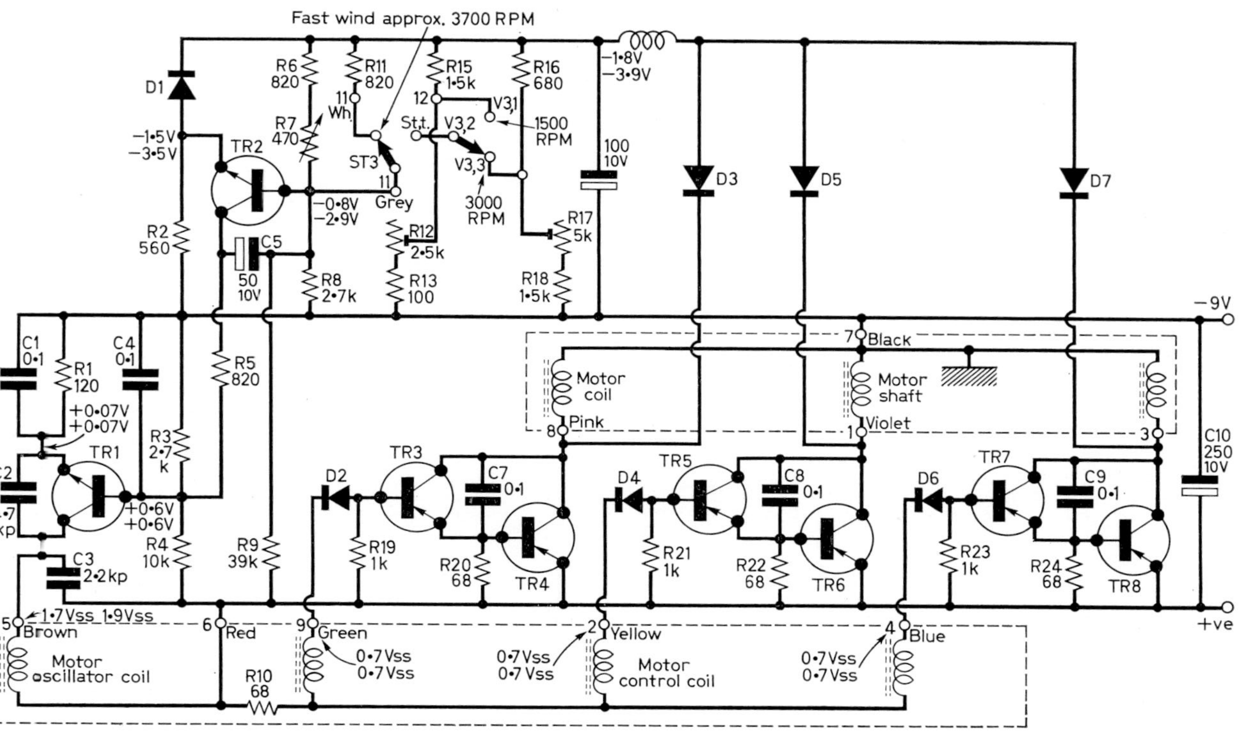

Fig. 5.7: Motor control circuit of Grundig TK2200, with fine speed control.

Motor Regulation

Motor regulation calls again for the zener diode, and in the examples that accompany this text we find a number of interesting variations. The problems are not quite the same as those which obtained for power supply regulation. Whereas the power supply had as its reference the zener breakdown voltage, the motor regulator has to refer to speed.

Applied voltage should be proportional to speed, when all else is equal, but as torques vary and d.c. motors tend to absorb some current and operate at different efficiencies over a fairly wide spread of applied voltages, there must be first some sort of operational reference, and then a method of allowing the supply to vary to meet the pre-set norm.

The motor control circuit of Fig. 5.4 employs a governor method with a 100kHz oscillator. The governor switch is adjusted to close when the speed drops below 3,000 r.p.m. This switch is connected to a coil which rotates with the rotor and the switch. On the stationary part of the motor there are two other coils forming a tank coil and an oscillator coupling coil. When the speed drops, S1 closes and the rotating coil is short-circuited, damping the oscillator so that it stops oscillating.

The base of Tr1 is part of the feedback coupling circuit for the oscillator. Tr2 is negative biased through R3 so the impedance of the resistor is low and the motor runs. When the speed achieves the correct value S1 opens and the oscillator is kicked into action. The negative swing of voltage across the K section of the windings causes Tr3 to appear as a low impedance via R7. So the negative bias at the base of Tr2 drops and the apparent impedance rises.

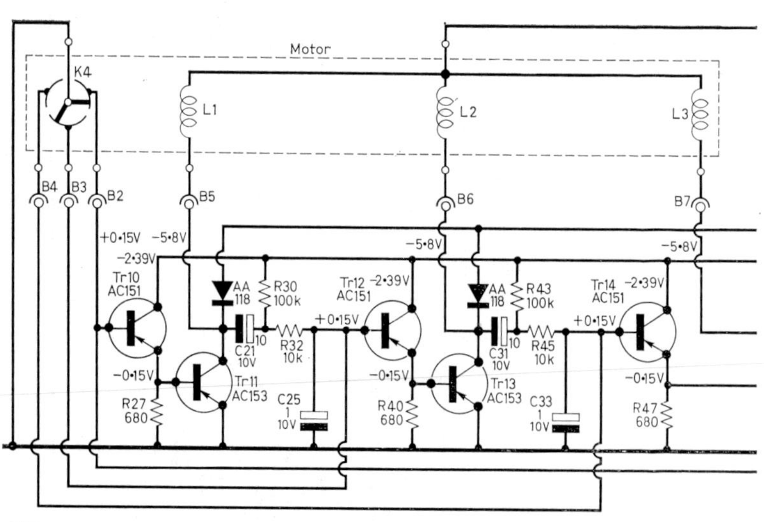

Fig. 5.8: Uher 4000L Motor control circuit and power supply section.

As the motor is fed through R6, the speeds drops, S1 closes and the oscillator again drops out. This action goes on all the time, maintaining the motor at a constant speed. But it does entail constant mechanical switch action and some interference can be caused and has to be guarded against.

The Grundig TK2200, like the Telefunken M300, whose circuit we have just been discussing, also uses two flywheels, contra-rotating, to achieve speed stability. First, the motor is accurately controlled, then the other parts of the mechanism have to be accurately held within close tolerance.

The motor control circuit of this later design of machine, shown in Fig. 5.7, also has an oscillator and several windings, but is much more complicated, making use of transistor switching, a device that Grundig brought to a high standard in their rudimentary circuit applied to the TK6 design. The current to each coil of the motor is switched in sequence through pairs of transistors which are biased 'on' by rectified high frequency signals derived from a rotating coil high frequency commutator.

The Uher 4000L employs a centrifugal switch and a high frequency generator, as shown in Fig. 5.8. Generator frequency is approximately 60kHz and the same system of oscillator damping we have seen before applies here. But the method works by controlling the collector current of Tr11 (and consequently the action of Tr12).

A very different method is favoured by Tandberg for their Model 11 portable, another of the top-class machines. A tachometer and a tone generator are features of this design. On the shaft of the motor there is a phonic wheel which generates an a.c. signal in proportion to speed. This

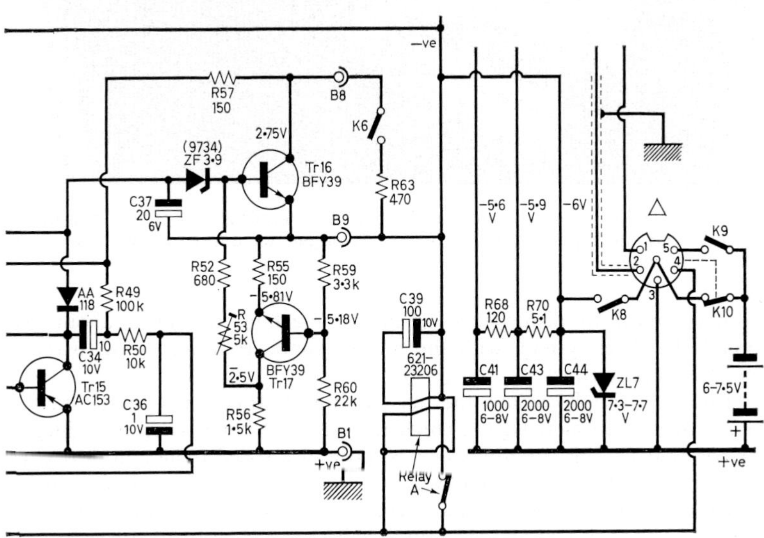

signal is fed to a tuned circuit and a discriminator which produces a d.c. voltage proportional to deviation from the required speed.

The control voltage alters the pulse width of a 4kHz signal and this drives the d.c. motor for intervals that depend on the deviation. So the mean speed tends to remain at a point where there is no deviation. A very similar arrangement is used by Revox in their studio model A77, but as this machine can by no stretch of the imagination be considered portable, it has no place in this chapter!

The use of a double flywheel has been mentioned as a device to 'iron out' short-term speed discrepancies. Tandberg go the other way in their construction of the Model 11. The argument is that a large diameter flywheel, having more mass, smooths out variations of speed, but then becomes subject to disturbance when the machine is moved about. The double flywheel system, with the masses contra-rotating, helps to reduce the disturbance effect.

Fig. 5.9: Using a tape recorder in the car requires a special adaptor to ensure that the input circuits are not damaged by overloads from the car's charging system.

Tandberg simply reduce the mass of the flywheel—it is quite small in this model—and increase the efficiency on the driving parts, including the motor system. This small flywheel is more of a speed reduction device and in consequence the measured wow at 19cm./S is below 0·08%, which is remarkably good. Mean tape speeds were within 0·4 and 0·5% from beginning to end of a reel, measured at beginning and end, at each speed, also excellent.

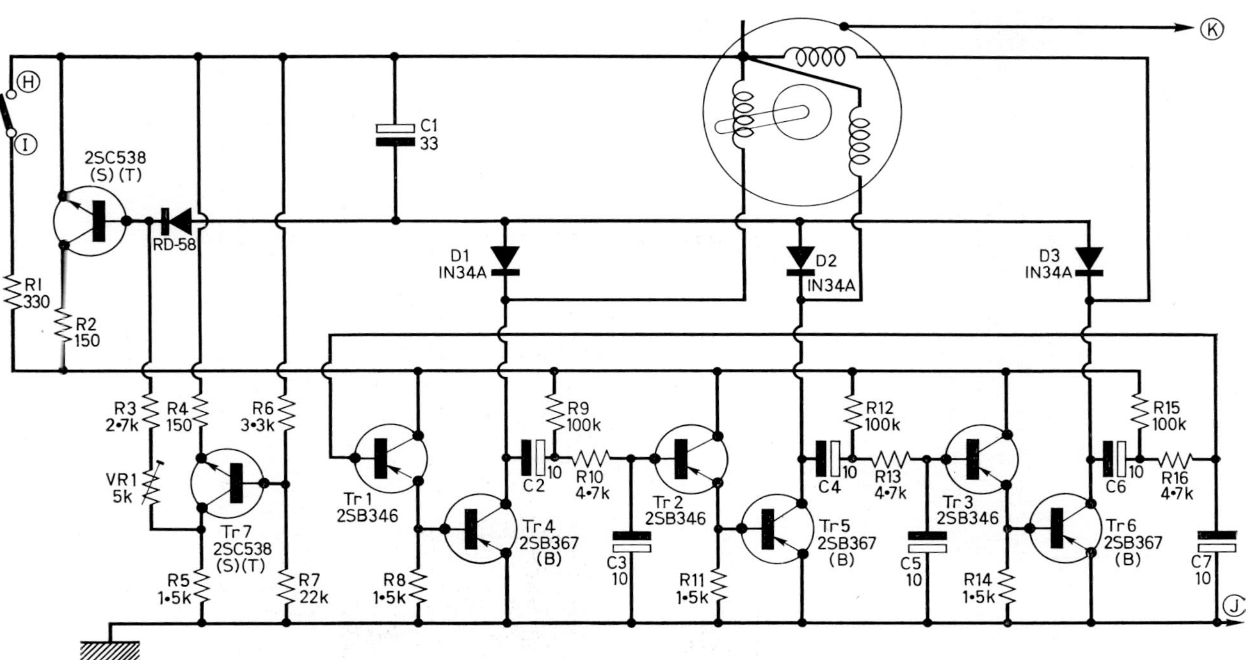

Fig. 5.10: Motor control circuit of the Akai X-5.

G

Servicing Problems

A price has to be paid for the complication of these control circuits and it is usually in the trouble encountered when some component fails. Testing some servo circuits is characterised by a complete abnormality of all voltage and current readings when any part of the system malfunctions. This can lead to some embarrassing situations, such as the one that ensnared the author once when servicing a machine similar to the Akai X-5, whose control circuit appears in Fig. 5.10.

In this design, a brushless motor has three coils switched sequentially by three pairs of transistors in a ring circuit. As one pair is switched off so the next switches on. The time interval is fixed by series and shunt 10 microfarad capacitors and their accompanying charging resistors. The voltage induced in the coils not switched is proportional to motor speed. This is rectified to produce a control voltage and this alters the time constant of each circuit, thus keeping the motor speed steady.

In my case, nothing appeared to work correctly, and the switching sequence, time constants, voltages as given by the distributors and currents as calculated were all wrong. Much time was wasted in proving tests before it was discovered that the problem was purely mechanical, a retardation that prevented the motor from attaining its limit speed to key the control circuits into correct action.

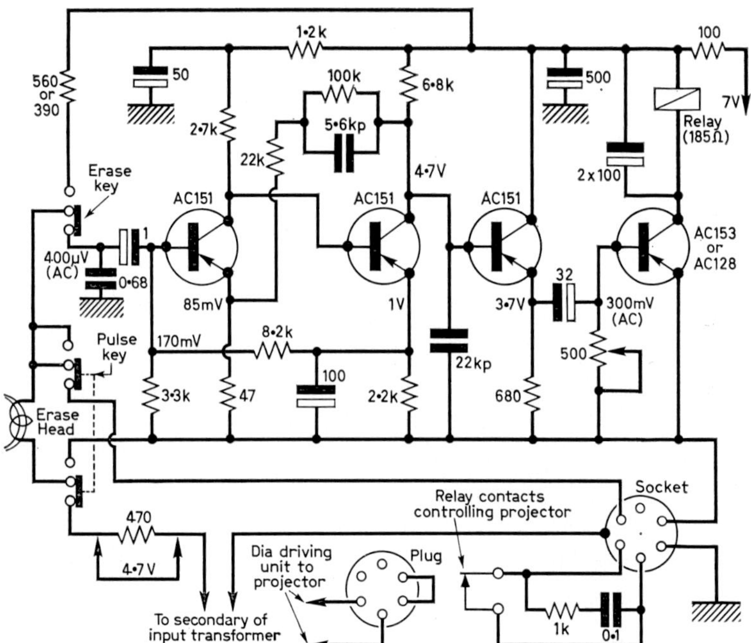

Fig. 5.11: Slide projector pulse circuit *(Sona-Dia)* used with Loewe-Opta 414 and 416 models.

The situation can be even worse with completely electronic controls, such as is used in the Sony TC800 and some of its successors, where hunting can make the control circuit go in and out of limits regularly—and the cause may be something as simple as a worn or dirty bearing!

Slide Projector Circuits

Simplicity is the keynote, too, of many slide projector pulse circuits, which portable tape recorders may have to take in their stride. The example given is that of the Loewe-Opta *Sona Dia*, which may be associated with several models but is most often found linked to the *Optacord* 416. Some pulse circuits can be fairly complicated, but the principle remains simple.

A signal is impressed on the tape coincident with a recorded audio signal, but if necessary at any time after the original signal has been recorded. This keying signal is then used to trigger the projector when the tape is replayed, telling it when to change slides. The snag comes when the recorded signal has to be reprocessed to provide this switching action, and hence some of the complication.

In Fig. 5.11 a four-transistor circuit is used and the first two are ordinary amplifiers. A combined record/erase head has the lower portion recording pulses on the tape. These are simply obtained by transforming down the mains supply to 7 volts and amplifying the third harmonic (150Hz). This gives a heavily saturated impulse to the tape. The erase head has erased previous pulses while the upper erase and record heads are not in operation, but a replay signal is being monitored. Thus, the pulse, is put on during the commentary at a time the operator selects.

On replay, the pulse is amplified, fed through an impedance transforming stage and by triggering the AC128 transistor actuates the relay and gives a switching action to the slide projector. The circuit is easily rendered inactive when the projector is not in use by making the chassis return via a shorting link on the projector plug.

Automatic Level Control

Simple in principle also, not quite as straightforward in practice, is the automatic level control system that we now meet on practically every portable tape recorder that is considered better than a toy. Auto Level is not just a matter of applying a bias in proportion to the signal going through the amplifier. If it were done this way the resultant sound would be a switchback. Instead, a circuit whose block form is shown at Fig. 5.12 has to be employed, to apply a control signal to a specially designed amplifier not only in proportion to the recording signal but also suitably delayed in time and level so that the dynamic range to be handled by the recording system shall not be impaired.

This works by selecting first a threshold above which the control will come into play and then determining the delay rate at which the control will die away so that the amplifier reverts to its full gain. The aim is to

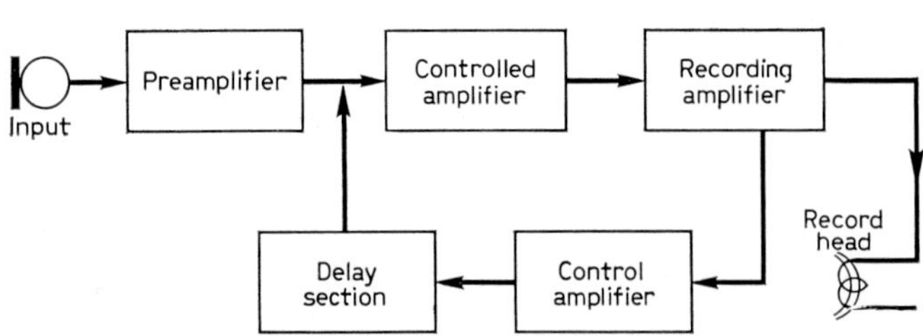

Fig. 5.12: Basic block diagram of auto-gain control system.

operate as near full gain as possible all the time, so that the best signal-to-noise ratio is achieved. Circuits which do this successfully can be quite complicated.

Fig. 5.13 shows first the control range (*a*) and then the effect of the control on a waveform such as a passage of music. These examples are borrowed from a review of the Philips EL3552, which is a small and not exactly portable model, but is excellent to illustrate the principle of ALC. Here we find the control range is 30dB, the signal level dropping this amount in a short space of time when the input signal made by a loud sound triggers the circuits into action.

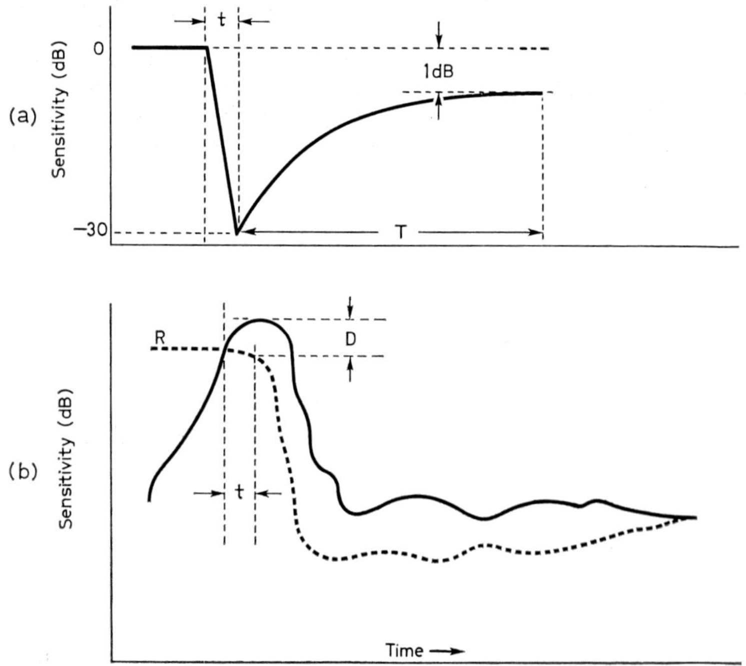

Fig. 5.13: Effect of control time on signal. Rise time response of auto circuits must be fast and delay time long.

This short period, which is very important, is the rise time of the circuit. If no further loud sounds occur, then the bias reduces gradually and the overall gain of the amplifier reaches within 1dB of the original level after some 60 seconds. (Other models have longer recovery times.) The curve of (*b*) gives a better impression of what actually happens. The hard line is the waveform that would be traced out by an uncontrolled signal and the dotted line represents the controlled signal. Time limits are carefully chosen to retain the overall dynamic range and the level R is normal modulation level, 0dB.

Fig. 5.14: 'Dismantled' view of the pocket portable design by Grundig which is widely used as a form of electronic notebook.

Early ALC Systems

Automatic level control has been used for a very long time. Many of the earlier tape recorders were designed as dictating machines. Indeed, as we have seen, it was for this function that the American development of the *Telegraphone* came about. An a.g.c. system of some sort was quickly seen to be a desirable feature for dictation, and some 'brute force' methods ensued. Grundig were the first to introduce refinements to allow for varying thresholds and delay times and their range of *Stenorettes*, some still giving sterling daily service, have been marketed for many years.

The relationship between delay time and the signal-to-noise ratio was the reason for their development of the '*Magic Ear*' principle in later machines, designed for domestic rather than office or industrial use. The best illustration of the technique is by using an idealised signal, as shown in Fig. 5.15. This, (*a*), forms a series of level changes above the system noise level, which is in turn a little way above a cut-off level.

Using the manual control, we should have to watch carefully for overloading and ensure that peaks were kept 'in the green'. The lowest tones would then be down among the noise levels unless we altered the recording gain control to suit. This can be done if we know exactly what is coming and can adjust our levels gradually and unobtrusively as the peaks and troughs approach.

The system of control devised relied upon a very swift rise time, so that the automatic function took over immediately a loud enough sound triggered it. Then, because the recovery time allowed a gradual approach to full gain after the loud sounds were over, the dotted line of (*b*) shows that the result is an overall improvement in signal-to-noise ratio.

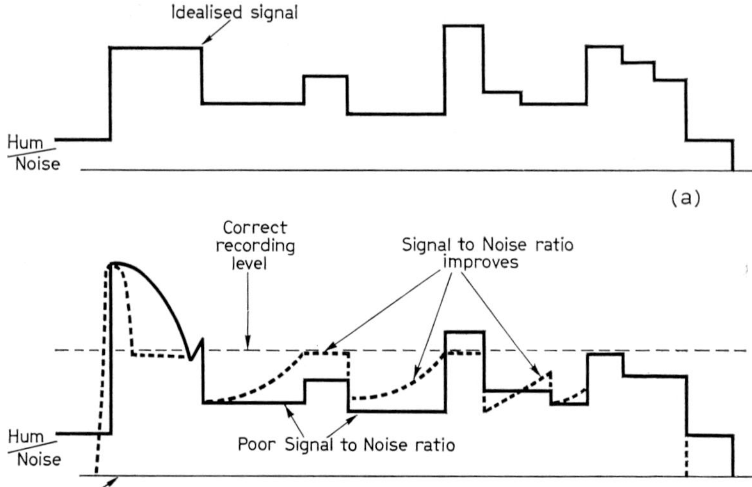

Fig. 5.15: Idealised input signal *(a)* with the result at *(b)* as recorded by manual control (hard line) and automatic level control (dotted line).

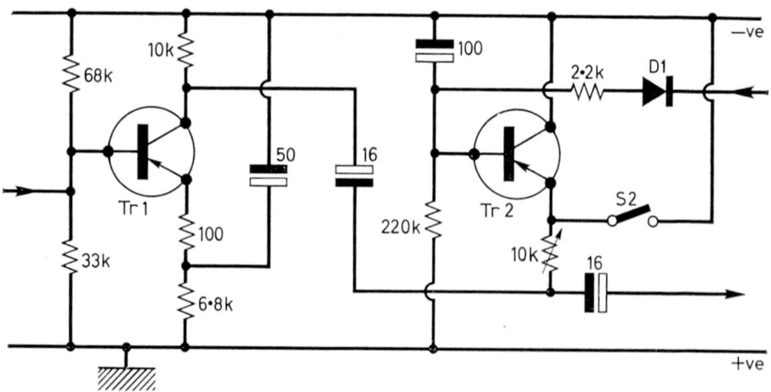

Fig. 5.16c: Early Fi-Cord auto-level circuit which was dropped from later versions of the 202a portable.

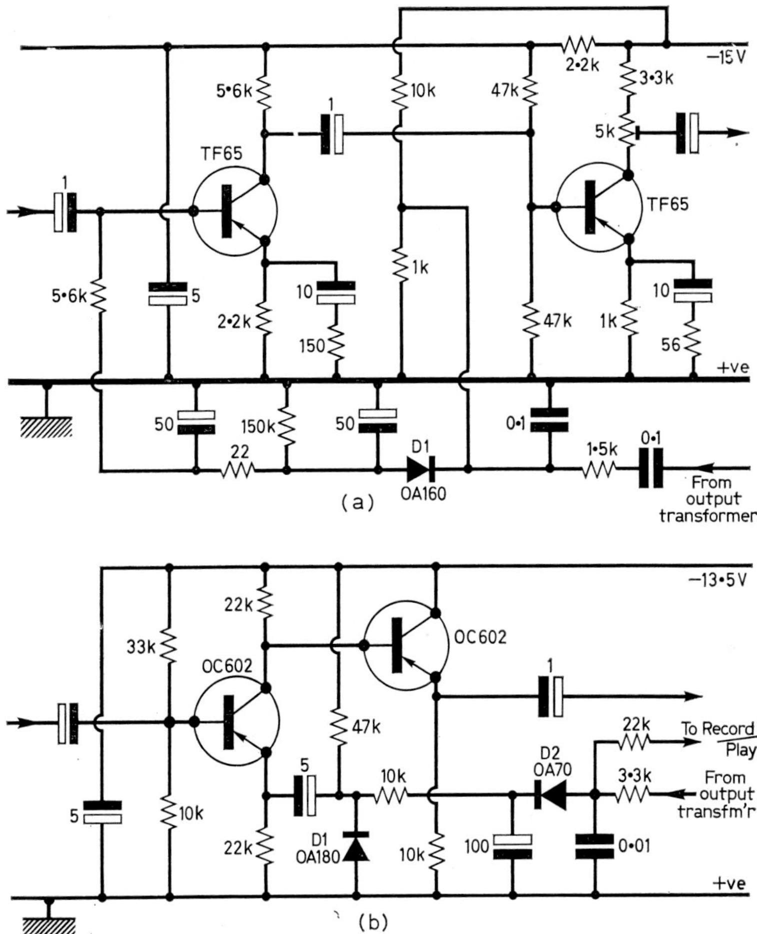

Fig. 5.16: (a) Early version of dictating machine control—Grundig *Stenorette* and *(b) Stenomatic* version with more refined control.

In the early transistored circuits, such as that of Fig. 5.16a/b, some difficulty was experienced. The control signal from the output transformer is applied to the base of the first transistor but a diode stabilising circuit has to be used as the impedance of the stage must not change with the bias—as it would if the control was applied more crudely. The audio signal causes the diode to conduct, applying a varying bias to the base of the transistor.

But this is a direct method, with little refinement. Trouble is that transistors are not so easy to control as valves, where the gain of a vari-mu amplifier stage is easily varied with no drastic changes in the accompanying circuit. Transistor impedances are more touchy than those of valves.

An example of an automatic control circuit that attempted to do the job differently but was not a great success, can be seen at Fig. 5.16c. When the gain control of the Fi-Cord 202A was turned fully anti-clockwise the switch S2 opened, making Tr2 part of the collector load of Tr1. A fixed 10kΩ collector load is added to prevent damage during switching. The emitter bias of Tr2 is set by VR1 whose resistance will now be in its minimum condition.

An audio signal, rectified by D1 is applied to the base of Tr2 and it changes impedance, varying the load of Tr1 collector. As impedance varies inversely with the applied audio signal, the gain passed on from the control circuit is nearly proportionate to the mean of the complete signal—which is not quite what we are striving for, after all!

Later ALC Systems

We have already seen the circuitry of the Akai X-5 and noted its individuality of design in the motor control section, so Fig. 5.17 comes as no surprise and we note that transistor regulation of the feed back signal now comes into play. The signal is again taken from the output transformer, as on previous occasions.

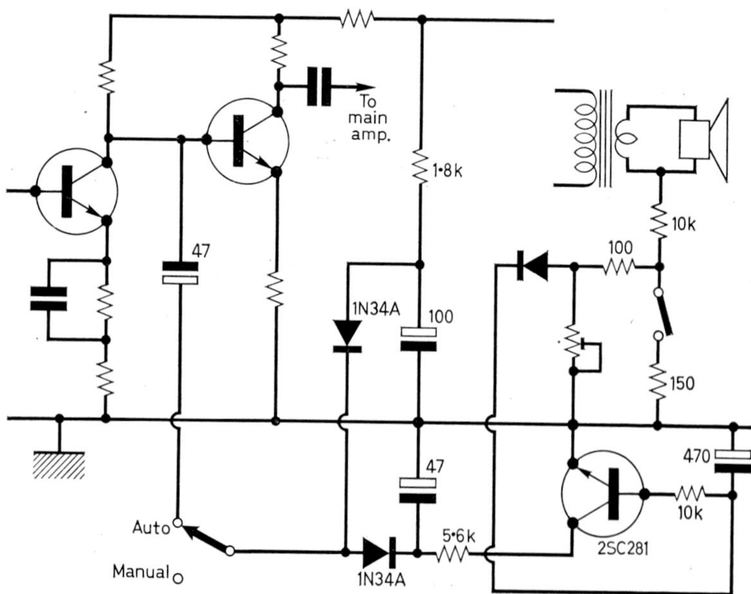

Fig. 5.17: Automatic level control of the Akai X-5 in basic form. This design includes transistor regulation of feedback from the output transformer to the input of the second stage.

As individual in their own way are AEG, whose Telefunken models exhibit some interesting circuitry. One small point that needs mentioning is the device employed to avoid the run-up time when the mechanism engages and recording or replay begins. The two preamplifiers shown in Fig. 5.18 receive their negative voltage for the collectors from Tr107. This AC122 transistor is controlled by the time constant so that the voltage rise across the 100 microfarad electrolytic makes the transistor conductive. Switching mutes the pre-amps for 1–2 seconds, just giving the motor time to get those two flywheels into action.

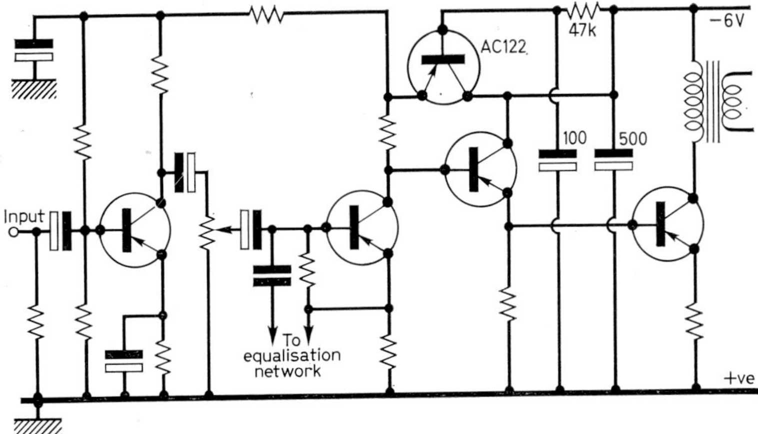

Fig. 5.18: Not strictly ALC, but an automatic muting circuit used by Telefunken on their model 300 to prevent 'start' errors.

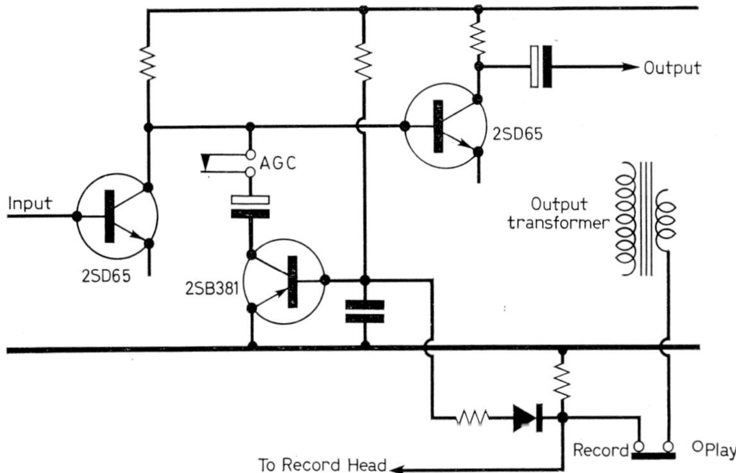

Fig. 5.19: Basic circuit of the much simplified but effective circuits employed by Sony in their TC9000 series.

Talk of portable tape recorders could hardly be concluded without mention of the incomparable Nagra. Most enthusiasts despise the automatic level control for serious recording as it limits their field of action. Nagra is a machine for enthusiasts. As one would expect, its concession to an automatic function is something of a compromise, as if it were grudged. They state, in their literature, that automatic level control can never give as faithful results as one would wish, so they fit instead a balancing circuit which takes the place of the microphone level control.

To avoid bass attenuation, but retain some independence of speech recording, the 6-position switch to the main amplifier bypasses the micro-

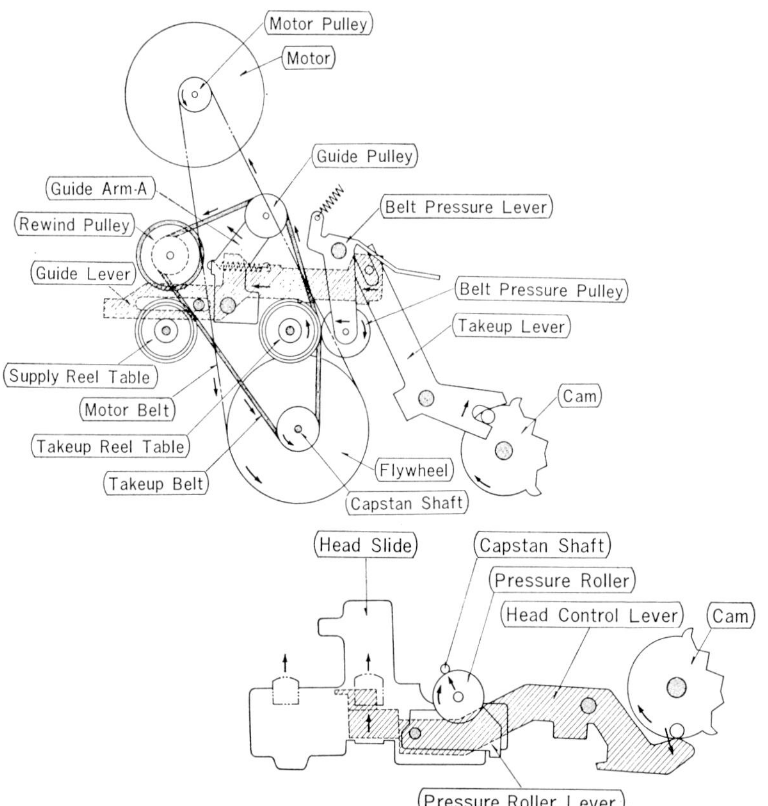

Fig. 5.20: Drive mechanism of the National RQ 204S portable with the function level set to 'Play'. This design is an adaption of the original Philips technique, using Compact Cassettes. The heads are mounted on a sliding plate which moves up to the front edge of the loaded cassette. Drive is via a belt from motor to flywheel, and via a shorter belt and pulleys to the reel hubs. The head slide assembly is separately depicted, showing its relationship with the main cam. This is a typical modern portable design.

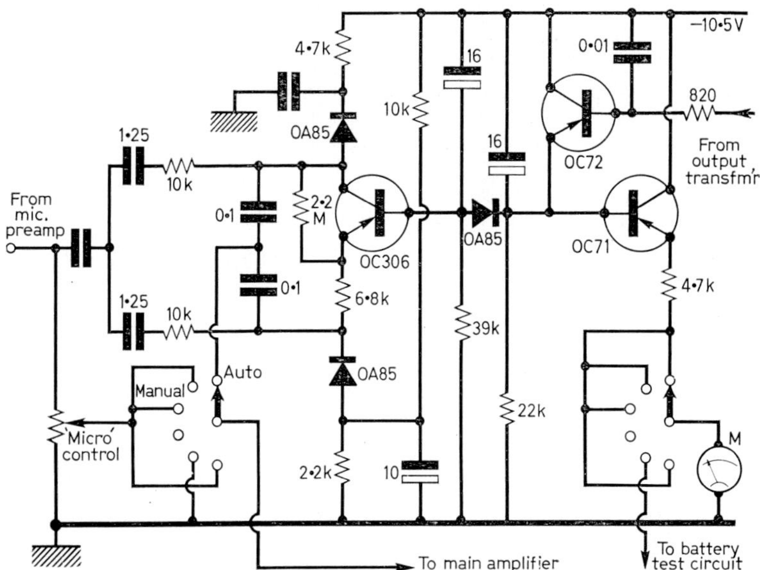

Fig. 5.21: Nagra employ a balancing circuit in place of a microphone level control, as a concession to those who insist on automatic level control systems.

phone level control and applies the signal to an OC306 transistor, controlled by the base bias derived from the control circuit of the OC72. Triggering is again from the output transformer. The stabilised signal is tapped off from the junction of the two 0·1μF capacitors across the OC306 and applied to the main amplifier.

At the other extreme of price, but with as simple a circuit is the excellent Sony TC900, which has a selector switch for a.l.c. Again, a transistor is used to regulate the bias and this time part of the signal fed to the record head is tapped off, rectified and, via the time constant of the 500μF and 20kΩ components, regulates the base bias of the 2SB381. The collector voltage of this transistor is held by the charge on a 30μF capacitor which is connected by the a.l.c. switch to a coupling between the first and second stages. So the gain of this pair of n-p-n transistors is controlled according to the signal level above threshold determined by the working voltages of the p-n-p shunt transistor.

Portability and Miniaturisation

Throughout this chapter we have tried to show that simplicity is often the keynote of good design, and this is especially true of the good portable. But the simplicity can be deceptive, and just as smallness and neatness require finer construction methods, so the whittled down circuitry requires a finer calculation during design.

Miniaturisation is now an accepted thing; not always good for its own sake, but often leading to the advances that can improve our studio machines as well. Examples are the development of the later silicon and field effect transistors, reduction in heat sink area and mass, and latterly the proliferation of integrated circuits which promise not only better serviceability but also a more trustworthy control of recording conditions under all sorts of different circumstances.

Portables have long since evolved beyond the 'toy' stage, and their only current limitation is the size of the loudspeaker from which their replay signals are heard. Anyone who has used an extension loudspeaker on a latter day portable will know that this is a limitation quite easily overcome.

As pointed out several times already, the real crux of portability has come when cassette loading can achieve the standards of performance we had previously come to expect from a reel-to-reel machine. Little has been said in this chapter about cassette mechanisms although one or two of the sub-circuits apply to machines using this style. In the author's opinion, we are facing an imminent revolution that threatens, with the wider release of better tape, to oust the reel-to-reel machine from all but the professional market.

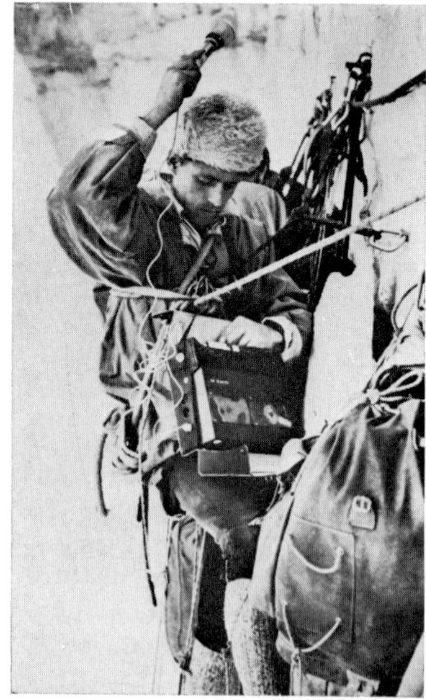

Fig. 5.22 (left): One of the most versatile of out-door machines, the Uher 4000 *Report* is easy to operate and capable of high quality performance; *(right)* making recordings half-way up a mountain is all in a day's work to the Uher 4000.

CHAPTER SIX

TRACKS AND SPEEDS

THE POINT HAS ALREADY been made that the tape recorder has a double personality. It can be entirely self-contained, an aid to study or business, a leisure companion; it can serve as the heart of a hi-fi outfit, a studio rig or a scientific hook-up. When choosing a tape recorder, some consideration of its future use must weight the decision.

For the recording of business conferences, for example, where the machine has to work for a long while unattended, but where the greater part of the material will be speech, a portable machine with automatic recording level facilities, running at a slow speed, but having a 'long-term' function may be chosen. Some of the modern types, with electreset microphones, mains or battery operated and quite unobtrusive in appearance, are ideal for the job.

Running Time

In the foregoing list of facilities, one small factor may be hidden, and needs bringing out. Let us suppose the purpose of the machine is to be, as suggested, conference note-taking. Many of the sessions last for an hour or so. It is neither convenient nor courteous to speakers to have to fiddle with a tape recorder, hastily changing spools, or even with easily loaded cassettes, to encompass a speech longer than the machine can record.

A cassette of the longest playing type at present available lasts for little more than 50 minutes before the need arises to remove and invert it. To be sure of an hour's recording, we need 4¼in. (10·8cm.) spools of triple play tape, which will give us 120 minutes of playing time at 4·75cm./S.

For dictation, where the periods of use are likely to be short, but where back spacing and pausing are both necessary, a slightly different machine will be chosen. The cassette machine comes into its own for this type of periodic employment. Its one drawback, still not solved despite a number of ingenious attempts, is the problem of cueing and indexing.

Whereas a spool of tape can be indexed by a counter driven from one of the spools, or even, ideally, by the tape itself to provide a linear relationship of time and tape length, the only method of indexing a cassette that has so far been used is the very rough and ready one of markings adjacent to the 'window' in the space between the hubs.

Remote control will be required for most machines used for dictating, and little harm is done to a battery-operated cassetted portable by merely interrupting the supply. The drive system is self-contained, and no problems of tape spillage are encountered. So long as it is remembered to neutralise the mechanism after a recording (or replay) session, no troubles should occur with flattened or distorted rubber drive parts.

For mains-operated reel-to-reel tape recorders, the problem is a little more involved and it is advisable to have a solenoid-operated mechanism for remote control, with brake linkage incorporated.

Small or Large?

Portability is an asset that can be very much taken for granted. When there are mains units, rechargeable lead-acid or nickel-alkaline or mercury cells available and a remarkably long life can be achieved, the small machine that can easily be added to a larger rig for quality replay has much in its favour. But there are some arguments against using a small machine where a larger one would probably do a better job.

Some advantages of the larger machine are (*a*) faster wind and rewind functions, (*b*) probably a choice of speeds and often of track systems, extending playing times where necessary, (*c*) improved frequency response and (*d*) greater power output. The facilities that can be incorporated in the larger machine, with power in reserve and more scope for switched refinements may only be used occasionally, but quite often the need for

Fig. 6.1: Not perhaps the best way to use equipment! The author's daughter has not yet taught her dog it is not the 'done thing' to sit on one's Uher 4000L.

Fig. 6.2: Tape recorders perform some unusual functions. This Grundig is apparently being used to con the farmyard fowls that Christmas is still a long way off.

such refinements makes itself felt at the most embarrassing times, and the tape recording enthusiast will generally find it an advantage to own more than one machine.

The main machine should be a multi-speed, multi-function type, as good as one can afford, without wasting money on any unnecessary facility. Such as, for instance, power output stages when the machine is to be part of a rig which already has a power amplifier. The second machine can then be a better, or mains-battery portable, matched to the main machine for dubbing.

Author's Choice

In Fig. 6.1 a selection of the author's personal collection can be seen, with, regrettably, his mainstay, the Bang & Olufsen 2000T, not plainly visible. The dog is nearly sitting on one of the best portables (for its price) on the market, the Uher 4000 Report L, while a smaller 'convenience' portable, a Philips EL3301A/15 sits atop the Telefunken 204. In the background, hidden this time by my daughter, is a Grundig TK400, which was acquired for the purpose of experiment and has proved useful for dubbing, while an Armstrong tuner-amplifier, Grundig and Sony phones and the loudspeakers for the B & O have also found their way into a hastily posed ensemble.

None of these things, not even the 2000T, can be called a fully professional model, but between them they are capable of doing all that the average tape recording enthusiast is likely to require. The range of facilities is enormous, thanks to the switching of the B & O and the input selection and quality of the Uher.

Adding these machines to the remainder of the rig, completes a true hi-fi ensemble. This consists of a Sony gramophone turntable—my pride and joy—a choice of several home built amplifiers, to Dinsdale, Bailey and, lately, Linsley Hood designs, and two sets of stereo loudspeakers, the smaller pair being Wharfedale 'Denton' types and the large pair the Sony version of the Bowers and Wilkin DM3.

It has taken a number of years, much domestic cajolery, hard work with targets in view and some anxious hours sweating over a choice to gather this collection. It is by no means the epitome of hi-fi. Many of my customers have superior equipment: I have to repair or adapt higher quality gear every day.

As can be seen from Fig. 6.3, the range of choice is very wide indeed. And Fig. 6.4., although only a suggestion, shows that the separate units can be shuffled around in a number of ways to make a complete hi-fi rig. The important thing is to make one's choice carefully, with full regard for the facilities one requires and not be misled by fulsome advertising, nor tempted by the glitter of a model with more ambition than achievement.

Track Dimensions

One of the factors that have to be explained to buyers of tape recording equipment is the difference between track dimensions, the way these differences are used and the extra facilities that become available when

Fig. 6.3: Plenty of choice. One view of the author's establishment in Bristol. On the opposite wall, out of view, a comparator allows a selection of equipment combining twelve amplifiers, twenty stereo pairs of loudspeakers, fourteen turntables, five tape decks and five radio tuners, plus remote 'take-anything' positions.

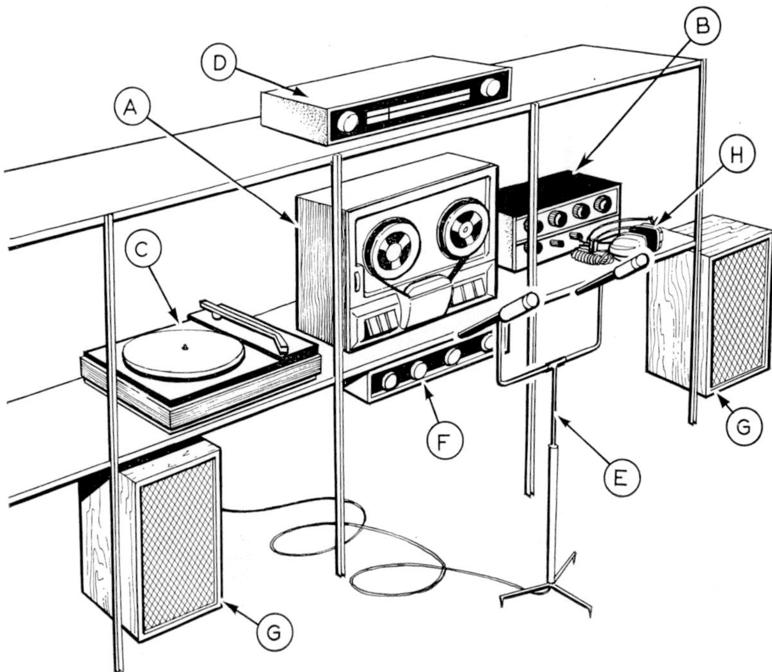

Fig. 6.4: A typical hi-fi set-up that incorporates tape. Items are lettered as follows; A, tape deck; B, power amplifier; C, gramophone turntable; D, radio tuner; E, matched stereo microphones; F, input mixer; G, G, stereo loudspeakers; H, monitoring headphones.

tracks are available simultaneously. Track systems can be baffling to the newcomer to tape recording because there is no visual analogy. He can *see* a disc going around and, if he peers closely, can even watch the oscillations of the needlepoint. But a tape is a tape is a tape, and unless the tracks are developed to show dimensions, could be almost anything to the naked eye.

Direction of travel is obvious, but 'turning over' becomes a tricky problem when the user is not fully aware of what tracks are being used and for which purpose. Fig. 6.5 outlines some of the track dimensions in common use, but it should always be remembered that track numbering and indeed nomenclature can vary from maker to maker.

The basic tape is plain and anonymous, oxidised across its width, and tracks are imposed upon it by the energy imparted by the recording heads. A full-track recording speaks for itself: the recording takes up the full width of the tape. There would be no point in turning it over for the result would simply be the same recording played backwards. The term 'single-track' may be used for 'full-track'.

Half-track recording implies that the width of the recorded band occupies half of the width of the tape. In fact, it takes up slightly less than half the width, as Fig. 6.5 illustrates. We can thus get two such tracks on the tape, and the term 'two-track' becomes synonymous with 'half-track'. Conventionally, the upper track is recorded from left to right.

Half-track stereo recording employs both half tracks, i.e. two-track in the correct sense, and again the tape travel is from left to right, so the tape cannot be inverted as again we would meet the problem of backwards play, there being no unused portion of the tape. Track notation for

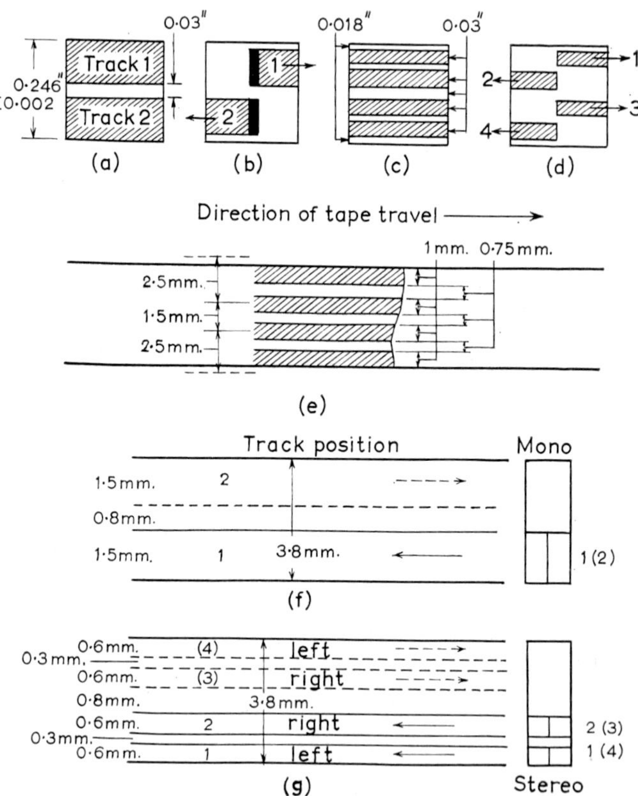

Fig. 6.5: Standard track dimensions. Note that guard tracks are incorporated at the edges of quarter-track recordings, and some half-track recordings also, but heads are sometimes adjusted to scan right to the edge, increasing the central guard track. Tape is not ¼-inch wide, but 0·246-in. ± 0·002-in. *(a)* and *(b)* are half-track dimensions, *(c)* and *(d)* quarter-track, with dimensions in inches and *(e)* has the equivalent metric dimensions. *(f)* and *(g)* show the mono and stereo track positions for cassette tapes. See text for further details.

such a two-track stereo recording is 2/2 with some manufacturers. For mono half-track recording, the equivalent method of notation would be 1/2.

Quarter-track recording occupies the first and third track positions, if we read four tracks on a so-called quarter-inch tape from top to bottom. Again the direction of tape travel is left to right, so the tape is run through first on track 1, inverted, then recorded on track 4, again inverted and by changing the track selector switch is then recorded on track 3, inverted and recorded on track 2. So the track switch will be marked 1–4 and 2–3. Stereo recording uses tracks 1 and 3 together, then 2 and 4

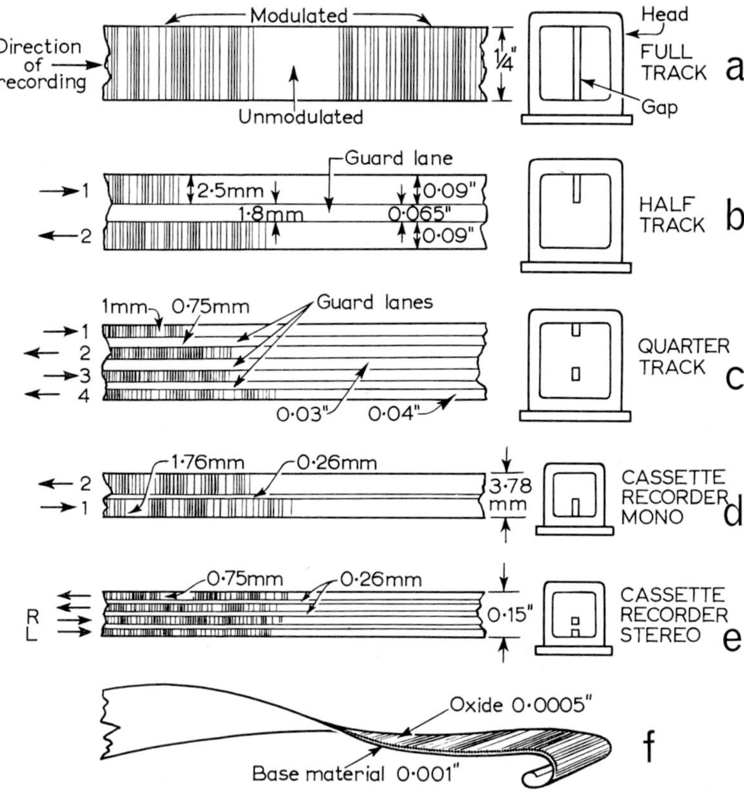

Fig. 6.6: Some additional track dimensions and spacings, showing also the effect of modulation and the position of the head gap. Note direction of each recorded track, and the accepted numbering. *(a)* full-track, *(b)* half-track, *(c)* quarter-track, *(d)* mono cassette tape, *(e)* stereo cassette tape and *(f)* the dimensions and formation of the coated tape.

together after inversion, making the stereo and mono machines compatible.

Compatibility is the big curse of the radio, television and audio industry. In an effort to avoid making any equipment obsolete and being faced with the charge of rousing business by converting standards, great compromises have taken their place in electronics history, to the ultimate benefit of no-one.

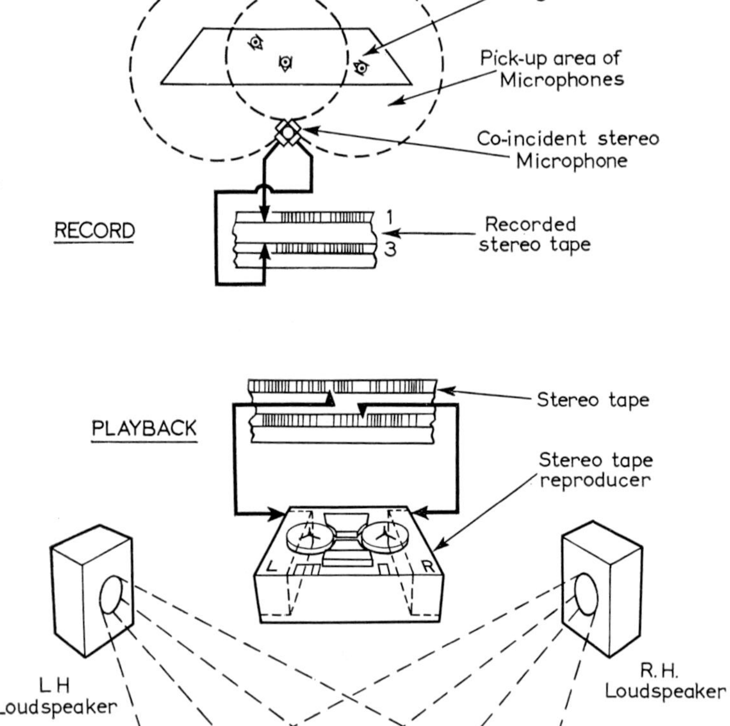

Fig. 6.7: Four-track stereo tape recording is now the norm (with 8-track, four channel stereo already past the experimental stage) and the way sounds are picked up, recorded, reproduced and heard is presented here diagramatically.

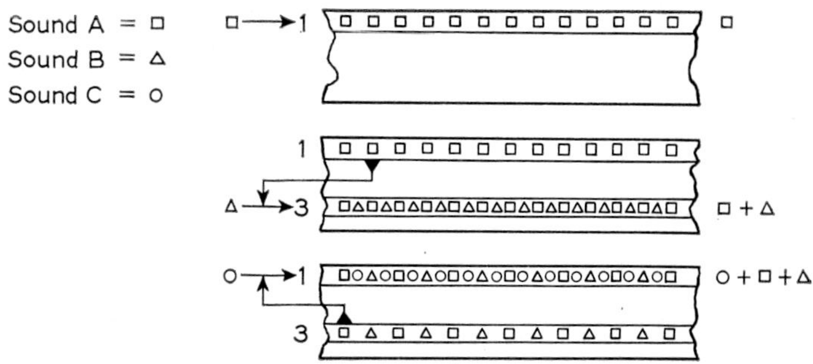

Fig. 6.8: Addition of sounds is possible by switching a stereo four-track tape recorder so that one channel records while the other plays. First, the original sound is recorded on track 1, the tape is rewound, this recording is replayed and monitored, and fed to track 3 at the same time as a new sound is recorded on. The process is repeated, adding the combined first and second recording to the new recording on track 1. In this way a complete ensemble of sound can be built, and the process has often been used professionally.

Cassette Tracks

Cassettes are recorded a little differently. The direction of travel of the tape is the same, left to right, but the mono version uses the lower half of the 0·015in.-wide tape while the stereo version uses two tracks within this same lower half. In this case, the tracks lie side by side, so the mono machine can still play back a stereo recording while the stereo machine will successfully handle a mono recording.

But there is insufficient separation on inexpensive domestic machines for the system of single 'stereo' tracks to be used with the narrower cassette tape. This does not mean that such narrow tracks are an impossibility. Eight, sixteen, and now it is reported, thirty-two track heads have been produced for professional machines.

In the 'pop' musical world, where studio time is the most expensive factor in production of records, a number of tracks can be used and mixed and 'trimmed' or tailored electronically by very highly skilled engineers long after the musicians have gone to their next appointment.

Multi-track Systems

Once the idea of a recorded track on a blank tape has been fully grasped, the added complication of transferred recordings is less of a hurdle. Multiplay, Duoplay, Sound-on-sound, Parallel tracking and Sound-with-sound are all terms that may be encountered and all depend on the provision of more than one track coincident on the tape. Stacked heads, i.e. those with track windings one above the other, are used for these facilities.

Multiplay is the recording of one track that has already been recorded on another track, with the ability to mix this with an independent input. To exemplify: a music background is recorded on track 1. The tape is rewound to zero, The Multiplay facility or Sound-on-sound is selected. Another recording is made on track 3, and as this is checked for modulation level, the sound already on track 1 is mixed with it.

The result could be the musical background with a vocal line added. It may then be necessary to intersperse some sound effects. So again the Multiplay facility is selected and the material on Track 3 is now re-recorded on track 1 while the effects can be added from an external source. In theory, this can go on indefinitely, and a complete orchestra can be built up from a number of individual instruments. In practice, the new recordings tend to weaken the older ones very slightly by the self-erasing effect of the bias, and the noise level increases as re-recordings are made.

The limit depends on the quality of the recordings and the complexity of the machine. It also depends on the ability of the operator—but that is quite another story. For true multiplay operation there must be stereo heads and a separate record and replay amplifier. The complete stereo tape recorder, with separate amplifiers for each channel should be adaptable for multiplay with the minimum of trouble.

When choosing, this point should be watched, for there are some on which the level of the signal being fed out from the replaying channel is not controllable, i.e. the gain control is subsequent to the point of line take-off. On others, input mixing is restricted, so that the replayed signal is possibly not controllable when the record gain is operating on the new source.

Although these problems are not insurmountable, because external mixing and attenuation can be done, it is much better to ensure that the facility is inbuilt if it may be required. A stereo machine need not necessarily include the multiplay facility. Four-track mono machines can be adapted with the aid of an external monitor amplifier, some of which are available from the major tape recorder manufacturers. Again, there are limits.

Synchronised channels are available by using an external amplifier on replay, where two simultaneous recordings can be replayed. For correct synchronisation it is necessary to record the second track while listening to the first. So the second track of a simple mono machine used in conjunction with an external preamplifier will have switching that brings its signal out to one of the sockets for this purpose, and not all four-track mono machines are so equipped.

The replay amplifier need not be particularly powerful, it is only used for monitoring, and it is generally desirable to use headphones for such monitoring. A typical application for such a facility is language training. More will be said about this in Chapter 8.

Duoplay is the ability to parallel the two recorded tracks to one output, and can be used to a limited extent for the production of tapes with sound effects, or for the making of trick recordings or, again, for langu-

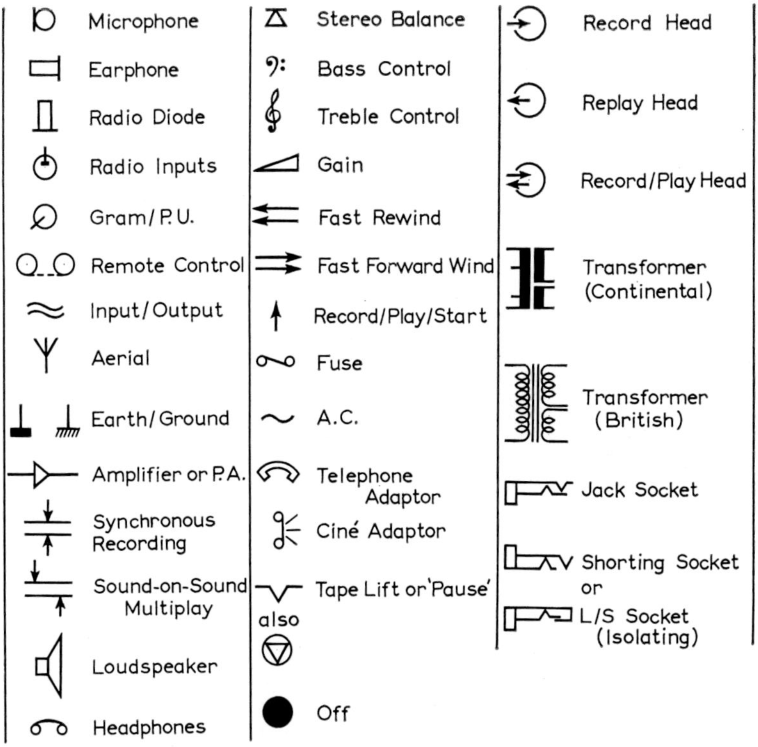

Microphone
Earphone
Radio Diode
Radio Inputs
Gram/P.U.
Remote Control
Input/Output
Aerial
Earth/Ground
Amplifier or P.A.
Synchronous Recording
Sound-on-Sound Multiplay
Loudspeaker
Headphones
Stereo Balance
Bass Control
Treble Control
Gain
Fast Rewind
Fast Forward Wind
Record/Play/Start
Fuse
A.C.
Telephone Adaptor
Ciné Adaptor
Tape Lift or 'Pause'
also
Off
Record Head
Replay Head
Record/Play Head
Transformer (Continental)
Transformer (British)
Jack Socket
Shorting Socket
or
L/S Socket (Isolating)

Fig. 6.9: Operational symbols.

a
Pin 2 is always earth or chassis connection
b
Common earth
Right channel input
Left channel input
Right channel output
Left channel output

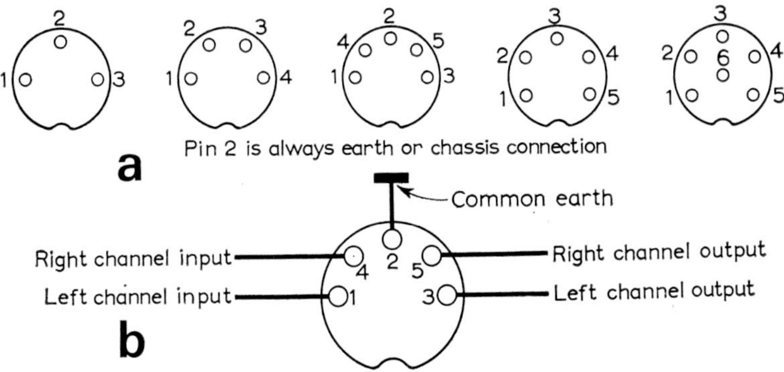

Fig. 6.10: Symbols used for the principal DIN sockets, showing five different standards of pin connection. *(b)* shows the accepted standard for input and output connections for stereo operation. There are many variations for parallel play, dubbing etc., and it is wise to check each individual socket from the maker's book of instructions.

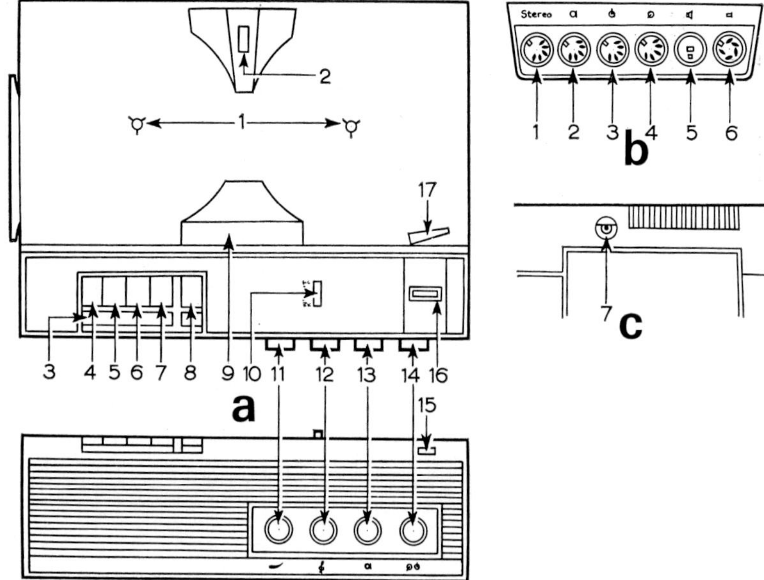

Fig. 6.11: Operational layout of a typical reel-to-reel tape recorder, with principal parts numbered. Code is as follows: *(a)*

1 Spool holders (7in. diameter spool).
2 Tape position indicator.
3 Stop key.
4 Record key.
5 Fast rewind.
6 Start.
7 Fast forward wind.
8 Pause.
9 Sound Channel.
10 Track selector.
11 Volume/Mains on-off.
12 Tone.
13 Recording level (microphone).
14 Recording level (radio/gram).
15 Control lamp.
16 Recording level indicator.
17 Speed selector: $3\frac{3}{4}$ & $1\frac{7}{8}$ips.

Sockets *(b)* and *(c)* are as follows:

1 Preamplifier and stereo output: Right channel, Pin 1; Screen, Pin 2; 16 V D.C., Pin 3.
2 Microphone: Pins 1 & 4 in parallel; Screen, Pin 2
3 Radio/amplifier/second recorder: (Record), Pins 1 & 4 in parallel; (Play back), Pins 3 & 5 in parallel; Earth Pin 2.
4 Gram: Pins 1, 3 & 5 in parallel; Earth Pin 2.
5 Extension speaker: Pins 1 & 2 in parallel; Pin 4.
6 Headphone: Pins 1 & 2 in parallel; Pin 4.
7 Foot switch (remote stop-start control).

age teaching. On a machine with all the above facilities one would expect to find separate record, play and erase heads, and then the added facility of 'echo' becomes available.

The signal read off by the replay track is fed round via the amplifiers and re-enters the recording channel of the same track. To do this, the record and play amplifiers must be cross-switched, i.e. the signal from the head winding for track 1 has to be replayed by amplifier 2 while the record amplifier for 1 is in operation. Again, separate record and replay amplifiers are a necessity. The amount of echo depends on the spacing between record and replay heads and the speed of the tape transport.

Some of the sound-on-sound, multiplay, duoplay, parallel play and other functions are illustrated graphically in Figs. 6.7 and 6.8, and it is often the case that the symbolic illustration is not fully understood by a prospective purchaser, so that he may buy a machine that proves to be unsuitable, simply because he was not conversant with the functions of the machine when it was originally demonstrated to him. Given a persuasive enough salesman, and a timid customer, quite an unsuitable sale could too easily be made.

Without wasting too many words on description, the illustrations Figs. 6.9 to 6.13 have been included. A study of the symbols in general use, plus a knowledge of the standard nomenclature and standard speeds, dimensions and principal functions may save the reader a few wasted pounds—certainly more than the cost of this modest volume!

Sizes and Speeds

Going on from there, we can give the list of principal conversions from British to Metric sizes and speeds, and in Table 6.2 we can show the tape length per spool diameter for different grades of tape, with playing times for a single track (i.e. multiply this time by four for 4-track mono and double it for stereo), as originally published by BASF. There may be small discrepancies between these figures and those published by other tape manufacturers, but they are certainly not of any significance to anyone except the professional tape recordist whose purchasing figure makes inches important.

Fig. 6.12: A combination of words and symbols may be found, as with the Bang & Olufsen 2000K.

Tape Speeds		**Tape Spool Sizes**	
15in./S	38·1cm./S*	7 inches	17·5cm.
7½in./S	19·1cm./S*	5¾ inches	14·6cm.
3¾in./S	9·5cm./S	5 inches	12·7cm.
1⅞in./S	4·8cm./S*	4 inches	10·2cm.
$\frac{15}{16}$in./S	2·4cm./S	3 inches	7·6cm.

* accepted figures are 38, 19 and 4·75cm./S respectively.

1 inch=2·54cm. 1 mil.=25μ (microns). 1μ (micron)=0·00004in.
1 thou'=0·001in.=25·4μ 1cm.=0·3937 inches (0·4in. approx.)

Table 6.1 Metric Conversions

Tape Thickness	*Spool Dia.*	*Tape Length*	*Playing Time per track (minutes at speed per sec.)*		
			1⅞″	3¾″	7½″
Standard Tape	5″	600′	60	30	15
	5¾″	900′	90	45	22½
	7″	1200′	120	60	30
	8¼″	1800′	180	90	45
Long Play Tape	3″	210′	22	11	5½
	4″	450′	45	22½	11
	4¼″	600′	60	30	15
	5″	900′	90	45	22½
	5¾″	1200′	120	60	30
	7″	1800′	180	90	45
	8¼″	2400′	240	120	60
	10″	3600′	360	180	90
Double Play Tape	3″	300′	30	15	7½
	4″	600′	60	30	15
	4¼″	900′	90	45	22½
	5″	1200′	120	60	30
	5¾″	1800′	180	90	45
	7″	2400′	240	120	60
Triple Play Tape	3″	450′	45	22½	11
	4″	900′	90	45	22½
	4¼″	1200′	120	60	30
	5″	1800′	180	90	45
	5¾″	2400′	240	120	60
	7″	3600′	360	180	90

Table 6.2 Tape Playing Times

Despite our avowed intention to retain the metric system through this book, we have set this table in the old nomenclature of inches of spool diameter and inches per second of tape speed, and feet of tape length, to allow correlation with the information that has been given elsewhere.

Used in conjunction with the table 6.1, which gives the necessary conversion factors, the diagrams and figures given here should aid choice and—we hope—facilitate the correct use of the tape recorder. Brief mention must also be made here of two more aspects of tape recorder usage that are of extreme importance already and likely to grow in importance as time goes by.

Storing Tape

First, tape storage, including the special library packages and protective devices. The way in which some users neglect their basic material—the tape—makes a service engineer shudder. We have already shown how small the discrepancy can be to cause a significant drop in quality and output. Tapes left lying about, unprotected, in the variations of temperature and humidity that can occur, even in normal domestic conditions, tapes begrimed and spools warped, tapes twisted, stretched and curled . . . we see these things every day.

Owners of discs are less inclined to treat their entertainment medium so

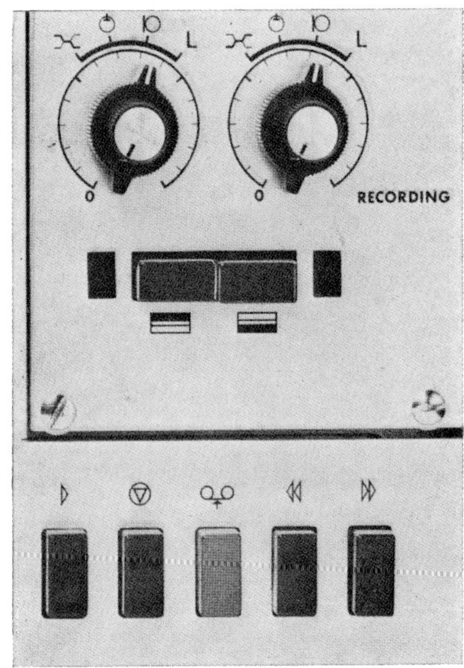

Fig. 6.13: A practical view of operational symbols as used on the Philips PRO12.

cavalierly. They usually sleeve and protect them, then store them upright, often in specially constructed library shelves or boxes. Tapes can be similarly stored and protected. There are numerous library systems, including those designed to conform with postal regulations and able to accept either cassettes or small spools. Prepacked message tapes can be purchased and are internationally recognized. Storage is now no problem with plastics library boxes that take single tapes or combinations of larger reels, with indexing facilities as well.

Storage can be made even easier, and another facility, endless loop running, may be added to the vast range of entertainment possibilities offered by tape. The Mobius loop, an endless reel of specially lubricated tape encapsulated so that the spool can be mounted on a single hub is in wide use for background music and other applications where a long programme and the minimum of attendance is required.

Provided the mounting hub has a small amount of back tensioning, and the head gate can accommodate the tape, this is the answer for the supermarket, the public house and other such places where a continuous programme, repeated at intervals, is the basic requirement. The tape only runs in one direction, being spooled off the outside of the reel to return to the inside, and indexing is not possible without some complications.

As a final note in this chapter on the practical significance of tape speeds and track dimensions, it should again be stressed that for higher quality the general rule is higher speed and a wider track, but modern tape developments have considerably narrowed the quality margin so that very acceptable results can be obtained at medium and even slow speed on track dimensions (as with cassette operation) that would have been scoffed at ten years ago.

What of tomorrow? Already, four-track stereo is the accepted norm, and although there are one or two companies concentrating on the low-noise aspect of two track stereo, this is strictly for the professional. Soon we shall all be involved in 8-track, four-channel stereo, with the rear of two pairs of loudspeakers supplying the ambience that duplicates the true sensation of being in the concert hall.

At the time of writing some interesting experiments are going on in America and elsewhere, Coupled with the keen competition by tape makers, this expansion of tape recording is another welcome aspect—even if it does make it more difficult for us to choose, and maybe use, the machine we want to buy.

CHAPTER SEVEN

MICROPHONES

THE MICROPHONE IS A TRANSDUCER; that is to say, a converter of energy. It receives the vibrations in the air, made by sounds, and changes them to electrical impulses which can be used to power an amplifier. These vibrations are very small. At a sound pressure of 0dB, the relative pressure in dynes/$cm.^2$ being 0·0002 (our reference value at 1kHz) the sound particle velocity will be as little as 0·0000048cm./S, the pressure gradient 0·000037 (at 1cm. distance) and the particle displacement only $0{\cdot}76 \times 10^{-9}$cm.

At 100dB, these figures can all be multiplied by 100,000, and still the actual air movement is extremely small, and the variations in pressure of the waveform are also minute. As an example, at the threshold of hearing, the movement at the diaphragm of a microphone caused by a 3kHz tone is 10^{-10}in., or one ten thousand millionth of an inch. The sound pressure fluctuations roughly correspond to a change in atmospheric pressure that would result from a vertical movement of 1/30,000in.

Intensity Range

These factors are applicable to hearing, reminding us how delicate our aural apparatus can be. If we were able to nod our heads (like those little dogs in the back windows of cars) at audio frequencies, the resultant motion would cause atmospheric pressure changes in the ear that would deafen us. The possible intensity range that has to be handled by our ears is about 20 million to 1. In terms of sound pressure, this is about 4,000 : 1. For example, a solo violin playing *ppp* gives about 0·0000038 accoustical watts, while a 75 piece orchestra at *fff* gives the acoustical equivalent of 70 electrical watts.

It has to be remembered that sound waves are pressure variations in both time and distance. If we trace out a graph of a waveform for the particle displacement and on the same time axis plot another of particle velocity we shall see that the pressure is greatest where the change is most rapid, i.e. at the peaks, and is normal (not zero, but normal) where the waveform crosses the line, i.e. where displacement is momentarily not changing.

The velocity of the air, however, is at maximum where the displacement changes most rapidly. So the magnitude of the velocity of a sound

Fig. 7.1: Small microphone capsules, such as the one depicted above, are being built into many portable tape recorders.

waveform depends on the magnitude of the pressure variation, and therefore on the intensity of the sound. But the velocity of the waveform through the air is a fixed figure, depending on temperature, mainly, and factors like wind direction and strength secondarily. The velocity at normal temperature is taken to be around 1,130ft./S (or 34,400cm./S). Sound, of course, travels through other media, but at different rates, and with different characteristics. We are not concerned, at this moment, with other than the effect on the microphone of a sound propagated through air.

Wave Motion

Sound moves through the atmosphere in a wave motion. There are three possible types of wave motion: (*a*) Longitudinal, with the direction of motion the same as propagation, (*b*) transverse, as the surface of water, often wrongly used as an analogy for sound waves, and (*c*) torsional. We need only concern ourselves with (*a*) but must differentiate between plane and spherical waves.

Plane waves are those whose whole front moves at right angles to the direction of rotation. The conditions where one encounters plane waves are rare. A piston in a pipe, for example, where the wavelength of the sound is large compared to the diameter of the tube, would produce a plane wave. We are more likely to be concerned with spherical waves, where the sound diverges outwards from the source which causes it.

It is convenient to consider a waveform as a plane wave when the microphone is some distance from the source, and as a spherical waveform when the microphone is near the source. Microphones have to work in both these extremes, and in addition are designed for omni-directional, concentrated direction, distant and close work, to operate in high background noise conditions or to be extremely sensitive to all sound.

Types have been developed to withstand the weather, to give good results in high winds, to 'focus' on distant sounds or to register close talking faithfully. Others are specially designed to be small and unobtrusive, to withstand physical shock and even to work successfully under water. We are not so much concerned with the vast variety of types as with the general divisions into which we may conveniently classify them.

Types of Microphone

There are four main classes of microphone:

(*a*) the carbon granule,
(*b*) the piezo-electric (crystal),
(*c*) the dynamic (moving coil) and
(*d*) the capacitor microphone.

As well as these main types, there are a number of special instruments such as the hot-wire microphone, where air particle velocity acts on a heated wire of low thermal capacity; the thermo-couple design, which is somewhat similar, but operates by the sound pressure variations; ionic transducers which employ the resistance variations of electric arcs; electronic microphones that operate directly into a thermionic valve or a magnetic coupling to its grid; capillary designs, where sound waves change the surface tension of an electrolyte to produce potential changes; micro-

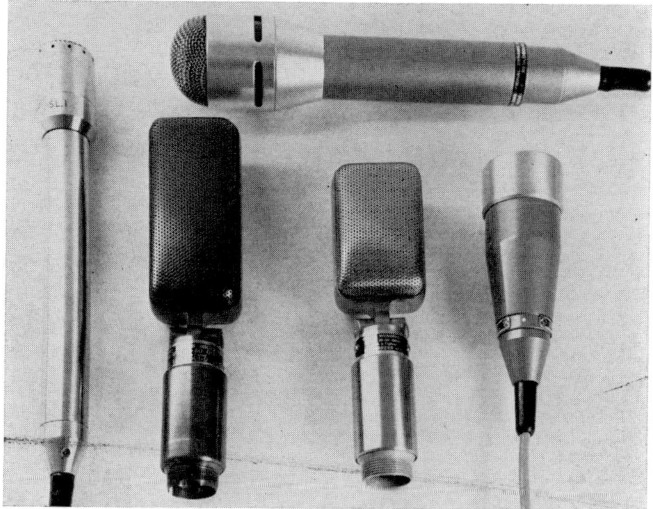

Fig. 7.2: A selection of ribbon and dynamic microphones by Reslosound, made to exacting specifications and tested in line with the recommendations by the International Electro-Technical Commission.

phones employing the magneto-striction principle and even one—about which more later—that takes advantage of radiation.

We can further reduce our list of four types by omitting (*a*), which operates by sound pressure variations on carbon granules, producing what is in fact a variable resistance. This is the type found in many telephones. It is adequate for speech, but subject to temperature variations and with a high inherent noise level and would never be used for any serious tape recording. Its only advantage is a high output; (subsidiary advantages such as a 'bend' in the characteristic which can protect the listener against sudden loud sounds and can suppress low intensity sounds are of interest only to telephony students).

Wave Type Microphones

Of the other three, we are concerned not only with their 'conversion efficiency' which may be less than 1%, but also by the way they operate in sound fields. Again we have to make some subdivision. Wave type microphones are constructed to have directional properties, and their size is larger than the wavelengths over the normal operating range, to take advantage of wave interference effects. The alternative, a 'point' type microphone operates by the action of a soundwave pressure at a point which is small (or points which are close together) and these are small compared to the wavelength.

It should be remembered that wavelength and frequency are inter-related, their product being the velocity of sound, i.e. $c = \lambda f$

Fig. 7.3 (left): Microphones have to stand up to a lot of pounding, and this AKG D119ES is designed specifically for this purpose.

Fig. 7.4 (right): A good quality directional dynamic microphone, such as this Beyer *Sound Star* X1, is capable of doing justice to that difficult instrument the flute.

Fig. 7.5: One of the most widely used microphones for years, the Sennheiser MD411 has three switched impedances and a very efficient cardioid polar response.

Fig. 7.6: An inexpensive dynamic microphone by AKG, the D7D-HL has two impedances and an omnidirectional polar diagram.

where c = 1,130ft./sec. (34,400cm./S), λ is the wavelength in the appropriate units and *f* the frequency in Hertz. For example, the wavelength of a 20Hz note is 56$\frac{1}{3}$ft. (1,720cm.), while the wavelength of a 20kHz note is 0·67in. (1·72cm.) and the wavelength of our 1kHz reference frequency is 1ft. 2in., or 34·4cm.

There are two ways in which this waveform can energise a microphone. Pressure operated microphones work by the sound impinging on one side of the diaphragm, the other side of the diaphragm being closed off by the structure. They are theoretically sensitive to sounds from all angles, although there are many designs whose housings modify this rule, and in all cases the upper frequency response, where the wavelength becomes near the physical size of the housing, is considerably affected by shape, giving some degree of directionality.

Velocity operated microphones work by the sound wave impinging on the diaphragm so that its displacement is proportional to the particle velocity. And as velocity has direction as well as magnitude, being a vector quality, then the velocity microphone is basically directional.

The free-ribbon variety of microphone and the pressure-gradient type both come into this category, with the sound wave acting on both sides of the diaphragm. In the case of the ribbon microphone, movement of the ribbon is caused by the pressure difference between the two sides. But although truly a pressure gradient device, it cannot be named absolutely as a velocity microphone: no ribbon can be made slender enough to respond *only* to velocity.

Nevertheless, we shall continue to be conventional and call the ribbon microphone a velocity mic. to distinguish it from its pressure-operated fellows. Just to confuse the issue, however, we find specially constructed ribbon microphones with many of the characteristics of moving-coil microphones, with modified housings to produce a cardioid response, and even, in some cases, with one side of the ribbon completely closed to the sound wave. So before life gets too confusing, let's take a look at the various types of microphone that are available and compare their characteristics.

The Piezo Microphone

Piezo-electric or crystal microphones depend for their operation on the peculiar characteristic of Rochelle salts, quartz or tourmaline to generate small voltages when physically stressed. A crystal wafer is cut and mounted in such a way that sound pressure on a diaphragm applies a force that tends to twist the crystal.

The crystal will have a high resonant frequency and is normally operated below its natural resonance. The upper frequency limit is determined by the resonance of the series mass and the compliance of the crystal and is seldom much better than 7 or 8kHz within ±3dB limits. They are largely capacitative, need to work into a high impedance load (see later notes on matching) and are temperature-sensitive.

They are quite efficient, an output level of −55dB being average into an amplifier impedance of 2MΩ or more. Normal practice is to damp the diaphragm with the acoustic resistance of a sintered porous-metal plate. or similar screen, which helps reduce unwanted resonances.

The Sound-cell Microphone

Sound-cell crystal microphones are a little more expensive and have correspondingly better properties (or, not so many drawbacks). In this design, two bi-morph 'bender' plates are sealed and attached together at their edges to form a 'box' round a small air cavity. Some types even have a solid construction, with flat diaphragms, approaching the ideal of the capacitor microphone, but without the frequency range that the latter can handle.

Their acoustic impedance is almost infinite and their sensitivity is high,

−50 to −70dB being typical. Stacks can be wired together to produce a composite unit, still small enough to retain the desired omni-directional quality. They are, of course, pressure-operated.

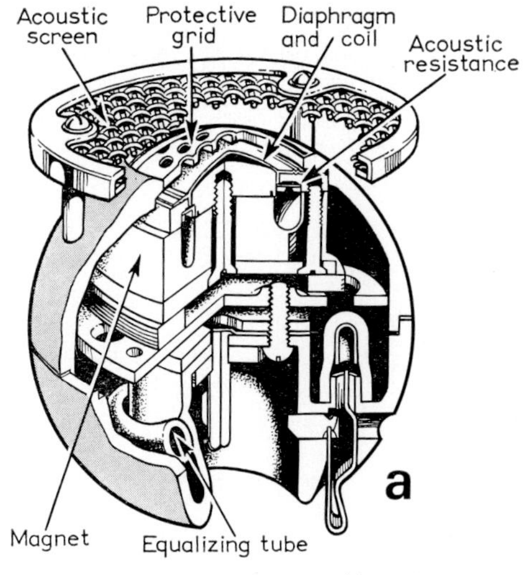

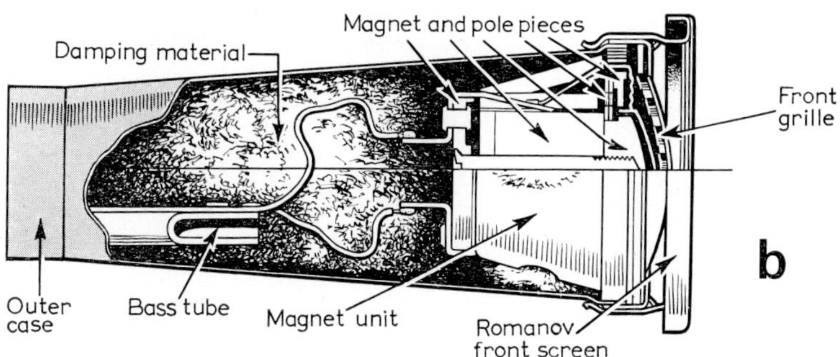

Fig. 7.7: Basic construc- of moving coil microphones. *(a)* the early ball and biscuit type, and *(b)* adaptation of the same principal to the smaller stick-type microphone. Both these designs are by Standard Telephones Ltd.

The ADP Type

The last type of crystal microphone that need concern us, more widely used in some public address applications than with domestic tape recorders, is the ADP type. The name is derived from the expander bars, which are usually of ammonium dihydrogen phosphate. As the construction makes them virtually solid, their frequency response is claimed to be linear up to nearly the resonant frequency of the crystal, which makes them very useful for high level measurements, as in some industrial applications. They normally match into a low-noise pre-amplifier with an input impedance of some hundreds of megohms.

Dynamic Microphones

Our second type, the dynamic range of microphones, is the most widely used, especially since the transistor revolution, when low impedance directly-matched devices were convenient. (That is not to say that the growing use of high impedance FET devices will cause a return of the crystal microphone, although it has certainly paved the way to better design of capacitor microphones, as we shall see.)

Moving coil microphones, as their name implies, operate by the pressure of the sound wave upon a diaphragm causing an affixed coil to move in a

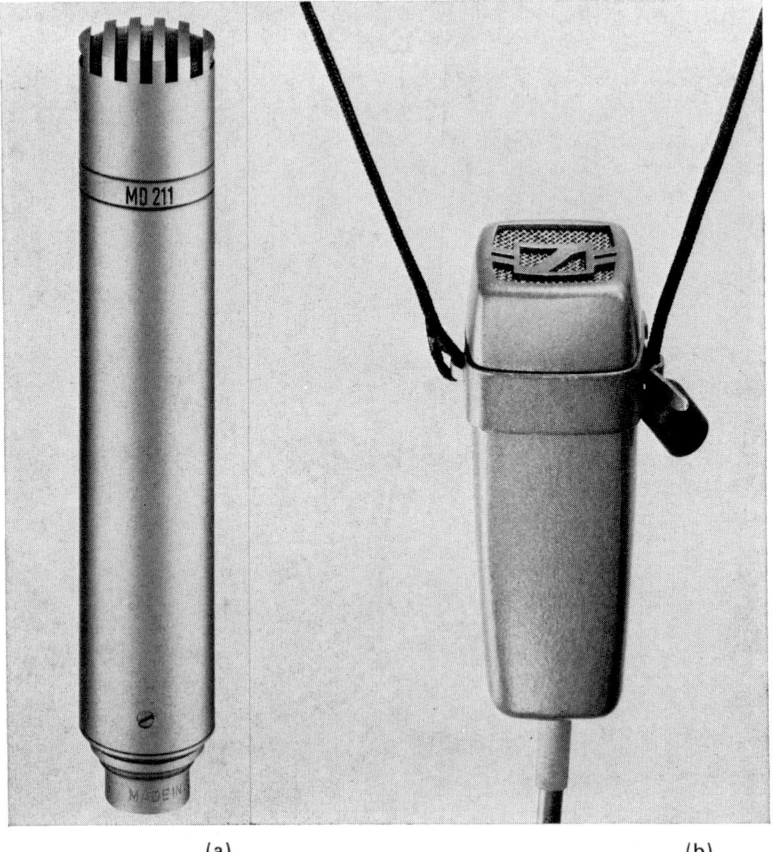

(a) (b)

Fig. 7.8: Wide differences in response and other characteristics are typified by these two Sennheiser microphones. The MD211 is a studio type, while the MD214 is a lavalier type designed to be hung round the neck and having a response tailored to eliminate the resultant chestiness.

magnetic field. The resultant cutting of lines of force produces an e.m.f. which is usually transformed up to match the input of the pre-amplifier.

Such a bald statement begs many questions. In the first place, a simple device as described would have a massive resonance at about 400Hz because of the physical structure of the cone system—the diaphragm usually being a shallow cone, similar to a small loudspeaker. Then, the coupling of the air in the pole gap as well as behind the cone will cause another peak, this time in the very sensitive 4–6kHz region. This is one reason why many cheap dynamic microphones produce such good results for plain communications—their resonance happens to fall smack in the middle of the speech frequency band!

To flatten the lower region resonance, an acoustic element, a piece of fabric or a ring of finely perforated or sintered porous metal, or even a narrow slit below the coil slot, is added. The compliance of the air within the main case causes a falling bass response and in many designs a form of equalising tube, or even a space that forms an acoustic leak, will allow air pressure to try to equalise from front to back of the diaphragm—all strictly controlled. The polar response is normally omni-directional, but modified by the shape of the housing and very easily controlled to make it the desirable cardioid shape.

Diaphragms are usually made from rolled aluminium alloy or plastics—the latter choice often determined as much to withstand blast as reduce price. Compliant surrounds are formed into tangential corrugations to achieve linear motion. Speech coils are usually wound from flat aluminium wire and may be cemented to the diaphragm as a formerless coil.

Even if a coil former is used, its material must be specially chosen to reduce weight, avoid resonances and preserve compliance of the cone. Modern shapes are generally tubular, but readers may have seen illustrations of the famous ball-and-biscuit microphone used in broadcast studios, and the construction here is so different as to merit explanation.

The biscuit is a frontal screen of porous material (design attributable to F. F. Romanow of Bell Laboratories) carefully dimensioned and spaced from the round body of the microphone so as to neutralise diffraction and give an accurate omni-directional response. Usually, artificial silk is supported between open-weave wire-mesh screens to form the biscuit. The material must have the exact acoustic resistance and the spacing is vital. Sound coming from the front is attenuated slightly, effectively boosting sound from the rear that would otherwise be impeded by the body of the microphone.

Small tubular designs may have a restricted low frequency response, but this is not always a bad thing in the applications for which they are most suitable, i.e. recording in the field with portable tape recorders. Quite often, a lavalier design which hangs round the neck (Fig. 7.8), has a deliberate bass cut below about 200Hz to prevent the inevitable 'chestiness' and to compensate for the losses at the treble end resultant from off-axis use.

The other advantage attendant on structure is that M/C microphones with a diameter of about 2½in. may exhibit omni-directional properties at low frequencies but increasingly become directional above about 2kHz. This is exactly what is wanted with most sound re-inforcement systems, where the directional factor helps reduce the howl of feedback, a familiar phenomenon which is always more prevalent at high frequencies.

Moving coil microphones have a basically low impedance and a low sensitivity, but the general practice is to build a small transformer in the body of the microphone, giving a voltage uplift and providing a more convenient match to the pre-amplifier, see Table 1 and the later section on matching. Basic impedance may be around 30Ω and the output with no transformer as low as −80dB.

Ribbon Microphones

Ribbon microphones can be pressure operated if they are expressly designed for the purpose, but are more often of the pressure gradient type, which we have agreed to call 'velocity' for convenience. Fig. 7.5 shows the basic construction, from which it is evident that the active part of the transducer is a very delicate piece of material. The ribbon is of soft aluminium leaf only a fraction of a micron thick, and is formed into a series of corrugations to give flexibility and to prevent edge curl.

A typical ribbon dimension for a practical microphone may be 1in. × $\frac{1}{4}$in. wide by 1/40mil. thick. It is clamped between polepieces, and the clearance at the sides is a vital design factor, as is the porous gauze which forms its baffle, and the strength of the magnet itself. Ribbon microphones should never be knocked, blown into, or laid aside casually among metallic objects. If you have one rattling about in your toolbox, get it out and have it serviced.

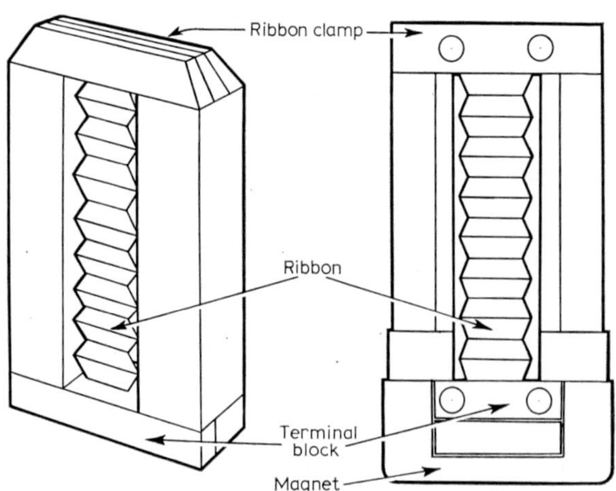

Fig. 7.9: Basic construction of the ribbon microphone. In the view on the left, the magnet is removed and the unit turned slightly to show the corrugations of the ribbon.

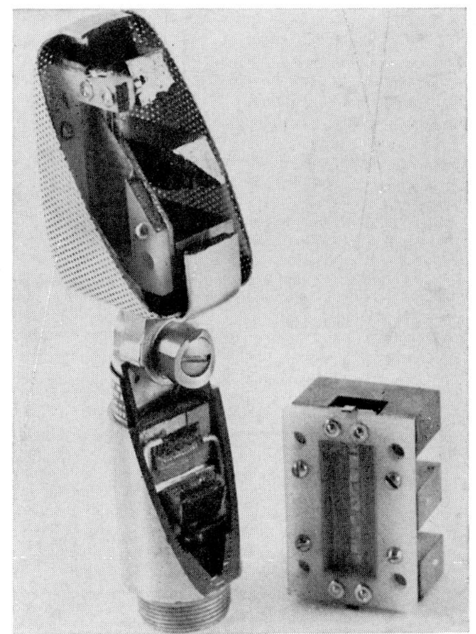

Fig. 7.10: A view of a ribbon microphone which we hope you will never see in practice! This is a sectionalised Reslo RB showing the principal parts, and with the replaceable insert duplicated beside it for clarity. The fine ribbon mounted between powerful magnets and protected by metallic gauze can be seen clearly. The matching transformer is housed in the metal barrel, also shown cut away.

Because the active element is effectively a single turn of a coil, the basic impedance of a ribbon microphone is very low—a mere fraction of an ohm. A step-up transformer is invariably built into the housing of the microphone to provide a more convenient matching impedance, generally 30Ω, and gives the necessary voltage step-up to load a pre-amplifier. Even so, the output from a ribbon microphone is low, but the quality is high and the 'figure-of-eight' response is capable of easy modification to cardioid, or other configuration by adaptation of the housing such as the addition of acoustic pads on one side of the ribbon, giving versatile performance.

The main drawback to the operator—apart from its dislike of rough treatment—is the response of the ribbon microphone at close quarters, which tends to give far too much bass lift for convenience. This proximity effect is a feature of velocity or pressure-gradient transducers, where the field due to a small sound source contains a factor inversely dependent on the product of frequency and distance.

The main advantage is the polar response, which can attenuate unwanted sounds by as much 4·8dB at the 90° 'dead' axis. The useful pick-up angle of a ribbon microphone may be around 60°, which is convenient for drama groups and similar stage arrangements.

Capacitor Microphones

Capacitor (or condenser) microphones are basically omni-directional and capable of a wide, smooth frequency response and a good transient

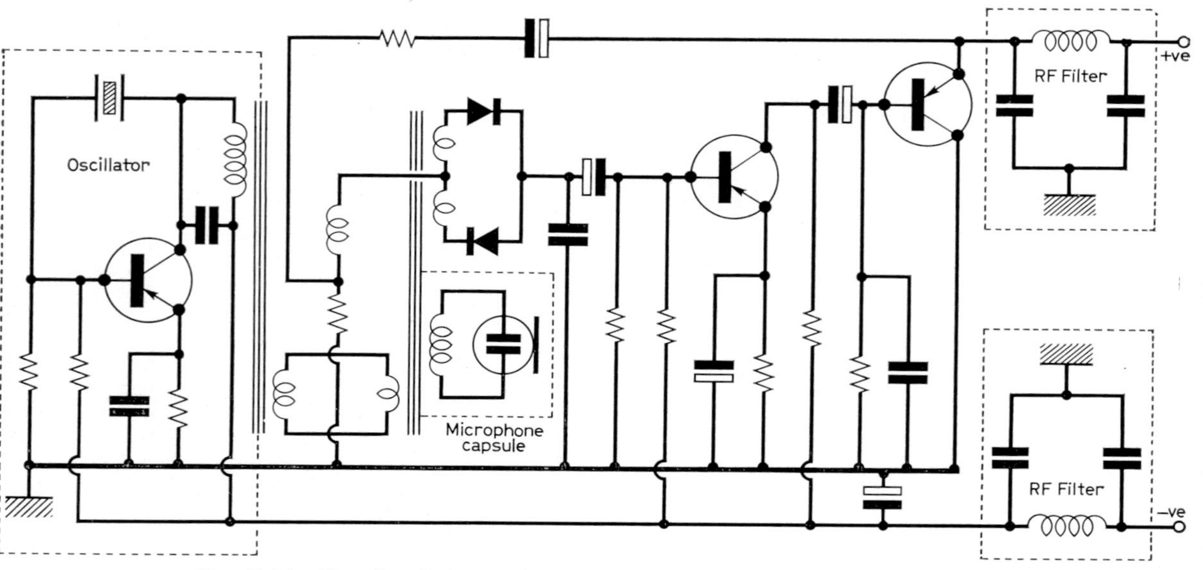

Fig. 7.11: The Sennheiser MKH105 capacitor microphone uses an r.f. oscillator, enabling the value of the capacitative elements (and thus the impedance) to be kept lower, reducing noise and increasing sensitivity. Careful r.f. filtering is needed to eliminate the 8MHz oscillator frequency from being developed across the power supply circuits.

response. The general construction consists of a diaphragm in a rigid enclosure spaced evenly from, but close to, a charged, insulated back plate. The two plates (for the diaphragm is a disc also) form a capacitor of between 5 to 75pF, whose value varies as the diaphragm is moved by sound pressure. A constant variation can be made at all frequencies by the 'linear' construction, but to preserve the low frequency response the input impedance and the impedance of the polarising voltage supply must both be quite high—100MΩ or more.

The usual practice is to mount a transistored pre-amplifier in the body of the capacitor microphone, which, with the advent of FET devices, and the latest insulating sheets between the plates which permit smaller construction and more rigid designs, has produced a generation of capacitor microphones of extremely small dimensions (improving the high frequency response) and very high quality.

The diaphragm tension has to be high, and this is usually effected by a locking ring. Clearance between diaphragm and backing plate may be in the order of a thousandth of an inch, and the plate has to be insulated from both the casing and the diaphragm. Quartz insulators have been used very successfully, but some recent small designs have employed melinex plastics which has been aluminium sputtered on one side, mounting this rigidly in a perspex ring, spaced about $1\frac{1}{2}$ thou' (37μ) from a grooved dural backplate. Other types of capacitor microphone have stainless steel, nickel and titanium diaphragms and very often the main structure of the microphone will be of the same material.

Single-sided systems allowing unimpeded acoustical access to the diaphragm may have a non-linear characteristic because of the relationship between electrostatic force and displacement. The polarising voltage has to be large in comparison with the generated e.m.f. and to reduce the generation of harmonics it may be necessary to settle for slightly less output—not such an important factor now that very efficient low-noise transistor circuits have evolved.

Capacitor microphones, because of their very special mechanical structure, can be made virtually impervious to shock and temperature change. By using thicker plates and diaphragms, probe microphones have been designed for measurement of the air in engine exhausts and similar industrial applications. From our point of view, as the microphone chosen to drive a tape recorder, we must first consider the capacitor microphone as one that will usually be of low-to-medium output, wide and even frequency response, good transient response but requiring a polarising voltage from a high impedance source and needing to be matched into a high impedance input. They will generally be fairly high in price as well.

Semiconductor Version

Just recently there has been an awakening of interest in the 'charge-potential' microphone of a rather different design from the capacitor microphone, using semiconductor techniques for its operation. A metal shell, coated on the inside with a semiconductor layer, with connections

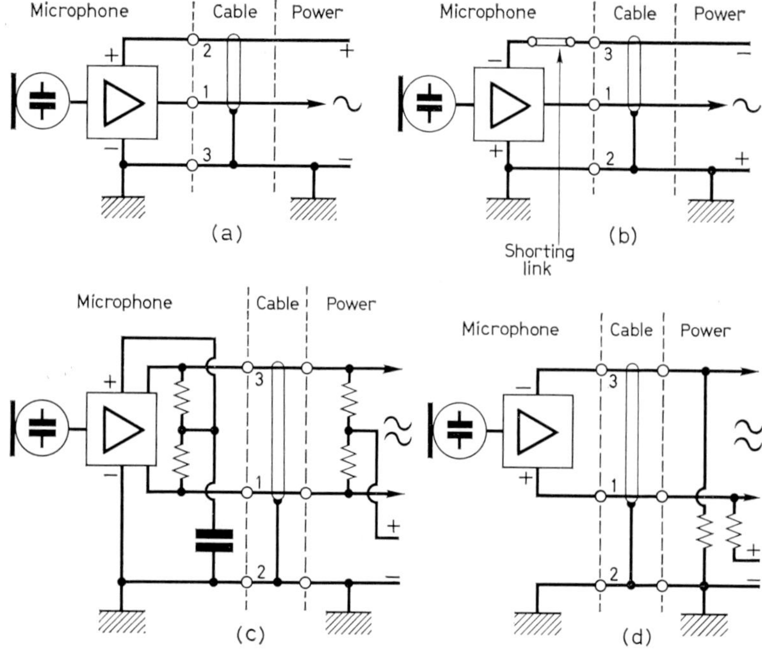

Fig. 7.12: Four different ways of powering capacitor microphones. *(a)* positive supply is applied along one core, the signal is passed along the other and the signal return line and negative supply line are combined in the screen, *(b)* a reversal of the above, with a shorting link—these microphones normally carry their own mercury cell supply, *(c)* phantom power supplies use an earth return as screen and negative, with the positive supply divided along the two signal lines by matched resistors at supply and microphone end, and *(d)* modulation lead power (to DIN specification 45 595), with both positive and negative supplies fed along the signal lines via balanced resistors at the supply end only.

to the outer and inner surfaces is coiled around a post consisting of a radioactive isotope (low-energy beta-emitting).

The principle is similar to that of a radioactive radiation type thickness gauge, the only moving part being the air itself. The design should thus, in theory, be completely linear and with an extremely wide frequency response. Because the beta-ray electrons travel at approaching the speed of light, the high frequency limit will be several megohms and the low frequency response will extend practically to zero. It sounds so simple that the only wonder is the market is not yet swamped with cut-price imported versions. We shall wait and see. Meanwhile we simply report what we have heard.

Polar Patterns

Polar response diagrams tell us a lot about microphone sensitivity. The curves are plotted graphically with the microphone shown as a small area or point, the distance from the microphone to each datum line of the response curve representing a voltage with reference to a fixed pressure and output.

Thus we find response curves scaled in volts, volts relative to 0·0002 dyne/cm.^{2}, microbars, and decibels below a reference level relative to 1 volt. The important factor is the shape of the response curve along each datum line. We see, for example, that the spherical distribution of the polar response of a pressure microphone at low and middle frequencies becomes increasingly directional as the frequency of the received sound is raised.

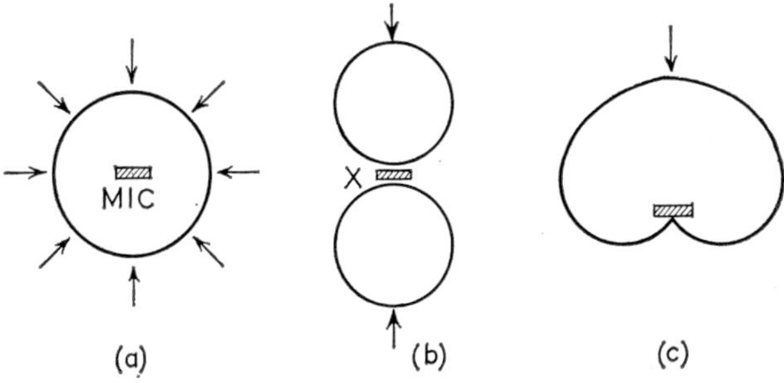

Fig. 7.13: Basic polar diagrams *(a)* omnidirectional, the microphone picking up sounds from all around with equal efficiency; *(b)* bi-directional, or figure-of-eight, with maximum front and back pick-up and minimum response from the sides; and *(c)* cardioid, with maximum pick-up in one direction and a null point in the opposite direction, providing a useful 'sound isolator'.

As a contrast to this, the polar response of a pressure-gradient microphone is virtually a figure-of-eight, with a reception angle up to 105° front and back and a virtually dead area at 90° to the plane of the microphone facing or diaphragm.

A cardioid (heart-shaped) response is very useful, offering the discrimination of the directional microphone with the width of response in one direction of the omni-directional. Cardioid microphones combine the qualities of pressure-operated and pressure-gradient microphones. Capacitor microphones with two diaphragms separated by a perforated plate can be used as a cardioid microphone and, as already noted, a quasi-cardioid response can be obtained from a ribbon microphone with acoustic pads filtering the sound from one side of the ribbon.

Directivity

Directionality is often used for special purposes, such as birdwatching, and the device of mounting a microphone in a paraboloid so that sounds are focused and concentrated at the diaphragm is a well-known one. Fig. 7.14 shows such a paraboloid.

Directional microphones whose 'aim' is achieved by sound—cancellation methods now permit the reception of minute sounds from remote points—making effective eavesdropping instruments. The main microphone points toward the sound source and subsidiary microphones are 'aimed' to pick up sounds in the unwanted area. These are then phase inverted and applied so as to cancel, leaving the required sound to be amplified.

Sensitivity of a microphone is expressed as an output voltage or in decibels relative to a fixed reference level. This is generally 1 volt (equalling OdB) when the sound pressure is 1 dyne per square centimetre, (1 dyne/cm.^{2}). This pressure is equal to 1 microbar (1μB), which is regarded as the peak level of normal conversational voice at a distance of 1 metre. Thus, a microphone with a sensitivity of −60dB would be expected to give an output of 1mV if the sound pressure was 1 dyne/cm.^{2}.

DIN Standards

It is interesting to note the minimum standards for microphones suggested in DIN–45 500, which can be summarised as follows.

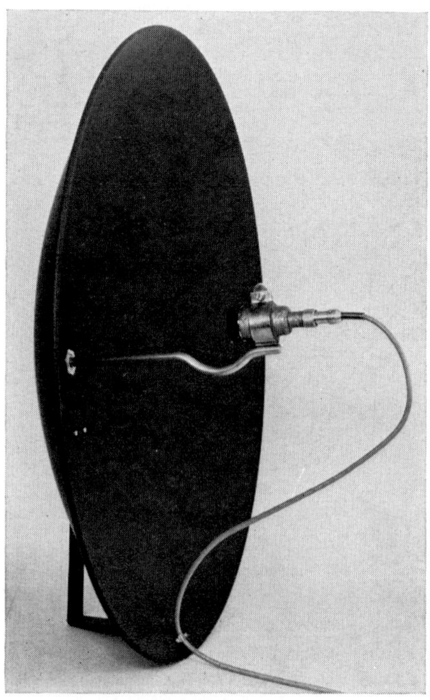

Fig. 7.14: Grampian have long been a famous name in the microphone and mixer world. Similar to the DP4 which for years was a prime example of high quality at modest price is this DP6 omnidirectional moving coil microphone with a −87dB sensitivity in its low impedance version, but a frequency response more restricted (200–15,000Hz). Models are available in four impedances, 25, 200, 600 and 50,000 ohms. The DP6 is shown mounted in a paraboloid by the same makers, used to focus the sound from a distance.

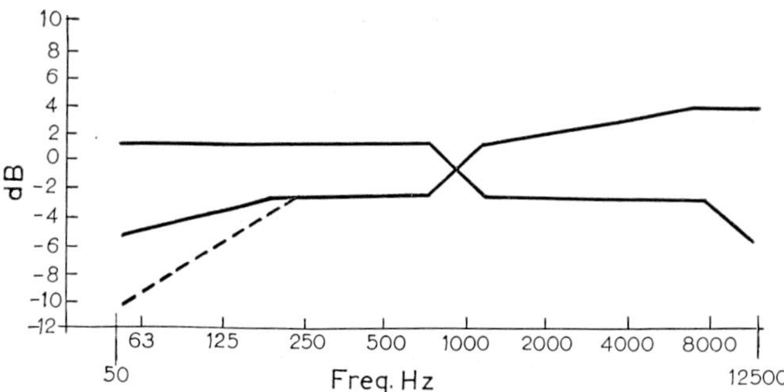

Fig. 7.15: Recommended frequency range of microphones according to DIN 45 500.

(1) Frequency range should lie within 3dB in any octave with a frequency range of 50 to 12,500Hz, the optimum curve lying within the limits portrayed in Fig. 7.15. Non-directional microphones have additional bass tolerance as shown by the dotted line. Tolerances permissible are ±4dB, 50–250Hz; ±3dB, 250–8kHz; ±4dB, 8kHz–12·5kHz.

(2) The amplitude of a practical curve should not exceed 12dB per octave at any frequency. Neither should directional characteristics be affected by frequency; the frequency curves for all angles other than zero degrees should show only a small variation from the frequency curve at a relative angle from zero degrees.

(3) Non-directional areas should not deviate in output by more than 12dB (when placed in a free area of sound) over the range 6kHz to 9kHz and altered in angle between zero and 90°.

(4) Directional microphones should not 'focus' the sound by more than two times (3dB–power) between 250 and 8,000Hz. Within this same range the amplitude of the frequency curve for any angle other than zero degrees should not differ by more than ±4dB from the zero curve. This requirement is relaxed for parts of the frequency curve that fall below −12dB, where the effect is virtually negligible.

(5) The distortion factor should be less than 1% from 250Hz to 8kHz at 100 microbar (equivalent to 114dB).

(6) Differences between stereo channels between the above limit frequencies should not exceed 3dB.

(7) Microphones are now required to be labelled indicating modulation principle, directional characteristics, field reproduction factor and electrical impedance. Plugs and sockets for microphones are specified separately in DIN 45–594.

Choosing a Microphone

Choice of microphone will be dictated by cost primarily, but the considerations of frequency response and the polar diagram of the unit must influence the final decision. To aid the reader's choice, a few notes on microphone applications are given, but it must be understood that every single recording session poses its individual problems. There are very few hard and fast rules, not always any easy solutions to such problems as reverberation or unwanted feedback.

The beginner usually cuts his teeth on the crystal microphone, which was often the type supplied with a valved tape recorder; nowadays, many transistorised portable machines will have moving coil units of quite reasonable quality for their price. The reason is simply that a valve presents a high impedance load to the input terminals, which suits a crystal unit, whereas the transistor circuits of simple common emitter mode

Fig. 7.16: The wrong way *(above)* and the right way to use a microphone at home. It should be far enough from the tape recorder to eliminate mechanical noise, should not be touched by hand or script and is best mounted on a stand to insulate it from vibration. *(Photos courtesy of BASF.)*

require a low impedance feed, and the moving coil microphone is a ready-made answer.

Difficulty with the crystal microphone is the losses incurred when the connecting cable has to be lengthened. Cable capacitance (single-screened type) can be 100 to 150pF per foot and the additional capacitance across the input very soon causes a deterioration in high frequency quality. Because of the high impedance, poor joints are very prone to hum pick-up and the cable itself can be noisy when moved. It is good practice, if you have to use a crystal microphone, to keep the connecting lead to no more than two metres and if an extension is necessary, employ a mixer unit.

Moving coil microphones are robust and versatile. They may be omni-directional but can be cardioid or with a modified cardioid response. They can be effectively shielded against wind and weather and by the inclusion of a transformer in the body of the microphone, they can be matched to most circuits. The directional polar responses that can be obtained are useful for special placings, especially indoors, where they can be placed farther from the sound source without picking up reverberation by angling them so that the 'dead' side is towards the unwanted sound and the major axis of the polar response towards the wanted sound.

Ribbon microphones tend to be more vulnerable, but this is the price one has to pay for an extended and smoother frequency response. The proximity effect argues against their being used for close-up work and the sensitivity to wind noises makes them an indoor choice. Not always, however, for one of the best sports commentator microphones, designed to be used close to the lips in noisy conditions, is a ribbon unit! Sound of broadcasting quality can be obtained from these devices when adequate care is taken in screening and mounting, and for indoor recording under reverberant conditions they are quite superior.

Omni-directional microphones have their special application when some reverberation may need to be extracted from a fairly 'dead' acoustic. Widely distributed sound can be picked up the same way, using the minimum of microphones. But in general, bidirectional and unidirectional microphones can be used with equally good effect if placed sensibly. Blending of sound and intelligent mixing is often the answer to awkward recording problems.

Phasing

When using more than one microphone, it is essential to see that they are correctly phased. This means that for a given sound impulse each diaphragm moves in or out at the same time. This way, the small e.m.f. generated by one microphone does not tend to cancel out that of the other and cause humped frequency responses or a deadened sound.

Some care is needed also when using more than one microphone and spacing them to achieve distance effects, as for example when several people are reading a play. The resultant differences in background noise level can be very evident. Indeed, one of the first things the listener notices when using a microphone for the first time (apart from how strange his own voice sounds) is the ease with which a sensitive microphone can pick up and record noises that had gone unnoticed.

Traffic noises through closed windows, the tick of a clock, even the rustle of clothing or the harshness of breath can spoil an otherwise good recording. The microphone should be mounted on a non-resonant surface. Noise can be reduced by seating it on foam rubber, and in all cases contact between the microphone and extraneous objects should be avoided.

When placing a microphone on a table, as for an interview, place it near a corner rather than in the middle of the table. Reflected sounds will take all life out of the voice, even if the table is padded. In broadcasting studios, this effect is reduced by the tables being vented—though the vents are concealed.

It is always advisable to avoid placing a microphone too close to the speaker. Breath noises and accentuated sibilants are added to the normal proximity effect and there is also a high frequency directional effect at close quarters that can make a voice sound most unnatural.

We normally listen with both ears, and the microphone should be at such a distance that a 'head' at the same place would hear the speaker normally. This is a very rough rule, and has not only the exceptions noted above but also those demanded by high ambient noise conditions, hard sound reflections and other phenomena.

Balance and Stereo

Balance has more than one meaning. Our primary interpretation is the proportionate volume of sound from separated and dissimilar sources—as for example, the instruments in an orchestra. It is sometimes necessary

Fig. 7.17: Good stereo recordings can be made in domestic conditions without recourse to prohibitively priced equipment. This amateur playgroup is using the Philips EL3537 stereo tape recorder with the RK57 stereo rig, which includes coincident microphones, one above the other, rotating for optional stereo angle. *(Photo courtesy of BASF.)*

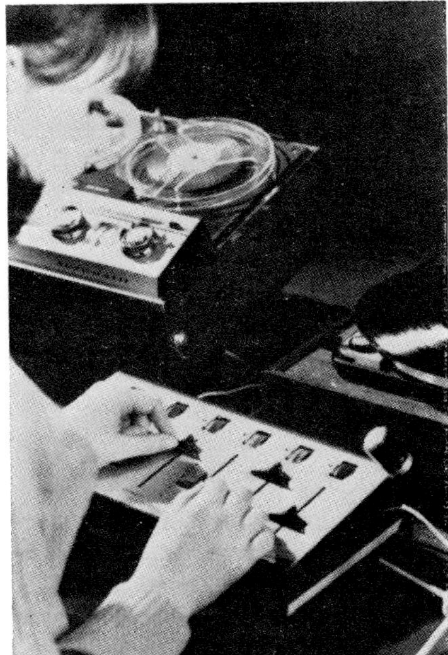

Fig. 7.18: Mixing microphone with other sources at home is possible in quite a professional fashion when you use equipment like this Grundig 422 stereo mixer.

Fig. 7.19: A useful 6-channel mixer by Grampian, with each input switched and controlled and a master fader provided. Balanced and unbalanced, high and low impedance inputs are available and monitoring is by output meter.

to allocate a number of microphones to a complicated source, mixing the outputs and feeding the mixed sound to the main amplifier.

In many recording situations, the mounting of one or two microphones above and at a fair distance from the orchestra can give a good and natural effect. Which brings us to stereo, for here 'balance' can often mean the matching of the two channels. In this case we are still referring to the relative siting of microphones and sound sources and we find that life may be considerably simplified by recording stereo!

Crossed directional dual microphones properly sited can give a much more realistic effect than scattered or spaced microphones with the signals carefully mixed and tailored. Many early stereo discs were made by this method of spaced microphones, and though they had a breathtaking difference from mono, they did not produce the natural sound that is desired. It must be remembered, too, that monophonic recording can be simply the sum of the stereo channels.

Mixers

Mixing has been mentioned so many times in the foregoing paragraphs that it would be invidious to go further while ignoring this subject. As the name implies, the procedure is to combine a number of signals for feeding to a common source. Mixers can be passive or active. Passive mixers contribute nothing to the signal, and some insertion loss will be inevitable when these are used between source and amplifier. Nevertheless, where signal strength is high enough for the noise figure not to be impaired by its insertion, the passive mixer can be quite effective and has the advantage that it needs no power supply.

The technique, with all mixers, is to design in such a way that the inputs are independent: adding a source, or changing the gain on one channel, should not affect the other channels or the overall signal. Too often it does. Design is by no means easy. Fig. 7.21 shows a simple mixer and it will be noted that the four inputs are all similar and balanced only by the 10kΩ resistors which feed the base of the transistor via the 10μF coupling capacitor.

This is not a passive mixer, but the input section is similar in principle, and as readily upset by a movement of controls once the levels have been set. The input section, up to the base of the transistor, can be regarded as a passive mixer. Taking this signal feed to a common 'fader' control would complete the type of easily built and quite useful mixer that the home user of a tape recorder could undertake.

Active mixers amplify the mixed signals in one of two ways. Either they boost each individual signal, then combine the outputs to a common line or they have a semi-passive input, perhaps with the low sensitivity sources amplified (inputs such as from tape head or magnetic cartridge) and then, after mixing, the whole signal again amplified up to line level, with a low impedance output to feed distributed amplifiers.

There are numerous public address mixers on the market with this kind of circuit. Fig. 7.20 shows the circuit (less power supply section) of such a mixer, widely used by tape recording enthusiasts, designed by Electronic & Scientific Instruments (Worthing) Ltd and sold under the trade name of Esimix—which describes its function exactly! The original circuit was, I believe, attributable to Messrs. Mullard.

Two microphone inputs are provided in this version, but there are several variations, some with four microphone inputs, others with four different inputs for widely varying sources. In Fig. 7.20 the microphone sensitivities are 2mV and impedance several megohms, suitable for crystal microphones. The Radio inputs are 100mV, again at high impedance, suitable for crystal and most ceramic cartridges.

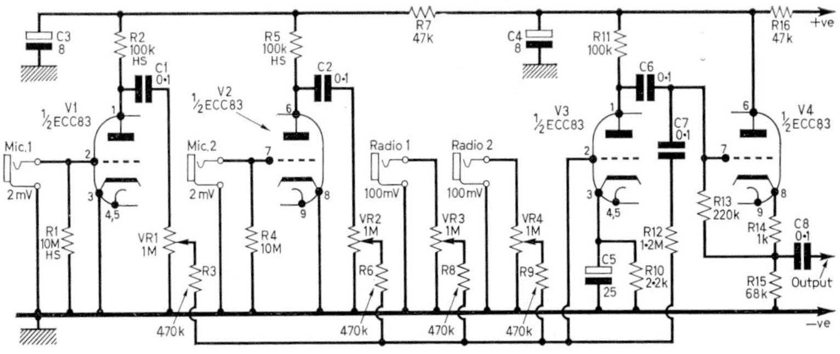

Fig. 7.20: A public address active mixer widely used by tape enthusiasts.

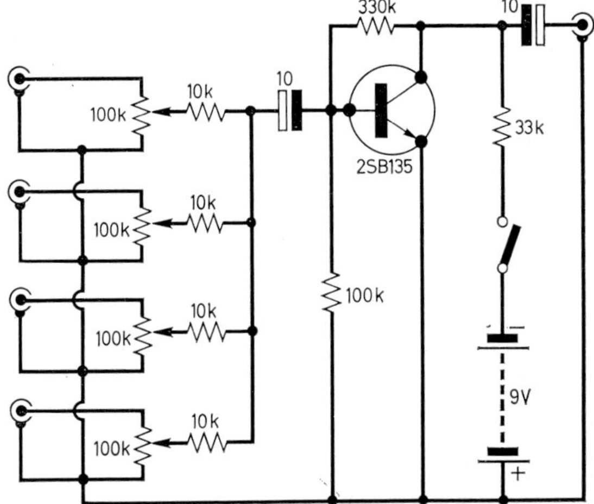

Fig. 7.21: A too-simple mixer with the drawbacks of the passive design and few of the advantages of amplification.

Gain on Channels 1 and 2 is approximately 40dB, and on Channels 3 and 4 about 6dB, with hum and noise at full gain better than −50dB and a frequency response of 15 to 20,000Hz±2dB. Crosstalk between channels is better than −45dB and the 600Ω cathode follower output delivers 200mV.

The inputs are each controlled and are quite independent and a master fader controls the combined signal. Method of setting is to apply a full level source with its gain control turned up, set the master fader to provide the tape recorder with adequate modulation level, then use the fader controls individually to set levels.

Another Mullard design, much simpler, suitable for the amateur to add to his tape recorder to extend its scope, is given in Fig. 7.22b. This has three silicon planar transistors, a very good performance specification, an input impedance of 2·5MΩ and a low output impedance of 70Ω to simplify matching and unity voltage gain for both inputs. The distortion is less than a half per cent for an output voltage of 2V.

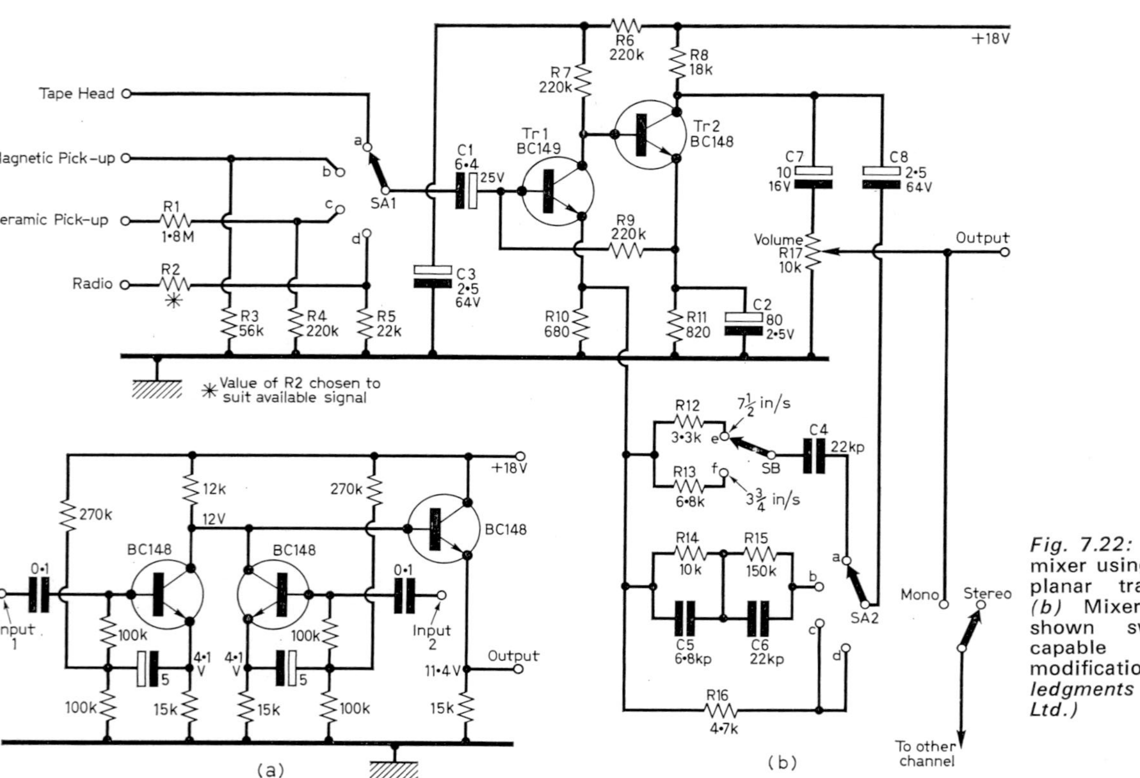

Fig. 7.22: (a) Two-input mixer using three silicon planar transistors and *(b)* Mixer preamplifier, shown switched, but capable of effective modification. *(Acknowledgments to Mullard Ltd.)*

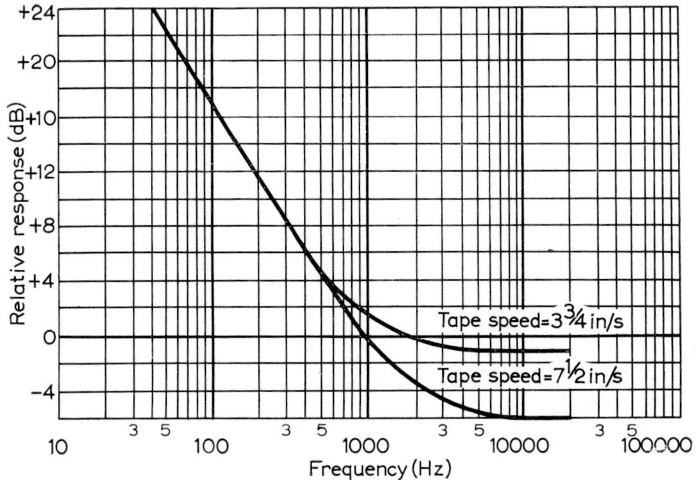

Fig. 7.23: Equalisation curves for non-linear inputs.

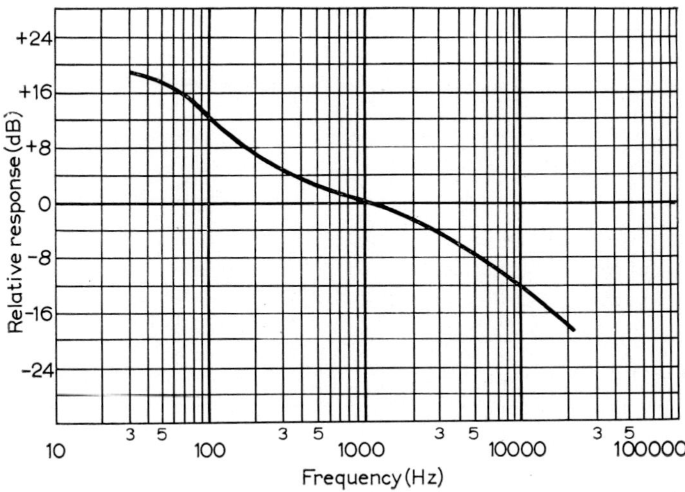

Driving this mixer-amplifier is a pre-amplifier circuit, shown in Fig. 7.22a with its specification and with equalisation curves for magnetic and tape head inputs Fig. 7.23. The only un-named component in this circuit is the Radio input resistor, R2, which will normally be chosen to suit the available signal from the tuner. This is done because tuners vary so much in their matching facilities.

I would have thought that an additional need in a circuit like this would

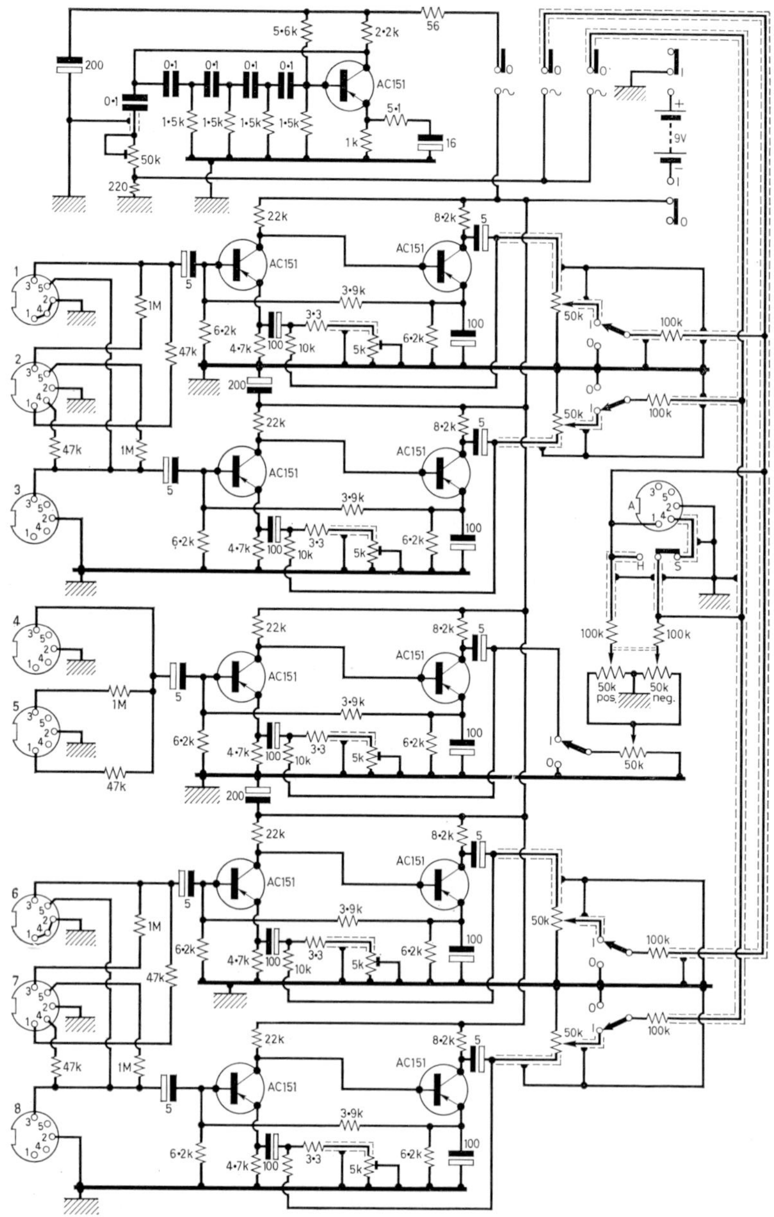

Fig. 7.24: Complete circuit diagram of the Uher 121A stereo mixer with several interesting features which are described in the text.

be a microphone input which would suit a low impedance moving coil instrument, and to make a really versatile unit, another magnetic pickup input capable of handling the rather higher outputs (10–15mV) of some latter-day cartridges.

Considerably different, capable of high quality results with remarkably small power supply requirements, is the Uher 121 mixer whose complete circuit is given in Fig. 7.24. This 5-source active mixer (5 mono or 2 stereo plus 1 mono) employs slider controls after pre-amplification, which gives the best noise performance, and a plastics locking device couples the adjacent knobs of the sliders for stereo operation when inputs 1+3 and 6+8 are in use.

Switches are fitted to neutralise each channel, with a mono stereo switch also fitted and separate control of the tone generator, seen at the top of the circuit. This device is used for setting the level of the applied signal to the main amplifier, and can be an incidental indication of battery deterioration, for this is the first part of the circuit to cease functioning when the supply voltage drops.

Most impressive point about this mixer is the wide dynamic range that is possible. Many units fall down on this point: though exhibiting high sensitivity figures, they overload and distort very easily when the programme source swings above a reasonable level. The 121 will accept a microphone input between 0·1 and 27mV at 3kΩ, stereo, with high impedance pickup inputs from 70mV to 10V at 1MΩ, an auxiliary input suitable for radio tuners, etc., accepting 3·5 to 500mV at 47kΩ, which will also suit dynamic cartridges, has the same impedances and sensitivities for the 5 mono inputs, three of which are connected to the balance control, and has an overall dynamic range of better than 60dB, which is very good. The linear distortion is less than 0·5% over the frequency range 20 to 20,000Hz and stereo channel separation is better than 55dB.

In testing this instrument, the only real criticism the author was inclined to make was the matching facility, which, though suitable for other Uher equipment, was not of a 'universal' nature—if such a term could ever be applied to such an unstandardised market. 30mV is all one can expect from this mixer, at an impedance of 20,000Ω.

Matching

The question of matching has arisen several times in the preceding notes on microphones and mixers. It is perhaps the biggest single problem the tape recording enthusiast has to face. As an example of the troubles that can beset one, take the case of the crystal microphone, matched wrongly into an impedance lower than it likes to 'see'. An immediate note is made of the loss of quality at the bass end of the sound spectrum. A male voice sounds hard and inadequate, a female voice is less affected, but compared with the original, may be squeaky. If we know why this happens, we are halfway to solving some of the other difficulties we may encounter.

The equivalent circuit of a crystal microphone is effectively a generator in series with a capacitance, as shown in Fig. 7.25a. This is matched into the load, Z, such as the input impedance of an amplifier, fixed by the circuit construction. The reactance of the capacitance C varies inversely with the frequency. C and Z form a potential divider and as long as Z is appreciably greater than C the larger portion of the microphone output will be developed across it, which is what we want. But at the bass frequencies, because reactance

$$X_c = \frac{1}{2\pi fC}, C$$

becomes more significant, more of the signal is 'lost' across the capacitative element of the microphone itself. Taking a practical example; a typical microphone capacitance may be 500pF, and the cable connecting it to the input of the amplifier can be 150pF per foot. For the response to be no more than 3dB down at 40Hz we need to make sure that C equals Z at this frequency.

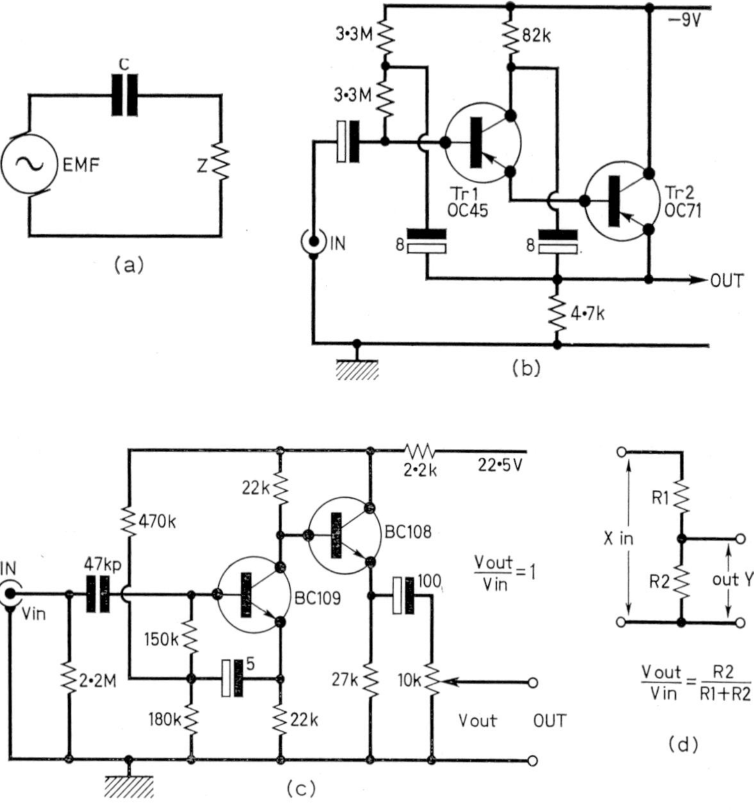

Fig. 7.25: Matching a crystal microphone which requires to 'look into' a high impedance can be tricky. See text for details of the diagrams shown above.

Working out the reactance sum, we find we need a matching input of 8 megohms to preserve our low frequency response. This may be possible with valves, as we saw with the Esimix circuit, but with modern transistor inputs a lot of fiddling is necessary to raise the matching impedance, and even when it can be done more easily, as with field effect devices, it is not always the best way to proceed from the point of view of noise performance.

However, the remedy for these problems comes from the bootstrap circuit, such as that depicted in Fig. 7.25b. The bias resistor of the first stage is split into two parts and the junction is a.c.—coupled to the second stage emitter. The output voltage therefore follows the input voltage. Overall gain is unity. The base of Tr1 and the emitter of Tr2 are at the same a.c. potential and the lower of the two sections base bias resistance is effectively open circuit to a.c. In practice there are some losses from this circuit, gain is less than unity, R2 becomes a high resistance to a.c. The collector of Tr1 is bootstrapped to the output and there is virtually no a.c. between Tr1 collector and the output, and very little a.c. flows in the first stage collector circuit, giving us an apparent increase in admittance. The use of d.c. coupling allows the collector current of the first stage to flow through the base circuit of the second and this is mainly leakage current because of the high value resistors. Thus, the transistors we use here should have as low leakage current as possible.

It is quite feasible to construct this very simple conversion circuit around cheap and easily available transistors. It works reasonably well with an OC45 first stage and an OC71 second stage. But for good results, silicon planar devices are recommended, and the alternative circuit of Fig. 7.25c is favoured. The circuit can give a frequency response of 20Hz to 20kHz ±1dB if enough care is taken in construction. Output impedance is 250Ω.

Input Requirements

The foregoing illustrates only one aspect of matching. If we are concerned with inputs, then voltages and sensitivities of equipment, with the required impedances will need to be known. There are one or two small points to watch when choosing a tape recorder and of these its match with other equipment can be high on the list of priorities. (It need never be the final arbiter, for external matching units can be constructed with no great difficulty, as we have seen, and for no exorbitant expense.)

When we know the impedance and the voltage ratings of two items of equipment X and Y, then we can work out what we need in the way of attenuation, coupling, or intermediate matching units. Taking X as the unit supplying the signal, whether this be another tape recorder, a tuner, a gramophone pickup cartridge or whatever, we need to observe that:

(1) The signal from X should be at least as much as the input sensitivity of Y, but

(2) It should not be more than about 5 times the sensitivity of Y, and

(3) The impedance of X should be less than that of Y.

The last point arises when coupling equipment needs a definite impedance to provide an accepted frequency response. For the same reasons that we have seen in the example of the crystal microphone, the coupling capacitor of X will cause a bass loss if the loading impedance across the output is lower than design stipulates.

The simple potential divider of Fig. 7.25d can be used where the output from X is much more than Y can tolerate. A variable potentiometer can be used and the values found by experiment, but the easiest and cheapest way of matching is to work out the required values of R1 and R2 from the specifications, then wire the necessary resistors into the connectors or near the sockets.

We must make sure that R1+R2 equals the loading that unit X needs to 'see', or is greater. We then need to determine what attenuation is needed, and for this we must know what limits of signal X will deliver into that load. Thus, a tuner with an output of 100mV for 50% deviation may be expected to deliver from about 50 to 200mV, and if the specification states a load of 100kΩ, then R1+R2 can be greater than this.

Suppose now that the input sensitivity of the tape recorder was given as 50mV at 50kΩ. From the foregoing rules we know that the tuner may possibly overload at 100% deviation, and that the best way of matching is to feed Y from an impedance lower than its rating. So, if we choose a 3 : 1 attenuation, making R1 68kΩ and R2 33kΩ, using preferred values, we shall satisfy the dynamic range and impedance match conditions. When in doubt, use the simple formula:

$$\frac{V_{out}}{V_{in}} = \frac{R2}{R1 + R2}$$

For low noise pre-amplification, simple circuits such as in Fig. 7.26 can be employed, and are not in the least expensive. In the given circuit, the input impedance can be anything up to a half megohm and it will accept

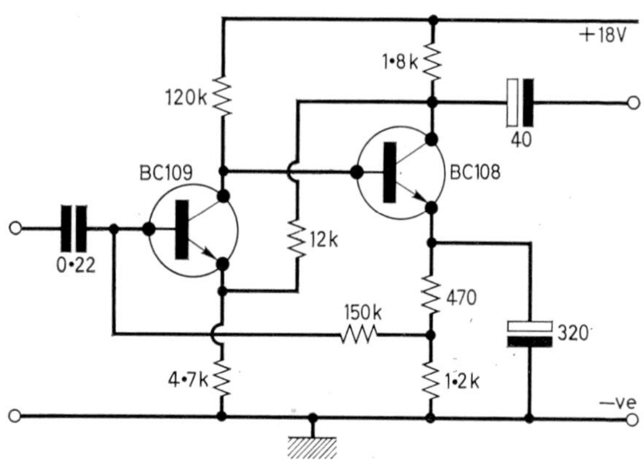

Fig. 7.26: A low noise preamplifier based on a Mullard design.

a maximum of 1 volt. The output impedance is low enough to suit practically any input and 10dB gain (little over three times) can be achieved.

Finally, when matching equipment, always ensure that there are no hum loops; earth return lines should all return to one point, preferably on the main amplifier. Earth only this unit to the supply earth.

Table 1

MICROPHONE DATA

Type	*Output (dB/m)*	*Frequency response*	*Impedance*
Crystal (diaphragm)	−41 to −62dB	50– 7,000Hz	2MΩ+900pF.
Crystal (sound cell)	−50 to −70dB	50–10,000Hz	5MΩ
Moving coil	−45 to −66dB	60–60,000Hz	30Ω
Ribbon (pressure)	−55 to −60dB	70–15,000Hz	0·2Ω
Ribbon (velocity)	−50 to −65Hz	30–15,000Hz	0·2/30Ω
Capacitor	−45 to −55dB	30–10,000Hz	Cap. 10MΩ

Output is given in decibels relative to the standard sound pressure, relative to 1mW (10dynes/cm.^{2}) the average peak r.m.s. sound pressure at a distance of 1ft. from a man's mouth in normal conversation. Frequency response is the range within the tolerance ±3dB.

Table 2

Mic. Output Impedance	*Transformer Turns ratio*	*Voltage step-up*	*Output level*	
			Decibels	*Microvolts*
25Ω	direct	0dB	−86	50
200Ω	1:2·83	9dB	−77	140
600Ω	1:4·9	14dB	−72	250
50,000Ω	1:44·8	33dB	53	2,000

Output relative to 1 volt/dyne/cm.^{2}, equivalent to 0·1 N/m^2 (Newtons/metre^2) MKS units, and to 1μB (Microbar) CGS units.

CHAPTER EIGHT

SPECIAL APPLICATIONS

IN A WELL-KNOWN DUTCH publication by C. G. Nijsen, of the Philips organisation a complete chapter was devoted to a list of the applications of the tape recorder, in alphabetical order. Without making this chapter so comprehensive, we must select and then describe a few of the more important applications of tape recording equipment, with special regard to those functions the amateur operator may require.

Slide Synchronising

High on the list of home entertainment needs is the adding of sound to pictures, Slide programmes can be made more interesting—dare I say more bearable?—with a little background music, and quite professional results may be obtained by the linking of slide projector and tape recorder to cue the slide changing process as the commentary and background take place.

There are numerous devices that make this task easier, but the onus for smooth operation is upon the editor of the tape. Slide synchronisers, such as illustrated in Fig. 8.4 offer very great assistance to the amateur photographer, whose interests may be widened by thinking aurally as well as visually when a series of pictures is planned.

For the lecturer or demonstrator the device of automatic triggering is invaluable. Programmes can be timed to the fraction of a second and ancillary effects, special lighting, sychronisation of additional sound sources and cues for other performers, for example, become a simple yet precise operation.

The slide synchroniser operates by a 'command' signal on the tape. There are several ways of obtaining this sound signal and, indeed, of processing it to be used as a trigger for the mechanism of the slide projector. In one popular method the add-on device is stationed adjacent to the tape recorder and the tape looped around it to pass across its auxiliary head.

The height of the pillar on which this head is mounted is made adjustable so that the minimum disturbance of the tape run is made. Short pulses are recorded on the tape in parallel with a recorded sound track. Such impulse recordings need only last a second or so and the recording level is uncritical. There is no need for recording bias or any frequency correc-

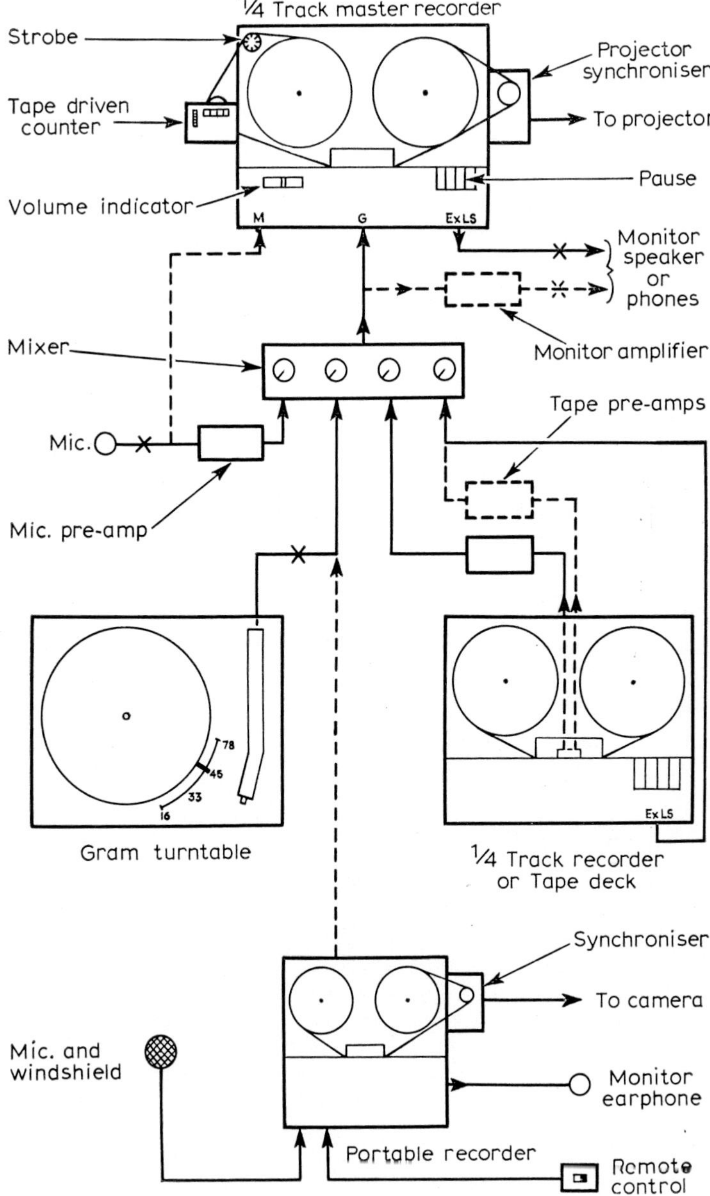

Fig. 8.1: Equipment set-up for making elaborate multi-track recordings, including lip-sync dialogue.

tion. Practically any frequency may be employed, so long as the playback head will respond to it, and indeed, the mains frequency or a harmonic of it is quite often used.

The level of the signal should be sufficiently high to let the playback

Fig. 8.2: A cine enthusiast's sound linkage system, with Eumig 709 projector (dual sound projector), a 4-track Tandberg tape recorder and Leak *Stereo 30* high fidelity amplifier.

head read it off with no delay. To achieve the best rise time, recordings are usually made up to saturation level. All this is incorporated in the design of the apparatus, and need not concern the operator, but it is a fairly simple matter to construct such impulse recording devices oneself.

An alternative method that has been favoured by some authorities is the addition of an impulse to an existing recording. The impulse must be of a frequency outside the normal audio band, so that on playback it is not heard, and the take-off is via steep-cut filters and limiting circuits so that the audio signal cannot itself provide a triggering impulse.

There are systems with tilted heads which use the gap effect to keep the impulse from the normal sound channel and others that use the guard channels between the recorded tracks. In our description of ciné synchronisers, a method of recording on the existing track and effecting a read-out that does not affect the recording is described.

The simplest method, undoubtedly, is the use of an adjacent track on the tape. Tape is cheap enough to justify the retention of one track for the occasional image pulses. The problem comes when a track has to be chosen. Some authorities favour the use of the lowest track of a four-track tape, so that stereo recordings, i.e. the use of tracks 1 and 3, are not affected by the addition of an impulse recording.

One head is used for the functions of erase, record and play. When

Fig. 8.3: Transferring tape track to magnetic stripe with the aid of the Carol *Cinesound* synchroniser.

switched to 'Record' this head acts as an erase head until the pulse is switched, then the mains frequency is doubled in a full-wave bridge rectifier circuit to impress a 100Hz signal on the tape. Replaying this tape with the synchroniser set to Play enables this pulse to be read off by the same head. The resultant signal is amplified, rectified, and fed to a switching transistor which is in series with a relay circuit.

As many slide projectors operate by switching heavy current (or mains voltage) circuits, it is common practice to arrange light switching at the impulse device and arranging that this be used as a sensor for a solenoid in a heavy-current circuit. There are many ways of achieving the same end. Ultimately, our choice will depend on convenience.

Synchronising Ciné

Synchronisers for use with ciné projectors pose some quite different problems. Their principal function is to 'tie' the speeds of the drive systems of tape recorder and projector so that a prepared commentary or background on tape will always be in step with the film. This is far from easy to achieve. It is generally advisable to match the projector and synchroniser, and thus we find makers producing matched equipment while others specialise in synchronisers that are especially made to match certain types of projector.

Care is needed in this choice and the dealer's advice is best sought before committing what can be a considerable sum to a lost cause. And in some cases it may be possible to use the facilities of the projector itself, or add yet another device to it, reading off signals from a magnetic stripe that is added to the film itself.

This method can, of course, afford a perfect synchronism and is used widely for situations where lip-synchronism is desired, but processing difficulties and cost militate against it for the amateur who is not requiring this added application very often. You can lose a lot of friends by showing your holiday shots every time they visit!

If there is any doubt about the matching of projector and tape recorder by a synchronising device, one must first ascertain whether the projector has a synchronous motor. Only if the projector speed can be regulated can these methods be used. Mechanical methods, including the use of flexible shafts from the projector motor to the sync unit, have been developed by some makers. Others rely on camera-tripped devices that are keyed to the shutter or frame speed.

In all cases, it is desirable to alter the speed of the projector while keeping the tape recorder speed constant. A variation of projector speed within small limits goes unnoticed: changing the tape recorder speed is noticeable very quickly and leads to undesirable effects. We have already noted the importance of correct and regular speed in preceding chapters.

Professional synchronising of film and sound is a complicated business. A close approach to professionalism can be made with devices such as those shown in Fig. 8.2 and 8.3. 100% synchronism is claimed for the Contronics system, which is priced well within the pocket of the amateur enthusiast. Electrical impulses from the tape are compared with impulses from the projector, maintaining a frame-by-frame synchronisation. The signals (which can also be initiated by a camera) start from a simple switch device, either mechanical like a reed switch, or electrical like a photocell system.

The basic principle can be applied to normal or sprocketed tape and is independent of the film type, speed or gauge. Camera synchronisation, post-synchronisation (putting the sound on after the original film has been

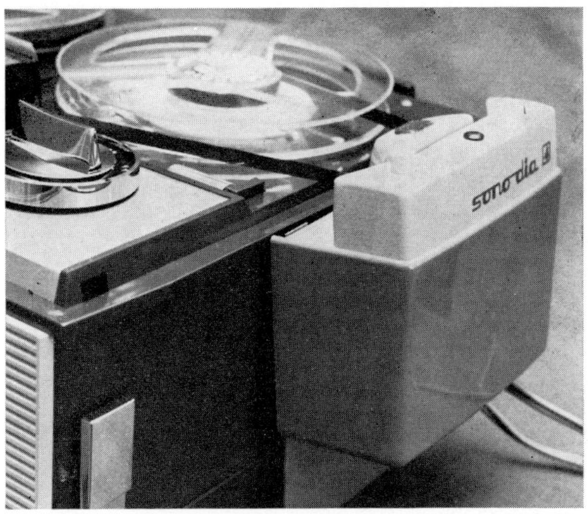

Fig. 8.4: One way of linking sound and vision is by the use of a slide synchroniser, such as the *Sono-Dia* from Grundig.

made) or simple dubbing can be carried out by using systems like this. Audible editing can be carried out by monitoring the sound of the pulse, moving the tape slowly past the sound head by hand and counting pulses.

When recording, the system generates a continuous tone which is then 'chopped' at pulse frequency determined by the frame rate. When replaying, the pulses on the tape are compared in an Eccles-Jordan bi-stable circuit after discrimination and shaping with pulses from the projector motor, which are also shaped. The output from the bistable feeds a silicon controlled rectifier which controls the voltage fed to the motor after mains rectification. The motor of the projector is then 'pulled' back into step with the pulses on the tape. The principle is broadly similar to the servo systems we considered in Chapter 5.

Pilot-tone System

Very different, more costly, and more professional in application is the pilot-tone system, a broad outline of which is given in Fig 8.5. Arising from the needs of the film industry, the pilot-tone system in its latest versions can achieve perfect sync and is not dependent on an error signal in the same way as less sophisticated systems have to be.

It may come as a surprise to know that synchronised sound was not used on film until 1940. To begin with, a non-synchronised tape recorder and a clapboard was used for short scenes in the studio. Then in 1950, perforated tape was used to achieve the multimix that more ambitious producers were wanting. The equipment was cumbersome and investigations went on apace for a better method. There had been a patent in 1941 (E. Schüller, A.E.G.) and in 1949 J. Schuerer of Munich put forward an idea on which the German pilot-tone system was based. The first pilot synchrone television recording was made at a Congo expedition in 1953 by German TV.

The main criteria that dictate a pilot-tone system are the need to preserve full audio signals and conserve the use of the tape, to maintain compatibility between studio and field equipment without crosstalk of sync or sound, and at the same time to ensure that there is neither a deterioration of the signal-to-noise ratio occasioned by transport errors, nor crosstalk at lower sound frequencies into the pilot tone system.

There are several alternative systems. The conventional recording method needs half-track or quarter-track systems, and is thus not compatible with studio equipment, which uses full-track. In one solution, the American Ranger system, the pilot frequency is recorded at an angle of 10° to the sound track and in the middle of it. The width of the sync head complies with the wavelength of the pilot frequency (or its harmonics).

During replay, the traversed pilot head activates its own recording and the pilot frequency is cancelled out in the sound channel, eliminating crosstalk because the head gap is at 90°. Pilot frequency magnetism is zero in the sound head. Crosstalk is governed by speed (tape wavelength) and the system operates on 60Hz which is $2\frac{1}{2}$ times the frame frequency of 24 used in the normal camera system.

In an alternative system, the Perfectone, a 100Hz pilot tone frequency is employed, recorded in push-pull on the outside edge of the tape. In this system, symmetry between record and play has to be guaranteed and the difficulty is to keep the two recording heads always exactly parallel, to maintain equal magnetic flux on the two tracks and to make sure complete physical alignment does not alter.

In yet another system, a proposal was made to modulate the pilot signal on the bias, which does not affect the sound track, but needs a complicated frequency selective amplifier and also circumscribes the bias. Suitable for high speed only, it is not a system that has been used to any extent.

The German Pilot system is recorded in transverse fashion in the centre of the tape. A pilot head width of 0·5mm. and gap width of between 0·4 and 0·5mm. are used. Sync pulses are recorded 90° to the sound track. Cancellation of the pilot frequency in the sound head then takes place. Frequency used is 50Hz.

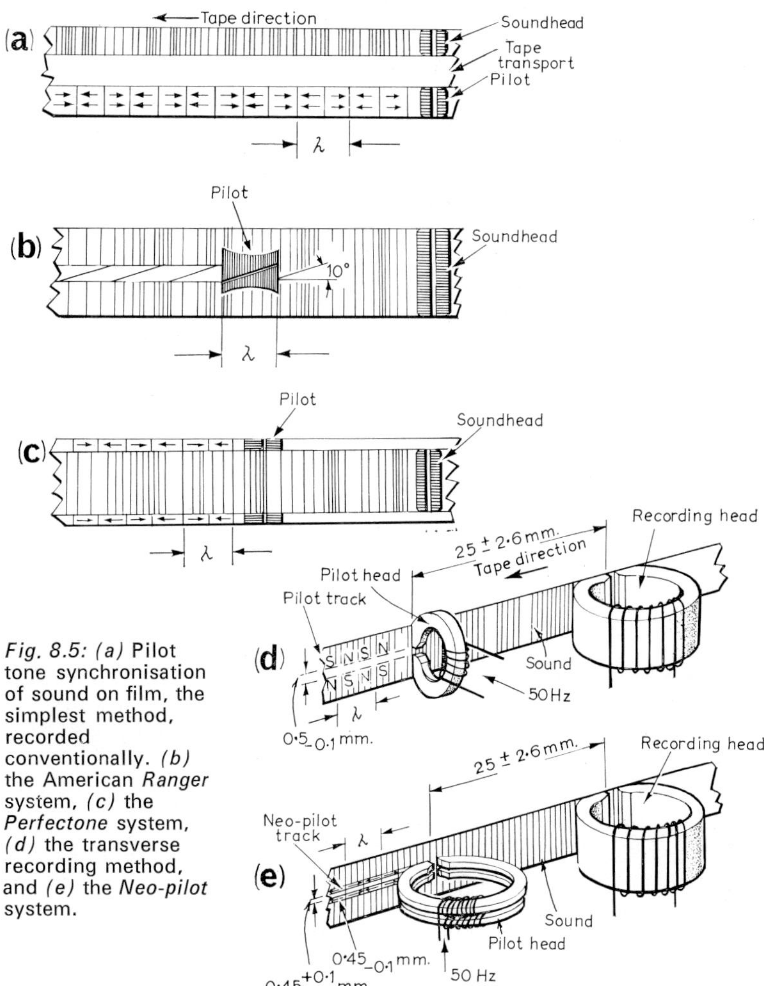

Fig. 8.5: (a) Pilot tone synchronisation of sound on film, the simplest method, recorded conventionally. *(b)* the American *Ranger* system, *(c)* the *Perfectone* system, *(d)* the transverse recording method, and *(e)* the *Neo-pilot* system.

Biggest difficulty was the provision of bias, which easily saturated a head with a 0·5mm. gap. A head was developed by Telefunken which dissipated only 150mW at a bias frequency of 80kHz. A further development was a push-pull pilot recording, now used by Nagra and Uher, with the two recorded pilot tracks in the centre of the sound channel. Track width is 0·45mm.–0·1mm. and pilot track clearance is 0·4mm. + 0·1mm.

The recording can be replayed by a standard transverse head because the position of the track as well as the magnetic intensity balances out quite easily by resistor adjustment and less bias power is needed. Compatibility with television equipment is ensured by using a 25 frame per second camera.

The Copyright Act

For the amateur, such complications may seem a little high-flown and all he thinks he will need is a tape recorder, a quick hand and a stop-watch plus an unlimited supply of music and effects from which he can choose his sound programme to accompany slide or film. And herein lies the snag.

Musical recordings are copyrighted and so are broadcast programmes. In some countries it is permissible to record from radio and gramophone records—the law has caught up with public practice. In this bastion of justice we are still bound by copyright regulations and it is as well to know them even if you have no intention of abiding by their edict.

We may not have snoopers listening at the keyhole of every den to catch us taping records, and the practice of taking down radio programmes for our personal enjoyment at a later date is too widespread to allow the law a swing of its long arm. But if we replay these recordings to others, and especially if we have the cheek to charge our neighbours an admission fee for coming to listen to our efforts, we are breaking the law.

Under the Copyright Act 1956 and the Performers' Protection Acts 1958 and 1963 permissions have to be obtained before a record or a film

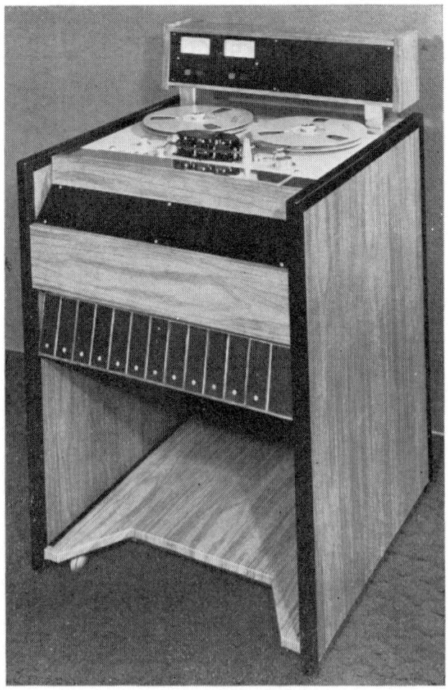

Fig. 8.6 (left): The 3M professional model PAR510 for studio use. It utilises 2 inch wide low noise tape and is capable of handling 16 separate tracks simultaneously to give recording engineers the ultimate in flexibility.

Fig. 8.7 (right): The prototype Leevers-Rich multitrack type E.

Right—the Ferrograph Series Seven

Below—the Revok A77

Left—the Philips PRO12

Below—the Chilton 100S

Fig. 8.8: A selection of tape recorders falling into the semi-professional classification.

is made of any radio or television programme. But in parts of the regulations there has crept in that face-saving phrase 'otherwise than for private purposes' and elsewhere there are mentions of 'research and private study'.

There are special arrangements with schools, and it is not likely that the B.B.C. would look unkindly on recordings made for a worthy cause, but there are so many ramifications of the law that not even they are sure how it should be interpreted. For example, although they may give permission for you to use their material, waiving their copyright for the once, there is still the right of the performer, and this includes not only actors and musicians but also the anonymous gentleman who is reading a script.

Worse than this, the gramophone record itself carries a copyright, usually owned by the company that made it. And their ruling is that you must not tape the record without their permission, whether for private purposes or not. This applies to direct recordings from a gramophone or recordings from radio of a gramophone disc.

It almost goes without saying that it is illegal to take a tape recorder to a public performance. The management may give prior consent under special circumstances, but it is not general practice.

The Synthesiser

Special applications that make great use of the tape recorder are so wide that we must perforce omit some, but cannot resist the temptation to include the Moog Synthesiser, which, at the time of writing, is catching

Fig. 8.9: A collection of disembowelled tape recorders and a few tape aids feature in this picture of the author with *(right)* Donald Aldous, well-known audiophile and journalist, at a servicing demonstration for the South Devon Tape Recording Club.

Fig. 8.10: The compactness of the cassette system has led to more flexibility in design ideas, such as the combined tape recorder and radio receiver. The one shown on the right is by Aiwa.

Fig. 8.11: One of the latest developments of cassette equipment is the Philips model 2502 cassette autochanger.

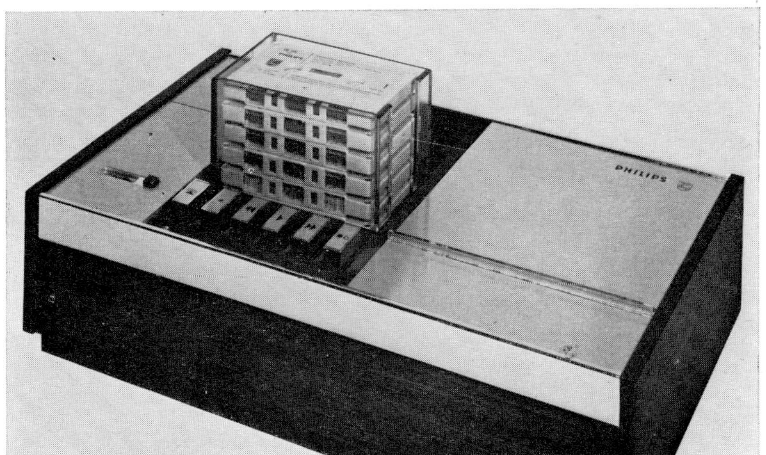

the imagination of audio enthusiasts and, much more quickly than innovations generally achieve, the mood of the general public.

Electronic music is nowadays held in high regard. It is no longer the province of the long-haired fringe. Even the most conservative musical schools will recognise, if not teach, composition of electronic music. It has become, as one authority puts it, '. . . a desirable outlet for original creative expression'.

Consisting of a mass of electronic wizardry, interconnected very cleverly so that signals can be the source for other channels than their own, and oscillators can be variably controlled by signals or non-signal sources, the synthesiser really comes into its own when combined with tape recording equipment to produce an external 'mix' of sound.

The tape recorder is an invaluable aid to the musician, both in its basic application, as a device for storing and reproducing sound, and also in its more refined function, a tool for producing electronic music. We looked briefly at some of the multi-tracking systems in Chapter 6, and can consider at this stage not only the requirements of the amateur enthusiast who wants to chip in with his own comments on a tape recording of the wedding breakfast, and also needs occasionally to combine and edit the efforts of the drama group, but also of the professional who is pressed by the remorseless hand of the clock and is forced to make many tracks of a similar piece of performance to select, mix, edit and transcribe the best bits and pieces into a finished product that comes to our ears as a continuous flow of virtuosity.

Many of the pop stars of today owe as much to the recording technicians of the half-dozen studios around the country as to the session men (musicians who anonymously fill in the real musical meat of the rendering), and little to their own talent.

Language Lab.

Special applications must include some reference to the language laboratory set-up, which also owes its existence to multi-tracking techniques. Even in its most obvious form, the home-made tape for studying a subject by careful repetition, the tape recorder's facility for language learning shows its superiority.

In a professional sense, the tape recorder has vast potentiality, a number of very effective language systems having been based on its versatile ability to repeat and parallel sequential signals. The student laboratory machine can be a simple adaptation of a standard tape recorder. Fit a stereo head, an external playback pre-amplifier and headphone amplifier and a little extra switching and any normal machine can be modified for study purposes.

Taking the basic system, in the normal position the main R/P head is connected to the upper track and the external pre-amplifier to the lower track. The master lesson is recorded on the upper track. In the 2nd position, the machine is set so that the upper track replays and is switched to be heard by the student. But the lower track is set to Record and the student can put his responses to the lesson on tape.

He should not be able to erase the master track while doing so, and this needs interlocking devices, which are quite simple to arrange, even on the normal stereo tape recorder, provided it is not the type with a single Record button. In the necessary third function, Duoplay, both the master track and the student track can be heard together so that corrections can be made and again, simple switching will provide this facility.

The advantage of a teaching recorder is its ability to compare and repeat. Various refinements have been incorporated, but most of them are toward a simplifying of these functions. Most important, in a machine designed specifically for language teaching, is absolute reliability.

The author has a true story about this factor. Quite recently a Tandberg Series 6 tape recorder was brought to the workshop for repair and all that was found wrong was a broken spring—the return spring of the pressure arm assembly. The young teacher who brought it in remarked that it had been in daily use, five hours a day, for five days a week and for three hours on the sixth day, even during normal vacations, for all of three years, to her knowledge.

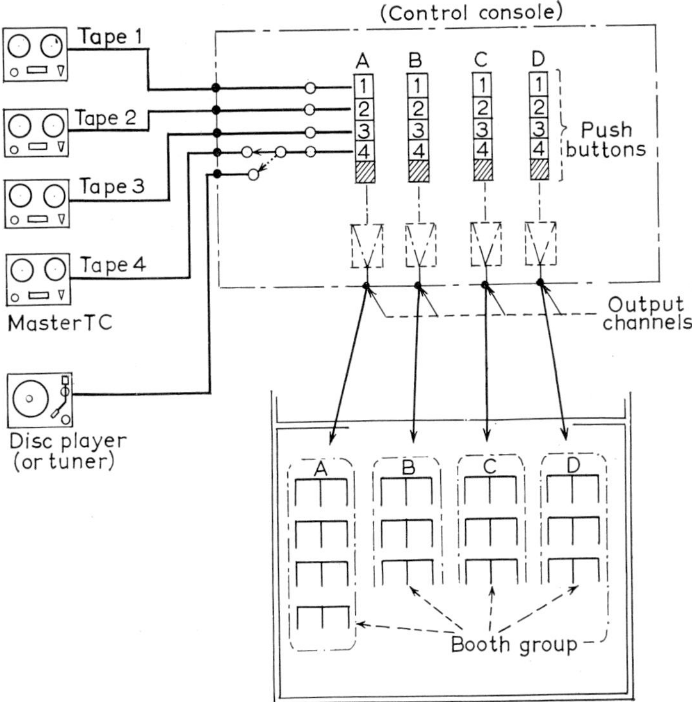

Fig. 8.12: A typical language laboratory set-up, with one or more programmes distributed to all students or to groups of students as required. In the example shown, a four-channel grouping is possible.

Accordingly, we proudly passed this information to the Tandberg representative when he next called. We were astounded to find him not the least impressed. 'We expect that sort of thing,' he said. 'Some of our language laboratory machines have been in use, non-stop, for six years.' Exeunt deflated servicemen!

The complete language laboratory is a sophisticated control system. Students can practice individually or in groups, can be interrupted individually or as a group by a master and can, in certain cases, communicate with the master also. Fig. 8.12 shows a typical layout. There are a number of minor variations.

Video Tape Recording

Video tape recording is an application that has taxed the resources of the tape recorder designer to the utmost. Theoretically, there is little difference in recording sound or pictures. Both are a series of electrical impulses. But whereas the sound bandwidth of from 20 to 20,000Hz, at the limits, can be accommodated by a good quality tape recorder at a reasonable speed of operation, the requirements of a video system are a bandwidth from zero to 6mHz and a synchronising system that requires a constancy of speed much superior to the audio counterpart.

A great deal of work has gone into VTR systems, and this is not the place to treat what has become a large and separate subject in a superficial way. A brief mention of the systems and the reasons for their development is the best the author can do in the space available.

In an effort to encompass the bandwidth, early systems speeded up the tape. But there are physical limitations to such accelerated systems, imposed by head wear, the inability to maintain good head-tape contact and the problems of mechanical drive. To achieve a simulated high speed, the relative head/tape velocity can be increased by rotating the heads in opposition to the direction of tape travel.

One system, now very complicated and very expensive but capable of superlative results, is a transverse, multi-head technique, where the heads rotate on a high-speed drum at right angles to the path of tape travel. Timing is controlled by a servo system, tied to pulses recorded on the tape. Exact head to tape spacing is maintained by vacuum pumps and other complications, and the overall system is an exercise in electromechanical ingenuity. Its effectiveness is apparent by the fact that we are quite unaware, when watching television, that a tape recorded insert has been made—given good editing.

Fig. 8.13: Compact design, reliability and a standard not far short of studio performance has made the Sony CV2100 videotape recorder a leader in its price bracket. The camera that goes with it is also a neat and compact piece of work as the 'open for inspection' view on the right demonstrates.

Fig. 8.14: A domestic set-up with Sony video recorder equipment.

A less expensive method, but one which has also been brought to a high level of efficiency, is the helical scan system, where the heads rotate in a drum across which the tape passes at an angle, thus tracing out paths or tracks that have a relation to the field timing of the television receiver/transmitter system.

A number of sophisticated circuits have been used, and the interesting factor, to the audio recordist, is that supersonic bias is dispensed with (as the bias has to be several times the frequency of the highest frequency to be recorded, the values would have been prohibitive). Instead a frequency modulated carrier is used and the audio or video signal modulates this to produce a tape flux taken to saturation but varying in intensity in proportion to the frequency change.

This is decoded, limited and used to drive an indicating device, or again used to modulate an r.f. oscillator and fed to a normal TV monitor as a 'standard' signal. Line and field pulses are used for locking by comparison rather than mere triggering methods and the camera is arranged so that it has its own timebase and can tie in with the display device to make a closed-circuit loop.

The author has been intimately involved with the installation and servicing of such semi-professional systems in the past three years and has seen a number of them adapted to the domestic setting. Here is the key to future progress in the tape recording world, as much as in movement to multi-track stereo and low-noise devices.

CHAPTER NINE

CLEANING, SPLICING AND LUBRICATION

A LARGE PROPORTION of the service jobs that the author has to handle require a general overhaul which must always include thorough cleaning and lubrication. It is sad to contemplate how many of these needed little more than the perfunctory clean-up that their owners could well have done themselves.

The losses that result from dust and dirt are so drastic that an unwary listener can easily blame the innocent tape recorder for defects that have arisen merely from neglect. In Chapter 3 we saw some of the details of head design and noted the effects of various kinds of losses. In this Chapter we are concerned principally with 'spacing loss', its causes and cures.

Spacing Loss

The magnetic recording process depends, as we have noted already, on the concentration of a magnetic flux at the head facing (recording) and on the transfer of magnetic flux from tape to head (replay). Anything that tends to prevent the tape running close to the head facing will result in spacing loss.

The easiest way to prove this effect is to turn a tape inside out and run it through the head channel. The thickness of the backing—no more than 23 micrometres for a long-play tape, with a magnetisable oxide coating of about half this thickness—comes between the vital gap area and the portion of the tape which does the work, and the recorded sound is so low as to be a muffled ghost of its former self.

Even the replay of an inverted tape, although not so low in volume, and backwards because of the inversion, loses so much of its high frequency content that it is a travesty of its original. So it can be seen that only a minute film of foreign matter is needed for the reproduction to be so badly impaired as to—apparently—merit the attentions of a tape recorder engineer.

The impairment can be calculated. Fig. 3.10 illustrated the attenuation curve, showing the relationship between the spacing and the wavelength

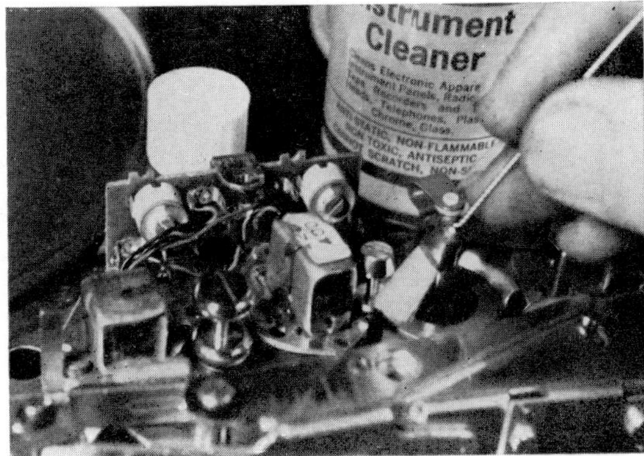

Fig. 9.1 (left): First rule: keep your head clean! Tape oxide and foreign matter quickly clutter up a neglected head channel. Before applying lubricants and solvents, brush away any loose dirt with a non-abrasive brush, such as this nylon type from the *Bib* kit.

Fig. 9.2 (right): Application of cleaning fluid can be done safely with the aid of a cotton bud. Nothing abrasive or ferrous should be used near the head assembly.

and the decibel loss. Attenuation is equal to a constant $(e^2\pi)$ multiplied by the distance over the wavelength, where the distance is the spacing between the head and the tape surface, and the wavelength is that of the signal recorded on the tape.

This, as we have seen, depends on both frequency and speed. Therefore we can say that the spacing effect is more severe, i.e. the attenuation is greater, when d is larger or when λ, the wavelength, is smaller. The wavelength is smaller when the frequency is higher or when the speed of tape travel is less. This is one reason for better performance at higher frequencies when we run the tape faster—but only one of the reasons.

Standard Figure

Some interesting facts arise from the study of spacing. Not least is the neat way the attenuation curve provides us with a standard figure for the spacing loss at a given wavelength. Taking the formula $A = e^{2\pi}.d/\lambda$ for the condition when the spacing is the same as the wavelength, we get the equation $A(dB) = 20\log e^{2\pi} = 40\log\pi e$ and as e is the basis of natural logarithms, i.e. 2·318, the attenuation becomes $A = 40\pi\ 0{\cdot}434$ or 54·5dB.

That is a lot of attenuation for a small spacing: In terms of voltage, 55dB is a ratio of 562.34 to 1. No wonder we can hardly hear the signal

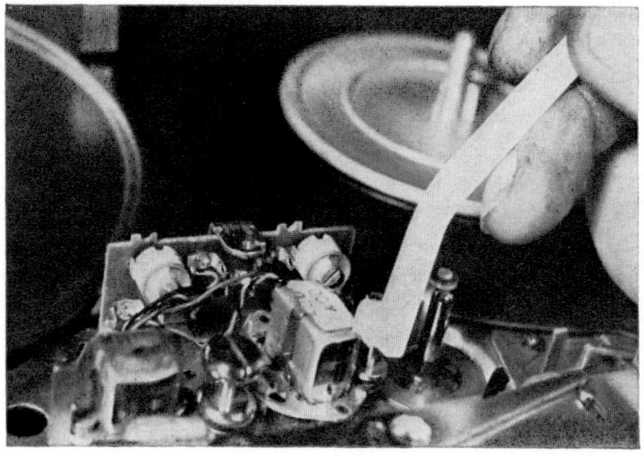

Fig. 9.3: Stubborn deposits will usually succumb to treatment from the double-grade felt pads in the head cleaning kits.

when we forget to clean the heads! And in terms of spacing, a frequency of 10kHz at 9·5cm./S represents a wavelength that is about half the thickness of the tape oxide. There are other reasons besides lack of cleanliness for this spacing loss when the tape is prevented from making its proper contact with the tape head. Depending on the type of head channel formation, it can be caused by lack of back tension, poor pressure pads, distorted guides and head shields and a twist in the tape for any one of a dozen different mechanical reasons. But first and foremost the rule should be—clean the heads regularly.

The loss is more noticeable on recording, as we have already said. This may seem like stating the obvious. But there are one or two factors which are easily overlooked. Firstly because the magnetisation factor varies with the square of the distance, the obvious double loss from record through the tape flux back to replay becomes a fourfold attenuation. And secondly, the bias effect is reduced drastically by the spacing and distortion sets in; so our resultant signal is not only low but distorted as well.

Add to this an increase of noise because the erase head will undoubtedly have lost some of its effectiveness by a film of impurity that has gathered during the same time the record and replay heads have been building up the attenuating film, and we get an overall loss that is so bad that it is small wonder unknowing owners bring their machines to the workshop for service when all they really wanted was a routine maintenance.

Regular Cleaning

The enthusiast is not so easily fooled. He cleans his tape heads and guides as meticulously and as regularly as he polishes his shoes. He is very well served by his accessory suppliers and can choose a number of different methods of cleaning and lubricating tapes and heads. Head cleaning kits are not at all expensive—neglecting to use them can be! Such diligent researchers as Multicore Solders Ltd., Metrosound Ltd, Messrs Colton and Filmagic are always searching out developments of the special

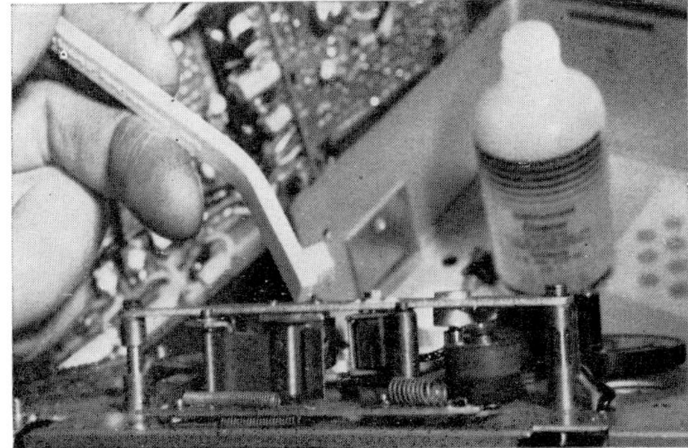

Fig. 9.4: Cleaning operations should include the whole head gate and sound channel assembly.

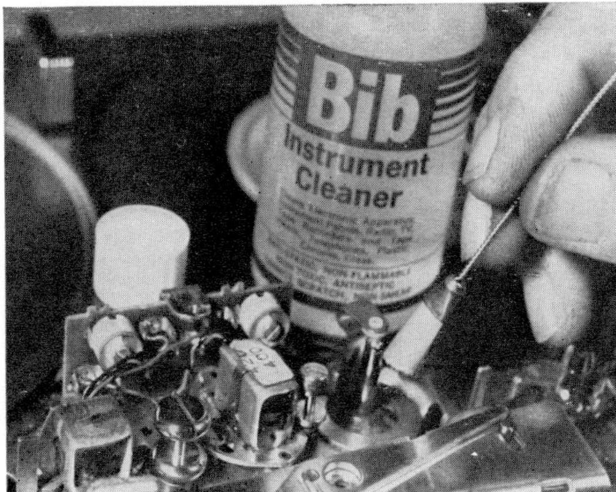

Fig. 9.5: The cleaning brushes are also useful for polishing vital running surfaces, such as the capstan spindle of this Tandberg. Dirt can be tracked between the claws of the bearing retainer at the base, and at the nylon pad of the limiter fitted to later models for vertical operation.

Fig. 9.6: Dust and dirt are the perpetual threats to trouble free operation. This Grundig tape deck was so begrimed that the tape position indicator refused to turn!

fluids and materials they have patented for the purpose of tape and disc cleaning and lubrication.

The tape head cleaning kits marketed by these people contain different kinds of brushes and pads to remove the caked oxide, solvents to aid the process, cleaning and polishing pads, cotton buds, felt-tipped rods, nylon brushes (as in Figs. 9.1, 9.2, 9.3,) and polishing cloths or materials.

First task is to remove the old deposits of dirt. Because of the constant friction and a polishing process that is bound to take place when the tape is run, the oxide film will have hardened considerably across running surfaces. It tends to cling and cake in shards across composition surfaces, to form in the corners of brass flanges, to seek out and fill any minor crevices of steel pins, etc., and to leave streaky bands of adhesion on aluminium.

These deposits should never be scraped off. Solvents must always be employed to soften and release the hardened oxide. Even the abrasive action of a plastics scraper, such as has been supplied with one or two cleaning kits, can cause scoring across the facing of some resin-potted heads. Nylon brushes (see Fig. 9.1) or the specially made felt pads on angled plastics rods (see Fig. 9.3) should be all that is needed. And if hard deposits do not succumb to this treatment, the answer is patience and a renewed application!

Leaving a solvent such as methylated or surgical spirit, denatured alcohol, or one of the proprietary brands of cleaner, allowing the coated surface to soak for a few hours and then swabbing the oxide skin with fresh alcohol is sometimes a success in dealing with stubborn deposits.

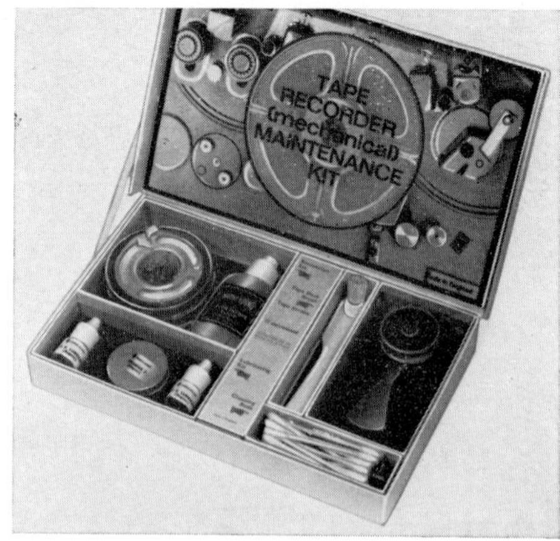

Fig. 9.7: On the left is shown one of the useful maintenance accessories from *Bib*.

Fig. 9.8: On the right is one of the more complete maintenance kits, this time from Metrosound. It includes not only cleaning fluids and the well-known *Klenzatape* on a 3 inch spool but also a useful tape stroboscope.

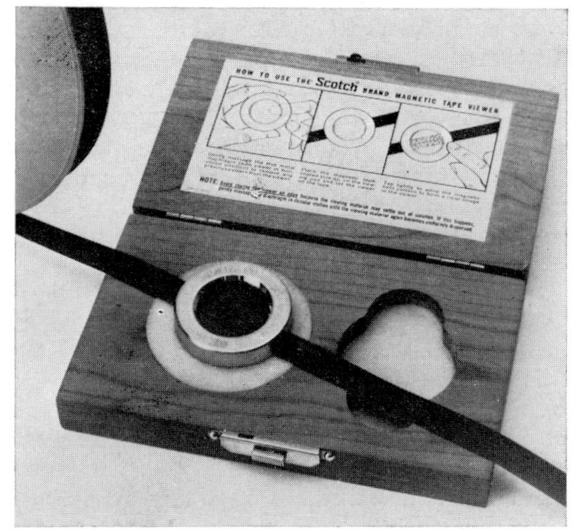

Fig. 9.9: Viewing the recorded tracks is a necessary operation for the professional recordist, who is served by this Scotch brand magnetic tape viewer from 3M.

Fig. 9.10: In addition to regular head degaussing, bulk erasure of unused tapes, or 'cleaning' before re-recording, can improve performance considerably. Below is shown the *Wal-bulk* eraser.

One way of treating guides (or barrel-type heads) is to wrap them in a close-fitting wad or cocoon of cotton wool, dampening this with methylated spirit at intervals to retain some moisture, and again tackling the surface with a nylon brush after several hours.

Take care when using the type of nylon-bristled brush that has a wire core and avoid this making contact with polished surfaces. For simple cleaning and final polishing of these surfaces the cotton-bud can hardly be bettered. These are available in separate packs and are cheap enough to be used liberally. Do not make the mistake of re-using an impregnated cleaning stick. Such false economy can be an eventual waste.

In the workshop, where a large amount over a long time can be a significant cost factor, the use of orange sticks (manicure sticks of hardwood with a point at one end and a flattened 'chisel' at the other) has grown. These have a number of handy purposes—including the cleaning of component holes in printed circuit boards for resoldering—and in conjunction with a small bale of cotton wool form an economical basis of cleaning operations.

Some such hard but non-abrasive tool is certainly needed to attack the kind of oxide deposits that build up in the flanged angles of guides, in the corners of mumetal shields and in tape-run forks fitted to certain kinds of recording heads. The deposits of oxide are insidious. They eventually form a glaze so smooth as to look part of the design. This is where experience helps, and the routine cleaning operation can make such a difference to performance.

An alternative method, once the heads are clean and when regular maintenance is all that is needed, is to run an impregnated tape regularly through the head gate. Impregnated tapes made of linen, wound on small spools and even in cassettes, with accompanying applicators and bottles of cleaning fluid are available in packs and kits and although a little more expensive than the 'open' kits, and not of any use unless the head channel is already clean, can be thoroughly recommended for regular maintenance.

One precaution must be taken, to observe very carefully the tape run as the cleaning linen goes through. This is necessarily thicker than recording tape and tends to spread so that undersized guides or parts of the head channel where some pressure is applied can trap the cleaning tape. There can also be a danger of pressure pads being disturbed, especially the small felt blocks on swivel plates that some Japanese designers have favoured.

On this subject, too, a warning is necessary against the ever-popular methylated spirit. Some pressure pads are secured with a type of gum, chosen to have least 'spread' and a non-soak action, which can be dissolved or softened by spirits. So cleaning operations here need to be even more careful. Felt is easily obtained and the pads can be renewed when they

Fig. 9.11: Switches are vulnerable, especially relay contacts. Brief treatment with cleaning fluid or an aerosol can improve performance. A touch of oil at the pivot of the armature can help, too.

harden, but because of their action, pressing on the polished back of the tape, they are less likely to suffer if the head channel is kept clean.

Pressure bands, such as those used by Grundig, one or two Truvox machines, Bang and Olufsen and others, need even more care. Because they engage the tape backing for a larger area they can, if neglected,

Fig. 9.12: Even the cruder mechanical switches need lubrication. The slider of this key-operated switch will work better for a removal of congealed grease, then relubrication.

cause a lot of friction. But the flock impregnated on the plastics or linen strip is very easily dislodged and cleaning operations need special diligence.

Below-Deck Care

Cleaning does not stop at the head, of course. Like the little boy sent back to wash the tidemark from his neck, we have to concentrate our attention on the area a little lower. It is necessary to remove from the deck area those loose particles of dust and oxide which can clutter up the mechanism, infiltrate the bearings and creep back to those heads we have just cleaned so assiduously. Method of approach can vary from the

Fig. 9.13: Cleaning operations will include removal of dirt and shine from rubber wheel edges. The tape head cleaning brush is handy for this job.

Fig. 9.14: Other surfaces that need cleaning include the drive flanges of spool carriers and brake drums, where rubber 'flash' can cause trouble.

'spread-it-around' technique of the feather duster to a careful collection of every particle with the nozzle of a suction cleaner. In the author's workshop a combination of these methods may be used.

We have small paint brushes with long, soft bristles. These we use to loosen the dirt, and as it is dislodged we apply the angled nozzle (corner or crevice nozzle) of a cylinder cleaner and whisk it away. The brush is useful to get under idler wheels and between belt runs, in the nooks of brackets and the crannies of lever systems. The only problem is the occasional smear of grease which must be avoided or separately cleaned in readiness for relubrication. For this it is best to resort to the swab, made from an orange stick or similar piece of non-metallic rod, wrapped at its end with lint-free cloth.

At all costs avoid the risk of getting oil or grease on any of the driving parts, and equally, avoid brushing the loosened dust *into* bearing caps or other vulnerable sections of the mechanism. When a deck gets into the condition of the old Grundig shown in our Fig. 9.6, it is difficult to know where to start renovations. Cleanliness is said to be next to godliness: for some tape recorder users it would seem to be next to impossible!

Tape Maintenance

It is of little sense to clean and polish the head channel and then neglect the tape. Poor storage is a major cause of the transfer from tape to heads of loose oxide, dirt and humid 'stickiness' which quickly traps dirt and leads to head wear. To leave tapes lying about is almost criminal, yet folk who would hesitate to put away a disc without carefully slipping it into its sleeve are capable of piling tapes in a convenient corner.

There is little excuse for this neglect. Storage systems are cheap enough, and even if this expense is grudged there are simple labelling methods that enable tapes, in their cardboard or plastics boxes, to be racked in a bookshelf and indexed. A complete tape library of reels or cassettes can be built up with the aid of a few packets of labels.

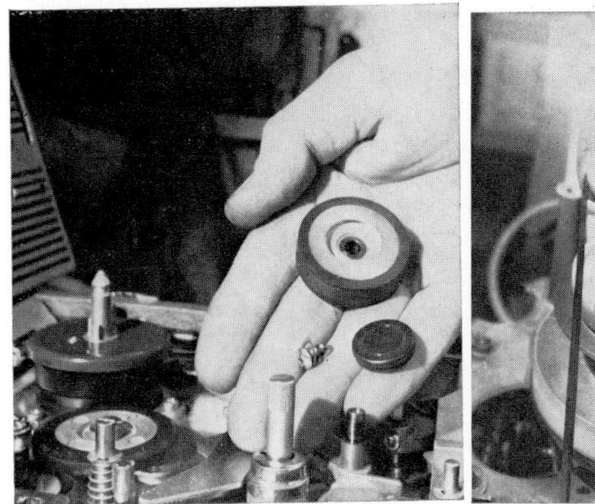

Fig. 9.15 (left): An obvious cleaning point, not always so easily accessible—the pressure roller assembly.

Fig. 9.16 (right): Often overlooked, rubber belts can become badly grimed and need occasional treatment.

Tape care includes sensible storage, and should include as well the occasional treatment of reels. Plastics reels of some types tend to collect the greasy smears of fingers and atmospheric pollution—just use your tape recorder near an open fire for a few days and you'll see what I mean! The empty reel can be washed in a mild detergent solution, with warm water, rinsed in clean cold water and dried with a lint-free cloth and will come up glitteringly new.

Take care with plastics spools, for they are easily broken, and in some cases strained into a warped position. One point on the circumference continually fouls the edge of the tape and is a major cause of drop-outs, developing into severe tape damage. Blocking up the spools with discs of cardboard, which seems to be a popular remedy, will only lead to uneven spooling and an aggravation of the trouble.

Tape Splicing

One of the prime causes of trouble is the fouling of a faulty splice. Splicing is something of an art and like most arts is made to look easy by the expert. Those indefatigable suppliers of tape recorder accessories we mentioned have catered well for the enthusiast and a wide range of splicers and splicing kits is available.

Despite the fact that many professionals still favour an open splicing block, a razor blade and a steady hand, the current models of tape splicers, properly employed, ensure that there are no stray edges, lumps, creases or weak spots to foul the head channel. Splicing, from the operational point of view, consists of cutting the tape just after the wanted sound and before the part to be excised, then joining to the cut another piece of tape which has been cut at precisely the same angle.

If several tracks have been recorded on the tape there must inevitably be an interruption of the signal where such a break is not wanted. Splicing, except for the obvious purpose of mending a broken tape or joining two lengths, is for the purpose of editing. and is only effective on one track.

The professionals, using single-track recording systems for the highest possible quality (full-track recording gives greatest output and less drop-outs) are not worried about cutting up tape. Wastage is an accountable extra. The amateur has to be more choosy and edits his first track with some care and is then stuck with the tape as it stands. Best method for him is to edit by dubbing—but that is another story, (see Chapter 6). His splicing consists of running repairs. The tape is laid, oxide side downwards, in the channel of the splicer, so that the broken ends overlap and can be trapped by the levers. Then a cut is made across the two thicknesses of tape, in the groove provided.

Splices can be angular or straight across (45° or butt joint). There is nothing to choose in terms of sound for an angle splice at 9·5cm./S only lasts for a fifteenth of a second for a full track recording and is proportionately shorter for multi-track systems.

Making the Joint

After having made the cut, the unwanted part of the upper layer of tape is drawn or lifted away and the splicing tape laid across and firmed down to overlap the cut. Note—splicing tape—not any of the transparent adhesive tapes that are used for packing parcels. It may be true that the 3-M boffins developed their original magnetic tape from a type used for packing and sealing, but we would be foolish to try to turn the recording wheel full circle.

Foolish because the adhesives of the handy rolls of packing tape have quite different characteristics and will 'spread' and leak so that the edges of adjacent turns of tape will tend to stick together. The adhesive will transfer to the heads, with disastrous effect and the tape can stick in guides and the head channel so that it is strained. Often the splice is the strongest part of the tape so we get another break, the need for another splice and finish with a patchwork quilt of sound.

When the joint is made, the edges of the tape can be 'waisted' slightly to prevent the cut edge from fouling, and most splicers have provision for this insetting of the tape edge by the grooves into which the blade of the cutter is inserted. The adhesive splicing tape is always laid across the backing, i.e. the polished side, of the recording tape.

For cassette repairs, a special kit is available, with a method of withdrawing the broken ends, which are then inverted, because a cassette tape runs with the oxide side toward the user. Jointing procedure is the same, but needs a trifle more care with this 0·15in.-wide tape.

Fig. 9.17: The Metrosound Professional Tape Editing Kit consists of a tape splicing block, three spools of coloured leader tape, one of jointing tape, one of metal stop-foil, a cutting blade and plastics cases for the spools.

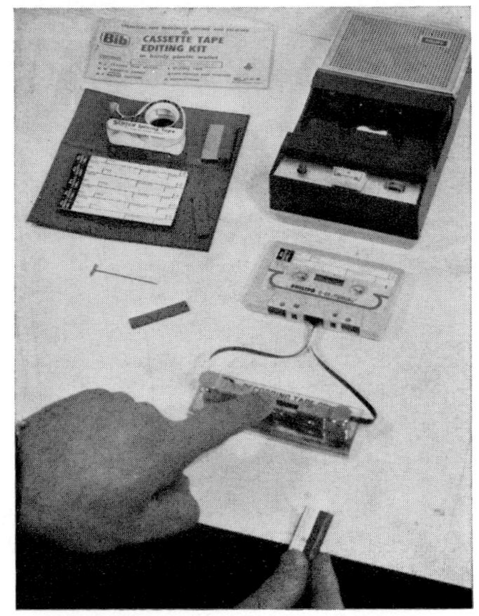

Fig. 9.18: An action shot using the *Bib* cassette tape editing and joining kit which comprises splicer, razor cutters, splicing tape, tape piercer, tape extractor and winder cards, cassette and container labels—all contained in a plastics wallet.

Fig. 9.19: From $\frac{1}{8}$ inch to $\frac{1}{2}$ inch tape, below is shown a special splicer for video tape which can be used to splice diagonally or with a butt joint.

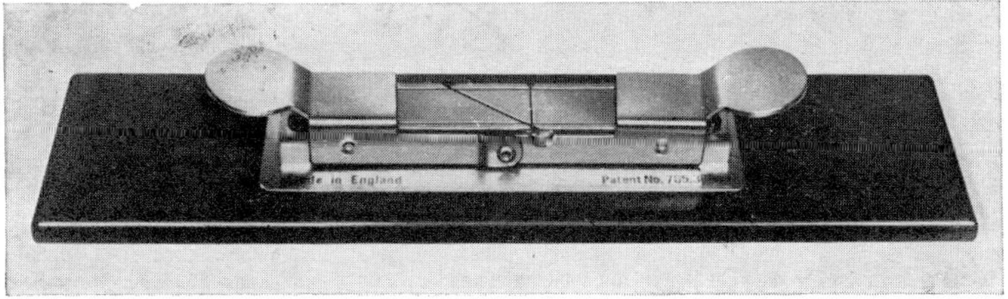

Degaussing

Care of the tape should include degaussing when the recording is no longer wanted. It is a mistake to leave tape stored until it is ready to be re-used. The recording can gradually print-through in heavily modulated passages and perhaps defeat the single erasure of the tape recorder when the re-run takes place. In addition, upgrading to a four-track tape recorder from a two-track seems a common practice, especially for those wishing to advance from mono to stereo. And when this happens, no four-track tape recorder is going to be capable of completely erasing the half-track recording.

The guard lane between the first and second tracks will still be there in part at least, and some inevitable tape wander and flux spread will at the best raise the noise level and at the worse sound like cross-tracking. So the answer is bulk erasure, and any serious tape recordist should think of this modest purchase which will enable him to enjoy recordings made on magnetically as well as physically clean tapes.

If the outlay is begrudged, a bulk eraser can be made from a discarded mains transformer, removing the laminations and rebuilding them to present an open magnetic circuit. This is not the place to give details of such subterfuges, and indeed it is doubtful whether there is much to be gained by the exercise, except for the fun it gives. A bulk-eraser such as that depicted in Fig. 9.10 is not costly, but is an indispensable addition to the tape recording enthusiast's workshop.

Lubrication

After the cleaning, lubrication. It is certainly no use attempting it before. The sight of a tape deck liberally smeared with grease that has thickened to the consistency of an abrasive paste by the admixture of oxide and dirt is painful to an enthusiast. The golden rule is 'a little in the right place' and the right place is that indicated by the manufacturer. Not necessarily the right oil, however, for tape recorder makers will always recommend the oils and greases they use.

Their choice will depend as much on a buyer's whim, or availability at some past period, as on the unique properties their brochure may lead you to expect their choice of lubricant to have. Nevertheless, as with choice of tape, choice of lubricant is made easier if you can follow the manufacturer's guidance.

Light oils are used for rotating parts such as idler bearings, pivots of lever systems, and those spindles that have felt washers for oil-retaining purposes. A slightly heavier oil is desirable where stainless steel or phosphor-bronze bearings have been fitted. For the motor and flywheel bearings, where so-called self-oiling cups and bearing barrels will be used, only a drop or two of light oil will be necessary. The oil has been held in the bearing by a sintering process, when the metal was pressurised into its form.

Sintering is a method of forcing oil into the porous metal of the bear-

(a) (b) (c) (d) (e)

Fig. 9.20: Lubrication points; *(a)* cup and ball bearings at base of flywheel, *(b)* motor spindles and bearings, (c) speed-change ramps and spindles, *(d)* shift levers and spring-loaded rods, and *(e)* the unsuspected friction points, such as shouldered screws that limit interlock levers.

Fig. 9.21: Dust caps are fitted on many pivot points to protect as well as to prevent 'scatter' of surplus lubricant. They must always be replaced.

ing under great pressure. The oil should be retained for a long time, even with extremes of temperature acting directly on the bearing—as happens with a motor running at 3,000 revolutions a minute. But if an attempt is made to lubricate too freely, the new oil will tend to run into the bearing and 'wash out' the old, with the end result that the spindle runs under high friction conditions, overheats and seizes.

For the same reason, care has to be exercised when cleaning the upper cup bearings of flywheel spindles, where tape oxide may have accumulated. Too liberal a use of spirit here can soon spoil the oil-retaining properties of the sintered cup and an infiltration of dust will soon cause hot running. Where dust caps are fitted, (see Fig. 9.21), they must always be replaced as soon as the cleaning operation is over. Lubrication points are shown in Fig. 9.20 and, although this is just a guide, some idea of the kinds of lubricant can be gained by a study of any maker's layout diagram, on which this is based. Graphite-based colloidal grease is often used for sliding levers.

One thing we always have to avoid when lubricating is the spillage of oil or grease onto rubber or composition surfaces, or indeed on any of the driving surfaces. Rubber hates oil. Too liberal a lubrication of a spindle can result in spin-off, not the useful sort that can benefit our tape recorder development such as from space research programmes, but fine particles of oil that are sprayed through the air to land on adjacent surfaces.

When idlers and rollers, drive belts and pulleys are damaged, whether by oil or any other cause, there is little we can do except clean them off with spirit, carefully wipe them, dust with French Chalk and remove surplus dusting, then rerun them with a careful ear for wow and flutter.

When cleaning around the deck, do not miss the chance to look for loose joints, worn screws or other fittings, chafed cables, rough soldering and damaged printed circuit boards. Dismantling can have disturbed a latent fault: hence our insistence, as stated at the outset of this chapter, to combine cleaning with overhaul.

CHAPTER TEN

FREQUENCY CORRECTION, BIAS AND ALIGNMENT

WE HAVE ALREADY NOTED (Chapter 2) the peculiar non-linearity of the amplifier curves of a tape recorder. Equalisation is necessary to compensate for the inability of the magnetic transducer to handle all frequencies with the same efficiency. By standardising the replay equalisation, some degree of compatibility can be obtained.

Tape recorders can then be adjusted to the 'standard' curve so that a tape which has been recorded to this standard will replay equally well on any machine. This is all very fine in theory: in practice, there is more than one standard, and manufacturers of tape recorders are often more concerned to adjust them for maximum performance than to adhere rigidly to the standard curves.

Before we can undertake any adjustment, we must be sure of our ground, and know what specification the maker of the tape recorder has followed. Too often, our brochure or operator's manual gives only a frequency *range*, as for example: 50–15,000Hz. To be correct, he should state a tolerance also, and confirm the standard to which his equalisation circuits are adjusted, as: 50–15,000Hz ± 2dB at 19cm./S, C.C.I.R.

Note that the above quotation from a semi-professional tape recorder brochure also states the speed at which the test is to be made. This is an important factor, and in this chapter we shall go over the matter of the relationship between head alignment, frequency response, tape speed and bias adjustment. This should underline the need for some precision in maintenance work on tape recording equipment.

Tape Flux

It may seem perverse to start with the playback process, but we must remember that the standardisation is of the *recorded tape flux*, and in practice we first adjust our machine to a pre-recorded standard tape and then adjust our recording circuits to produce this standard tape flux under the correctly controlled conditions. So our first requirement is a pre-recorded tape.

If this tape had been recorded with the flux strength equal at all frequencies, as in curve (*a*) of Fig. 10.1, which is, of course, a straight, horizontal line, then a measurement of the output of our playback amplifier would show a tremendous accentuation of the treble notes, and, in any case, our recording amplifier circuits would have presented us with some pretty design problems to achieve this end.

A more practical curve is that of (*b*), with the tape flux falling off in the treble. From such a tape we would obtain, after equalisation, a fairly constant output. Theoretically, the output from the replay head, following the laws of induction, will increase with increasing frequency.

The more lines of force that are cut per unit time, the higher the induced voltage. Twice the frequency should, theoretically, give twice the voltage. The curve thus produced would be a '6dB per octave' straight line, as (*a*) in Fig. 10.2.

6dB per octave because a voltage ratio of 2 : 1 (i.e. double the output) is equivalent in the logarithmic scale to 20*log*2, which is 6 decibels; and twice the frequency represents an octave in the musical scale.

Losses

In practice, this 6dB per octave rise applies only up to about 500Hz (depending on several factors), after which the output begins to droop. Gap effect (see Chapter 3) accounts for further losses at the treble end, and there is a spontaneous demagnetisation effect also, producing the curve of (*b*) Fig. 10.2 instead of the theoretical straight line.

Demagnetisation depends on the wavelengths of the recorded 'magnets' on the tape, and is therefore worse at higher frequencies and slower speeds. The smaller the wavelengths, the closer are the terminal poles of the 'magnets' together. Some of the flux, instead of running outside the

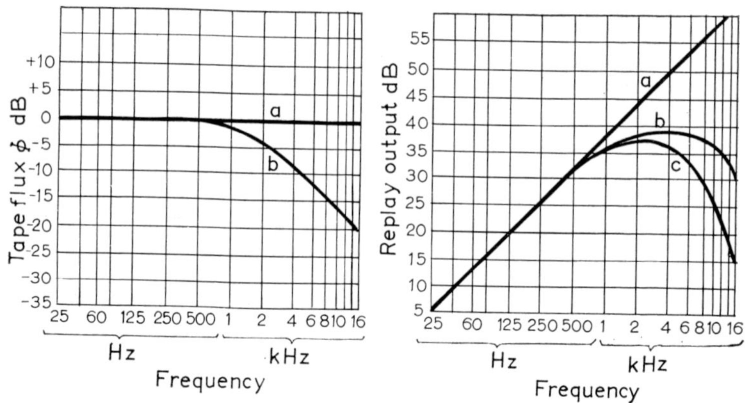

Fig. 10.1 (left): Tape flux *(a)* ideal and *(b)* allowing for various losses.

Fig. 10.2 (right): Curves plotted for output from a replay head: *(a)* under ideal conditions, i.e. 6dB per octave, *(b)* allowing for tape and gap losses and *(c)* the curve that would be produced if a constant current recording were replayed, i.e. without pre-emphasis.

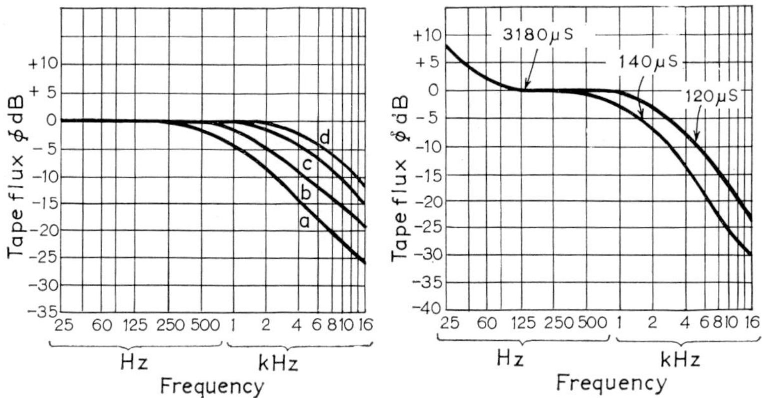

Fig. 10.3 (left): Tape flux curves (see Fig. 10.1 also), plotted with different equalisation standards. *(a)* 200μS, *(b)* 100μS, *(c)* 50μS and *(d)* 35μS.

Fig. 10.4 (right): Tape flux curves, allowing for full pre-emphasis.

oxide layer of the tape through the pole-gap of the head, ceases to have an effect beyond the surface of the tape.

The flux runs inside the oxide coating from pole to pole of the magnets and is lost. This effect can be measured and calculated. The tape flux attenuation follows the law

$$S = \frac{e^{\lambda_1}}{\lambda}$$

where e is 2·718, the base of natural logarithms, lambda is the tape wavelength and λ_1 a constant that depends on the magnetic properties and thickness of the coating of oxide.

As an example of the loss effect, also applicable during recording but for different reasons, curve (*c*) of Fig. 10.2 is what we would have had as a result of playing back a recording made with constant current at all frequencies. Treble lift has to be applied in the recording amplifier to achieve the standard replay curve. Which brings us to the vital question: what are the standards and how are they defined?

Standards

International standards specify that the recording amplifier, when supplied with a series of frequencies at equal level, should be able to make a recording whose magnetic remanence follows a definite law. The tape flux plotted against the frequency is a definite curve for each tape speed.

This curve can be defined as a time constant, because it corresponds to the frequency response of a simple resistor-capacitor network. The RC network has a time-constant which has a definition, in microseconds, from which we can determine the 'turnover frequency' at which the curve has fallen 3dB below the straight line.

Fig. 10.3 shows a family of curves which are produced from the original standards drawn up by the CCIR (Comité Consultatif International des Radiocommunications) at Geneva in 1953. These were incorporated into the German revised DIN–45 513 standards in 1955, but the USA still went their own way, using the standards recommended by the National Association of Radio & Television Broadcasters (NARTB), which differ in several ways.

For example, the NARTB (or NAB) time constant is 50 microseconds instead of 100 microseconds at the 19cm./S tape speed. This is the treble lift; at the base end the turnover frequency remains the same and a time constant of 3180 microseconds at all tape speeds is general.

The practical result of this is that the NAB standard means a little extra treble lift for recording and less treble lift for replay. Because the amplitudes of the upper harmonics of sound fall rapidly with increasing frequency, it is possible to provide some extra treble lift during recording, even when the low and middle frequencies have magnetised the tape to the limit.

This makes it less necessary to lift the treble during replay, and as the greater part of noise, tape hiss etc. is attributable to amplifier conditions that are accentuated by a treble lift, we can say that the use of NAB standards will give us the best signal-to-noise ratio. But—and this is a big BUT nowadays when so many tape recorders have been imported from Japan and made to American standards and specifications—replay of a tape recorded to CCIR specifications on one of these machines may sound dull and lifeless, whereas a tape recorded to NAB specification and then replayed on a European machine will sound over-brilliant.

This was, in fact, the criticism levelled against some of the early CBS stereo tapes, quite unfairly, for all that was required was that they should be replayed on machines whose circuits had been 'tailored' to suit the standards to which the recordings had been made.

Time Constants

Which brings us to the matter of the time constants and the method whereby the replay and recording amplifier circuits are designed and adjusted to conform with international standards. Not only is the de-emphasis time constant for the upper end of the frequency spectrum stated (de-emphasis, because on replay, these upper frequencies are not amplified to the extent of the lower ones) but there is also a turnover frequency time constant stated at the lower end.

Fig. 10.4 gives tape flux curves recommended by CCIR less than ten years ago. It seems likely that with the advent of improved tapes, we shall soon see a revision of the curves and time constants on both sides of the Atlantic, and it should be stressed that the following table of time constants includes both the old recommendations, the revised standards and

Fig. 10.5: Equalisation is combined with speed-change switching in several different ways. *(a)* Reps R10 added a switch wafer to the speed change mechanism, mounting the components directly on the switch; *(b)* in some cases a separate speed/equalisation switch has been used, making for a great deal of wiring, and *(c)* most modern units, like the Grundig TK47, use slide switches on printed circuits to perform the same function.

(a)

(b)

(c)

the proposed new ones at the time of writing, but cannot take into account any standards arising from the development of chromium dioxide tape, which the author sees as a revolutionary step in the history of tape recording.

Tape Speed	Time constant	Turnover frequency
9·5cm./S	200μS	800Hz
19cm./S	100μS	1·6kHz
38cm./S	35μS	4·55kHz
76cm./S	35μS	4·55kHz

No figure is given for 4·75cm./S, which will normally be recorded to the same standards as 9·5cm./S. In the following table of compared time constants, we can see also the relationship between the time constant figure and the turnover frequency.

It should be remembered that the lower the time constant, the greater the treble lift the recording amplifier gives to the signal producing the tape flux by constant current recording methods. A 100μS correction gives a lift of 20dB at 10kHz; a 200μS correction gives a lift of 14dB at 10kHz.

Standard	*4·75cm./S*		*9·5cm./S*		*19cm./S*	
	Bass	*Treble*	*Bass*	*Treble*	*Bass*	*Treble*
CCIR	—	400	3180	140	3180	100
CCIR (new)	—	400	3180	200	3180	100
CCIR (proposed)	—	140	3180	120	3180	100
DIN	1590	120	3180	90	3180	50
NARTB	—	—	3180	100	3180	50

(Time constants in microseconds)

Equalisation

Playback amplifiers have to be corrected to reproduce a linear output from these varying curves. The response of the amplifier will depend on the replay head characteristics, and some of the factors influencing design have already been discussed in Chapter 3. The replay amplifier response curves given in Fig. 10.6 make allowance not only for the speed of the tape but also for the different head gaps.

The method whereby this frequency correction is carried out varies from maker to maker, and, indeed, from model to model within the wide range produced by some of the leading manufacturers. Examples can be given to demonstrate the procedure, but as the usual method is the application of frequency-dependent feedback, and this is affected by the related circuits before and after the controlled stages of the amplifier, the best way of understanding any particular circuit is a patient and careful inspection and a comparison with known designs.

Fig. 10.7 shows a block diagram of a typical single-speed machine. This is, in fact, one of the early versions of the Philips cassette portable. The values of the important components in the feedback chains are given, and it will be noted that there are two separate networks. R1, C1, R2, C2 act during recording. R1, C1 form a frequency-selective potential divider.

Treble emphasis is given during recording by a decreasing negative feedback as the frequency of the signal rises. To improve the signal-to-noise ratio and flatten the peaks slightly, a little bass boost is given by the series network C2, R2.

During replay, the network C3, C4/R3 is switched in, producing treble attenuation of 6dB per octave modified by the losses we have mentioned before. Fig. 10.8 shows an alternative method, again as a block diagram, used by Grundig in their TK340 model. Here, a quite complicated network is used during recording, but switching is considerably simplified so that the replay feedback loop is returned to virtually the same circuit point.

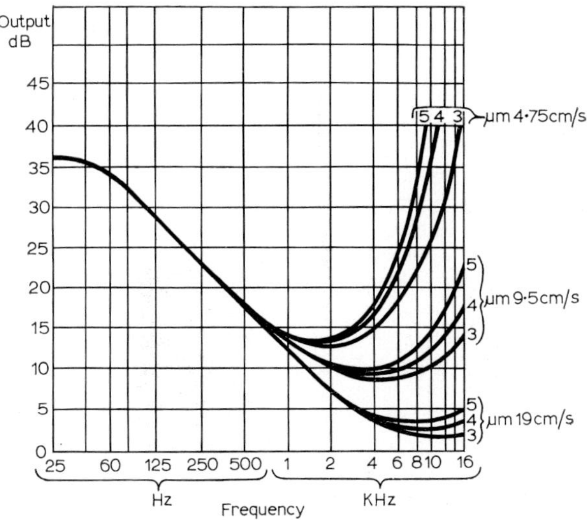

Fig. 10.6: Replay curves, allowing for differing head-gaps at the three principal speeds.

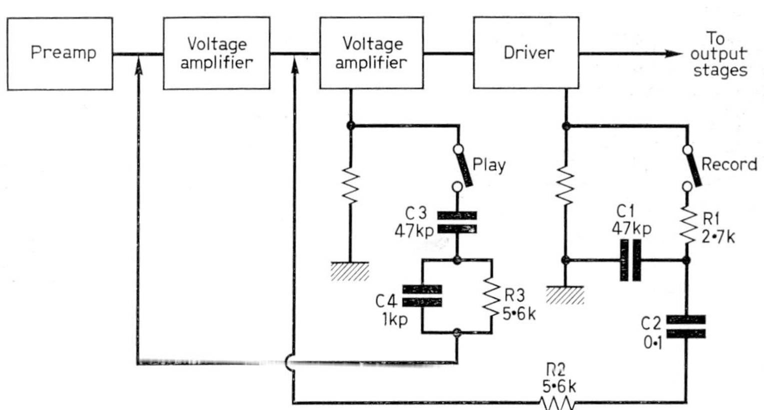

Fig. 10.7: Pre- and de-emphasis networks are switched during the appropriate function.

While recording, C119 limits the bass feedback, giving some bass lift; C115/L1 limit the feedback at upper frequencies, their tuned circuit giving a fairly sharply defined pre-emphasis. R132 flattens peaks and the combination of R127, R128 and C118 give a rising characteristic to the upper middle frequencies.

Playback brings a different network into use. C114 limits bass feedback, lifting the lower frequencies. R23 is fitted to prevent instability at the lower end of the frequency spectrum. C119/R121 and the combination R126, R 132, C115 and L1 modify the curve, giving bass and treble lift. Note, however, that the switching has now effectively put R126 in series with R132, which reduces the treble emphasis.

Feedback

When looking at these feedback loops—not always an easy matter, for the circuit layout 'buries' the relevant components and requires much patient tracing to resolve—one must bear in mind that the usual procedure is to feed back part of the amplified signal in antiphase (i.e. negative feedback) so that it reduces the gain of the controlled stage in proportion to its amplitude.

With frequency selective feedback, the gain of the amplifier is now made to vary in proportion to the frequency, as well as the amplitude, of the signal passing through it. A series capacitor in a feedback loop, for example, will more easily pass high frequencies than low, and thus will apply more feedback at the higher frequencies, so will therefore give treble de-emphasis (or, conversely, bass lift).

The larger the value of the capacitor, the greater its effect at low frequencies, but it is on the combination of the capacitor with the resistance in the circuit that the slope of the curve of response depends.

After all the concentration on replay response curves, time constants and equalisation, we must go back over some of the same ground and consider some of the recording factors that affect the standardisation. Our aim, while recording, is to make as 'strong' an impression on the tape as we can, to modulate the tape oxide up to its fullest capacity without producing distortion.

If we employ constant current recording techniques, as we have already determined we must, then the head characteristics and some of the factors introduced by the medium, will give us a slight droop of the curve, as we have noted. We can apply a little treble and bass pre-emphasis quite usefully to get the best possible recording, while still keeping the upper middle and low-to-mid frequencies below the tape saturation point. This way we shall get the best signal-to-noise ratio. But only if the bias is correct.

HF Bias

The amount of treble lift we need to give will depend on the h.f. bias. Magnitude of bias current affects the tape magnetisation at high frequencies. The ironical fact is that a reduction of bias may seem to *improve*

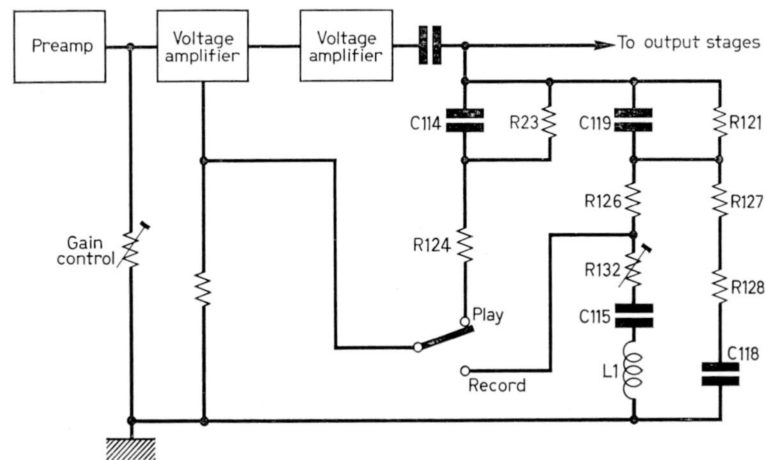

Fig. 10.8: An alternative method of switching equalisation, using common components in a network changed by the switching.

the treble response. In fact, all it has done is to increase the non-linear distortion, slightly emphasising some of the upper frequencies. Too much bias while recording will always lead to treble attenuation.

If we plot a graph of bias current against the measured distortion of the recording thus made, we find some rather peculiar variations. To begin with, distortion must be refined in some way: the blanket term can include hum, system noise such as hiss, and any non-linear contribution our whole chain of amplification may offer.

Laboratory tests prove that the significant factor is third-harmonic distortion. This will be the most troublesome factor influenced by the h.f. bias. Third harmonic distortion is high when the bias current is low. As the current is increased, a sharp drop in third harmonic distortion becomes noticeable and there is a well-defined 'dip'. Fig. 10.9 shows this effect clearly.

It might be thought that an operating current in line with this dip would be the ideal—and so it would, if all other things remained equal. But variations in the properties of magnetic tape, of mains and internal power supplies, even of temperature, will cause the position of this dip to change slightly, and as we can see, the slope of the sides is so sharp that a slight variation of bias current will produce a large change in distortion. So the alternative is to take a point on the less rapidly varying slope of the graph.

At this operating point, the bias current is higher, and there will be a small range within which only slight changes of third harmonic distortion will be registered, and where other considerations will affect the exact choice of operating point.

Professional tape recorders, and one or two of the better semi-professional machines, allow the operator to set the bias for every recording, and indicate the bias current (or some equivalent evaluation) on a special meter, or on the normal modulation level meter switched for the temporary purpose of bias setting. The good operator will check his bias, at least, and reset its value for optimum conditions—always a compromise—according to the characteristics of the tape he is using.

The author has strong feelings about this point. I once 'sat-in' during a recording session which was ultimately ruined because two successive tapes of a batch from a single maker (mercifully unnamed) had widely differing characteristics, and the recording engineer did not take the precaution of checking bias when reloading tape. In my view, bias adjustment should be available on any machine with pretensions to quality. Those that have this facility, however, may be numbered on the fingers of one hand.

Bias setting and output

After which bit of tub-thumping, we can progress to some of the other factors influenced by our setting of bias current. One of the first points we must remember is that any distortion caused during recording is likely to be enhanced by the frequency-conscious equalisation networks of the replay amplifier.

As an example, reverting to our discussion of third harmonic distortion: recording a signal of 1kHz, we would require a replay signal of that frequency and would get, with K3 distortion, another tone at a frequency of 3kHz superimposed. The new tone would be small in amplitude, say 5% of the wanted 1kHz signal. But our replay circuits provide a boost of (ideally) 6dB per octave, and the uplift afforded to the harmonic may bring its level up to 8 or 9 per cent, which cannot be tolerated. All of which serves to emphasise the importance of correct bias.

The effect of bias setting upon audio output can be seen by plotting playback voltage against bias current, as in Fig. 10.10. But here we have one or two conflicting ideas, so instead of simply choosing a test frequency and producing a neat curve (*a*), we can plot a family of curves and find that the peak point, where maximum audio output is produced, occurs at a lower bias current setting as the frequency of the test tone is raised.

For clarity, these I-optimum curves, as they are called, have been reduced to two only, and Fig. 10.10 shows the readings taken with a 1kHz and a 10kHz tone. Note that the 1kHz curve is fairly flat, so that an alteration of the bias current will not have a great effect on output; but the 10kHz curve is very markedly humped, and a change in bias current has a pronounced altering effect on output.

The logical setting for our operating point would seem to be somewhere between the two humps. And if we study the graph, we can see that the ideal operating point may be where the two curves cross. In practice it can be much simpler. Specification for a professional machine may state optimum bias current for a given tape and include the cryptic remark (. . . 1·25I_b(8·5kHz)/9·5cm./S).

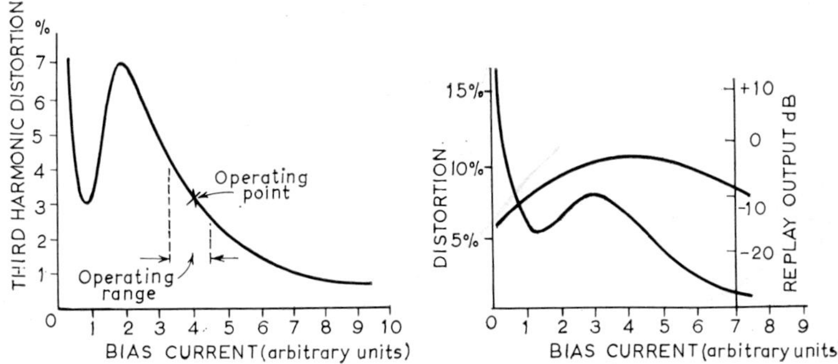

Fig. 10.9 (left): Third harmonic distortion alters drastically with a change in bias amplitude.

Fig. 10.10 (right): Difficulty in choosing the operating point is exemplified by plotting distortion and output curves on the common axis of bias amplitude.

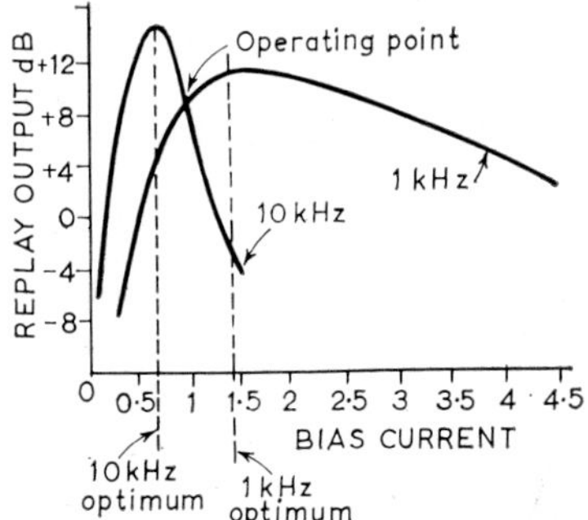

Fig. 10.11: The choice of bias operating point depends on several factors. In this graph, the operating point falls conveniently where the replay output curves at low and high frequency happen to cross, but this is not always the case.

This simply means that the bias current is one and a quarter the peak producing current for a signal of 8·5kHz at the given tape speed. Note that because tape magnet wavelengths are longer at higher speeds, bias current has less effect on frequency response.

Compromise Setting

We have now seen that it is frequency response and not merely audio output that the new bias setting can affect. Also that a compromise will be necessary to find a value of bias current that is best for good frequency response and low distortion. Fig. 10.11 combines the curves for distortion factor and audio output on the common base of a scale of arbitrary units of bias current.

Selecting the operating point on such a curve combination could be a tricky business, but luckily for us, manufacturers have done a lot of work on this problem, and a general rule to be followed is to adjust bias first for maximum audio output then increase the bias current until the output falls 2dB from this setting. A number of precautions must be taken when these adjustments are made, and these are outlined in the succeeding chapters on maintenance and testing.

Two other points have to be considered when choosing the bias operating point. These are signal-to-noise ratio and dropouts. As might be expected, there is a well-defined peak for the S/N ratio plotted against bias current, but as so many other considerations are involved, and overall noise measurement itself is a complicated matter, we can only say that design is oriented to the least noise and distortion at the optimum bias setting, and in this matter we are very much in the hands of the manufacturer. There is much to discuss on the subject of noise and its measurement, and this must be left to a later chapter dealing with tests and adjustments.

Dropouts

Dropouts, however, are a different matter entirely. With slow-speed, narrow track machines, which is the way the art is currently progressing, the length of the 'magnets' on the tape becomes less, and any physical deterioration of the tape surface, its oxide properties, or the contact with the head facing will have a drastic effect. We shall return to this point in a moment but must first look at the effect of incorrect bias on the problem of dropouts.

Some of the limitations are imposed by the self-demagnetisation previously mentioned. This is most marked when the tape wavelength of the

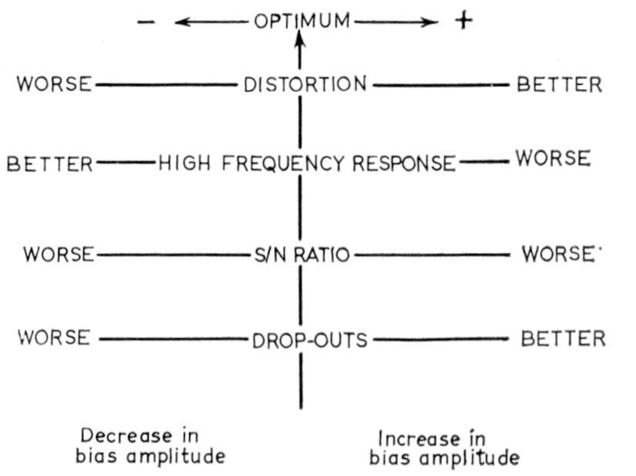

Fig. 10.12: Alteration in bias from the optimum value (for a given tape characteristic) will produce changes in the four main factors.

programme signal approaches the width of the recording zone (see Chapter 3). It is aggravated by the use of narrower tracks, slower speeds and thinner coatings on the tape. It is necessary to make the recording zone as narrow as possible. The effect is even more marked with thinner tapes as the available playback signal is lower. Any discrepancies will have more 'signal-spoiling' influence.

Reducing bias amplitude has a similar effect to reducing the recording

Fig. 10.13: View of the head assembly used by Tandberg for their crossfield design, with the bias head hidden in the flange of the pressure arm, ready to swing forward to its position close to the R/P head facing.

zone-width. There is then a chance of distortion at highest audio levels because the bias signal has not reached the deepest parts of the coating —an effect not often taken into account, especially as it is more noticeable at the middle and lower frequencies.

So, to balance matters, the signal amplitude has to be reduced to avoid distortion, it is more 'touchy' in the regions where the least good is being done by the equalisation and pre-emphasis, and the overall effect is that the full thickness of the oxide coating is not being employed efficiently. So the smallest physical variation, i.e. tendency to dropout, is aggravated by the incorrect bias.

Summing all these things up is not easy, but a small diagram, Fig. 10.12 demonstrates the way any alteration of bias current from its optimum value will cause a variation in one or other of the important factors during recording, and why a compromise often has to be effected.

Crossfield Bias

Which brings us, inevitably, to crossfield bias, a system employed by one or two makers to obtain the best possible recording conditions. Akai used the system for some time before other makers considered it worthwhile to attempt any improvement at what would be, for them, considerable expense. But the Akai system has always been aimed at an extended frequency response, and many users have claimed that this has been achieved at the expense of an enhanced noise level.

More recently, Tandberg have produced their own crossfield system, which relies on a slightly different approach, the head which supplies the bias waveform being offset a little toward the trailing edge of the recording head gap. According to their designers, the recording zone is confined to the area around the trailing edge of the record head gap.

In this zone the bias field comprises two components: one originates from the field between the two headfronts; the other emanates from the stray field across the gap of the recording head. At the trailing edge of the head gap the two fields are in opposition and partly cancel. The net result is that the effective recording zone becomes narrower.

This makes the critical self-erasure frequency higher, a thick tape coating can be more readily penetrated and the frequency response is improved. Crossfield techniques give the same signal amplitude at lower and middle frequencies coupled with greatly improved performance at higher frequencies.

The significant point is that thinner tapes can be used, and at slower speeds, for the same frequency response as with conventional recording. This means that all the other factors can be upgraded, giving greater scope for design improvement. Pre-emphasis can now be decreased—a good point when we consider that much modern music has a high amount of energy concentrated in the upper frequency spectrum, where too much pre-emphasis could so easily lead to distortion.

Conventional bias and thick tape require some 20dB of pre-emphasis at 10kHz. This is at 9·5cm./S. The use of crossfield bias reduces wavelength-dependent losses to the point where only 12dB pre-emphasis is needed. This is for a small increase in tape noise, however, a factor that is too often skated over lightly by the protagonists of X-bias.

However, when we reduce speed to 4·75, using the same tape, the case looks more favourable. Pre-emphasis has to be 18dB, with an increased S/N figure of 2dB, but the overall S/N increase is still only 4dB above what could have been achieved at 19cm./S using conventional bias.

For thick tape, crossfield biasing is some 6dB better than conventional biasing at all tape speeds (signal-to-noise). But the frequency range is considerably enhanced, and more effective recordings can be made at lower speeds. For thin tape, the corresponding noise figure at the same speed (4·75cm./S) would be nearer 20dB. This shows quite clearly that crossfield biasing is not the panacea to all our recording ills, but when it is properly designed and allied to the use of tape with much lower noise figures than that we use at present, without any increased thickness, we may be well on the way toward a recording revolution. I make no apology for repeating that statement, and am well aware that the speed of advance of modern technology could outdate my words as soon as they appear in print.

Head Alignment

In our earlier look at the subject of heads, (Chapter 3), we noted the importance of gap dimensions and touched upon the need for correct azimuth adjustment. In this chapter, concerned as we are with frequency response and the quality of recording, we should investigate the business of head alignment a little more deeply.

We know already that gap width affects the head sensitivity. The aim is to achieve as narrow a gap as possible. If we look at Fig. 10.14 we see that not only does the tilt of a head from its true azimuth (i.e. at right angles to the direction of tape travel) effectively increase the gap width, but also that the increase is proportionately more for a half-track recording. From this we conclude that quarter-track azimuth setting is not quite so critical. But this need never be an excuse: setting the heads correctly is a small job, easily within the capabilities of the owner, and should never be neglected.

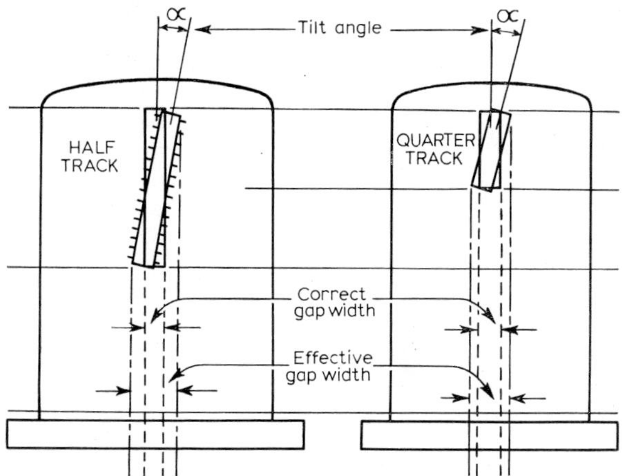

Fig. 10.14: The effective gap width is increased by head misalignment. This is more pronounced for half-track than quarter-track recording.

The high frequency response is governed by the gap width. Enlarging the gap, or tilting the head with the same ultimate effect, causes a severe high frequency loss. The tolerance regarded as acceptable by the makers of many domestic tape recorders, even if rather wide for professional operators, is approximately one-quarter of the width of the gap for half-track machines.

Gap width can be, as we have already noted, as little as 0·8 of a tenth of a thousandth of an inch, (0·00008-inch) so a tilt of quite minute proportions will be needed to give an effective alteration in gap width of 0·00002 inches. We know that replay output is theoretically zero when the wavelength of the signal is reduced to the gap width. The gap width must always be less than the shortest wavelength to be recorded—i.e. the highest frequency.

To take an example: at 16kHz, replaying at 9·5cm./S, the wavelength would be, nearly 6μm. The gap in the playback head must be less than this. In practice, it would be 0·6 to 0·7λ, the wavelength, say 4μm.

Gap loss can be calculated if we know the width of the gap. A formula for the so-called gap function is as follows:

$$S = \frac{\text{Sin } \pi s/\lambda}{\pi s/\lambda}$$

where s is the gap width and λ the wavelength to be recorded. From this formula a whole family of curves can be built up. These will show that for a decreasing gap width the high frequency response will improve, but also that the droop of the curve as the frequency increases is much the same for all gap widths.

Gap Azimuth

A further effect that must be taken into account is the gap azimuth effect. Although tapes recorded on one particular machine with its head offset will play back quite well on the same machine, to interchange tapes between machines with an offset head on one is asking for trouble.

Replacing the gap width s in the above formula by b tan α we can calculate attenuation due to tilt. This is where b is the track width and α the angle of tilt in minutes of arc. For a half-track machine at 9·5cm./S we get an attenuation at 12kHz of 7dB if there is as little as an 8 minute tilt.

Fig. 10.15 shows the alignment assembly of a good quality machine (in this case the Uher 4000) where the erase head E is fixed and provides a a reference for the level of the adjustable tape guides A, B and C. The overall height of the Record Play head is set by the screw S and the tilt adjusted by the screw D. There are very few machines on which this adjustment cannot be made.

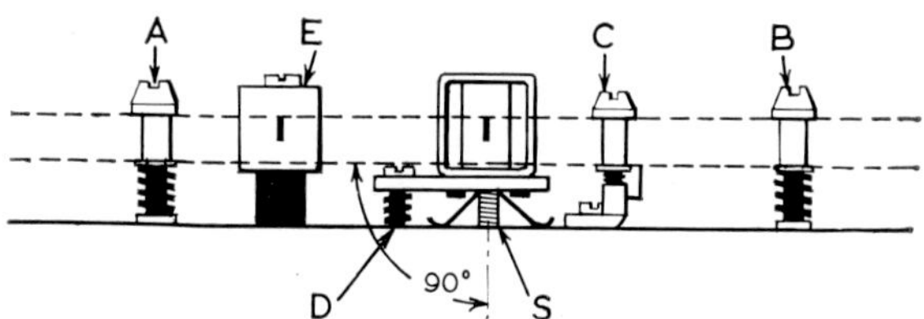

Fig. 10.15: Head alignment is generally simple, but should always start with a reference or datum. In this example (Uher 4000), the erase head is fixed.

Normal setting is for maximum replay output of a pre-recorded test tape, and white noise is accepted as the easiest 'programme' to aid an aural assessment. But the eye is much more accurate than the ear when making measurements, and the correct way is to measure the output from the replay amplifier while tilting the head, adjusting for what should be a quite definable peak. More on the subject of adjustments later, but mention must be made here also of the importance of an all-round adjustment, not simply a setting of the head azimuth.

A tilt from the vertical in the backwards or forwards direction can cause severe attenuation. Spacing losses due to separation of the tape from the gap facing can be calculated from the formula

$$A = e^{2\pi}\frac{d}{\lambda} \text{ or } 55\frac{d}{\lambda}\text{ dB}$$

where d is the distance in the same units as the wavelength, λ. If $\frac{d}{\lambda} = 1$, i.e. if the spacing is just equal to the wavelength, the attenuation is $A(dB) = 20\log e^{2\pi} = 40\pi\log e = 40\pi\ 0{\cdot}434 = 54{\cdot}5dB$.

Reverting to our previous example of a 6μm gap, and a wavelength of the same amount (16kHz at 9·5cm./S) we can see from the playback output curves that such an attenuation is equivalent to a serious dropout for as long as the tape is held off by this spacing. When you consider that the

Fig. 10.16: Adjustment of azimuth on one of the older Grundig models. Apart from head shape, the principle of azimuth alignment has not altered greatly. Adjustment is nearly always a matter of the turn of a screw.

overall thickness of double-play tape is only 26μm you can see what a proportionately small offsetting of the head is needed to produce severe deterioration in recording and playback results.

For a different reason, but with a similar effect, the positioning of the replay head, where some rotation is possible, can have dire results. In Chapter 3 we have noted the influence of head contouring on the efficiency of recording, and refer to the fluctuation in the playback output curve when the length of contact between tape and head is of the same order as the tape wavelength.

Unfortunately, these 'bass resonances' we have noted are more pronounced at higher tape speeds. The more suddenly the tape leaves the contact area of the head, the greater the amplitude of the face resonance. Wrongly positioning a rounded-faced or contoured head can have a similar effect to changing the contour.

It has been emphasised before, and needs no apology for repetition, that all these adjustments, and meticulous design, are annulled by a lack of maintenance. Head cleaning is the first job the owner should tackle, once he has chosen and learned to use his tape recorder.

CHAPTER ELEVEN

SERVICING THE DECK

THERE ARE ALMOST as many styles of tape recorder mechanism as there are model numbers. Any attempt to be more than general in this chapter would make it ten times as long. Perhaps the best way to describe the ruses and problems of tape deck servicing is to show it being done, so the bulk of this chapter is its illustrations and the following text can be read in conjunction with the pictures, which are all of equipment that has gone through the author's workshop. Apologies may be due for some of the photography: I keep a camera in a drawer beneath the bench, with a flash unit and spot lamps all ready for an on-the-spot shot when time and circumstances permit.

Such a system is not conducive to award-winning photography! But it has the advantage of making direct illustration of adjustments possible, where masses of textual description would only tend to confuse. Very often, the adjustments and repairs are empirical—a matter of 'bend this, twist that, and try, try again'. In such cases an exact guide to procedure is impossible, so these notes may be taken as personal descriptions of prevalent faults, their treatment and, it is to be hoped, their cure.

Application and Adaptability

To begin with an admonition: Fig. 11.1 is not merely a joke. How efficiently we are able to maintain our apparatus depends on how good our tools are as much as on how well we can use them. Hitting plastics handles is only one of the small crimes that marks out the careless workman, so perhaps I should emphasise that one of my colleagues posed especially for this picture!

Tape recorder repairs call for some special tools, and over a long period the average workshop handling such repairs in any quantity will have built up a rack of home-made or specially adapted tools. Benders for resetting levers in confined spaces, various hooks and clamps, spring balances with extended crooks, slot-grip and notched screwdrivers and the cleaning items detailed in Chapter 9 are a few of the items that do not generally have their place in a radio and television workshop.

We have to find ways of dealing with springs, slotted levers with inserted screws, some tiny screws that would not be out of place in a

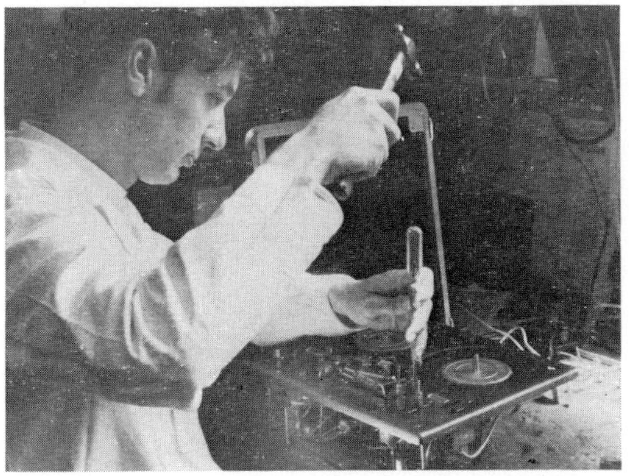

Fig. 11.1: Not the best way to carry out servicing! But Bob is only pretending to attack the Tandberg and knows better than to compound the felony by hitting a plastics-handled screwdriver with his knocking stick.

jeweller's department, and cleaning, skimming, resetting and testing rotating parts from the slack-tape idler to the motor armature itself. Small wonder that the number of specialist dealers capable of handling tape recorder repairs efficiently is dwindling.

Rotating Parts

Rotating parts, and the bearings in which they run, are prime causes of tape deck trouble. Infiltration of dust, absorption of lubricant, heat and friction can cause erratic running, slow but regular running or even a

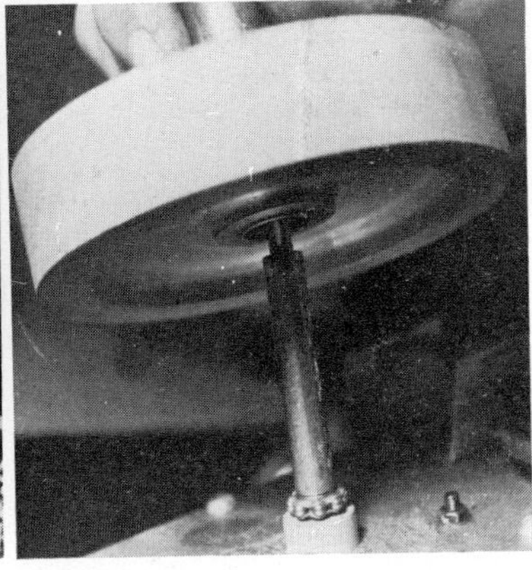

Fig. 11.2 (left): Motors, their mountings, pulleys and bearings are the major items in service work, and need close attention. This Ferrograph example, because of its known reliability, has been neglected until the bearings dried completely and seized.

Fig. 11.3 (right): Flywheel bearings are closely machined and demand careful cleaning and lubricating.

complete seizure. In Chapter 9 we saw some of the problems and considered the merits of correct cleaning and lubrication.

In an ideal world, half the tape deck troubles would be absent, for a regular regime of maintenance would not allow them to develop. But our problem, once the trouble has arisen, is how to save what is left of the situation. First job is a complete dismantling and cleaning. It is of little use swabbing a bearing down with spirits or other solvents when the end result is going to be more dirt washed into the porous metal and the vital oil washed out.

Cleaning should be done with a minimum of spirit, and after reassembly a couple of drops of machine oil can be allowed to run into the bearing block. If there is a special place for application, use it. Some manufacturers have even gone to the length of extending a tube from the lubricating point to the bearing surface. It is asking for trouble to pour lubricant indiscriminately down a rotating spindle.

Oil Creep

One of the problems following poor lubrication is oil creep. Capillary action will allow the thin film of oil to work its way upwards, centrifugal force does the rest. Some oil gets onto the driving or driven surface in

Fig. 11.4 (top left): Ball-races are rarer now that nylon, neoprene and other plastics bearings have been developed. They need careful cleaning and lubricating to reduce noise and wow.

Fig. 11.5 (top right): Do not neglect the upper holder of the flywheel spindle which, in its various forms, acts as a locator bearing. Its setting is often adjustable.

Fig. 11.6 (lower right): Neglect of a bearing. Overheating through lack of lubrication has caused the lower brake section to deform and seize.

Fig. 11.7: Small spindles on which rotating wheels move must be kept clean and correctly angled. This Sony example requires that the take-up idler slides to the upper position for fast winding. Note return spring.

contact with the spindle, and more may be thrown off by the spinning member to arrive on other moving parts such as rubber pulleys or drive belts, brakes or friction pads. In any of these places it spells trouble and can sometimes be difficult to remove.

Closely machined bearings may require special lubricants and the types with ball-race end-pieces need careful attention in reassembly. They must be seated and 'run-in'. This sometimes means a period of running with bearing clamps not fully tightened and with the help of a knock from a wood mallet—not a steel hammer or the heel of a shoe, please! In Fig. 11.4 we see the ball-race of an older type of tape recorder—but one, which like the Rolls Royce, seems destined to go on for ever. Removing, cleaning and replacing this with a smear of clean grease is not a difficult task, once the rest of the mounting assembly has been dismantled.

But after reassembly there may be a temptation to neglect the final item, the upper locator—hardly a bearing at all in the case of some lesser machines. This item, shown in Fig. 11.5 can be critical in its final setting. Taking it off for normal cleaning operations is temptingly simple. Refitting it may take some time, for the correct adjustment is not easy to judge.

Neglected bearings can seize, as we have pointed out. Where rubber floats and spacers are used, the ingress of oil and foreign matter and the build-up of heat can cause dire results. The debacle of Fig. 11.6 is fortunately rare—which is just as well because that particular machine was purchased in Singapore and spare parts were a long time a-coming. In this case it was the lower brake section that suffered and may well have been where the fault originally happened.

In many tape recorder designs we see the method of rotating a disc on a spindle within the fixed barrel of a bearing mounted in the deck plate. Some of these mountings, I regret to say, leave a lot to be desired. They are too easily disturbed from verticality. Where such spindle bearings are held in the deck by a form of open rivet, and where perhaps the deckplate itself may be less than completely rigid, it is sometimes possible to prise the tube to a correct setting, but this is a very unsatisfactory solution. Unfortunately it is the only solution short of changing the whole deck.

The opposite case, where a pulley or other moving part depends on the vertical setting of a spindle, also calls for a little 'brute force' when things get out of line. The easiest method of straightening these spindles—bearing in mind that the bending is more often of the lever on which the spindle is mounted—is to fit a suitable diameter of tube over it and gently apply a force in the required direction, holding the mounting piece firm as this is done. A tubular box spanner is an excellent tool for this job.

The difficulty comes when the mounting piece, often no more than a splayed end of the pin, has worked loose in the lever or bracket. Then, tightening is imperative before any straightening can be done, otherwise the pin swivels and is worse than before. To tighten, either mount in a vice and use a pin punch to clip the cinch or cut across the base of the pin and the lever with a fine saw so that the splay of newly cut metal helps to clamp it. In a properly equipped workshop, brazing or spot-welding would be called on to make the spindle seating permanent.

Sliding Parts

Very often, as in Fig. 11.7 the action depends on sliding parts, slotted levers and so on, and the relationship between spindle and slot is critical. If the angle is wrong, the slot binds on the spindle. Enlarging the slot is no answer—decks are noisy enough already—and it may be necessary to adjust the angle of the lever or the set of the spindle. The need for this is not always obvious, and the position of the idler or other borne part must be checked at the beginning and the end of travel for assessment of the angle of 'throw'.

Where an aiding spring is incorporated, either a simple compression

Fig. 11.8: A common 'bent spindle' problem is found when large, thin idler wheels are loosely suspended, as in this Philips example.

Fig. 11.9 (left): Spindles such as the small type used for this rewind wheel (Philips) can get grimed easily, especially when the belt (removed here for clarity) becomes damaged and sheds rubber particles. The result, poor torque.

Fig. 11.10 (right): Many idlers depend on spring tension for their correct operation. Look for distorted spring anchor points.

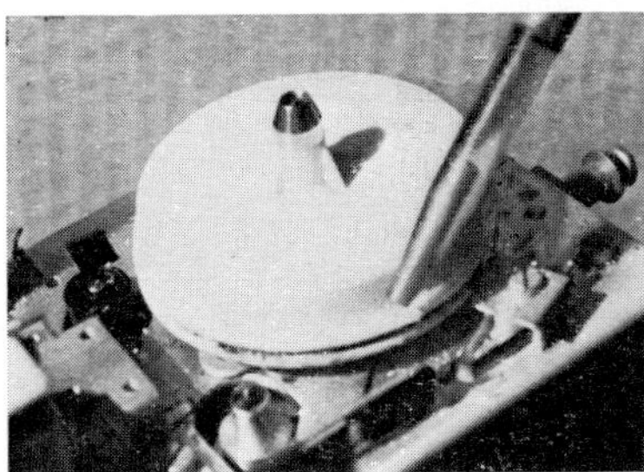

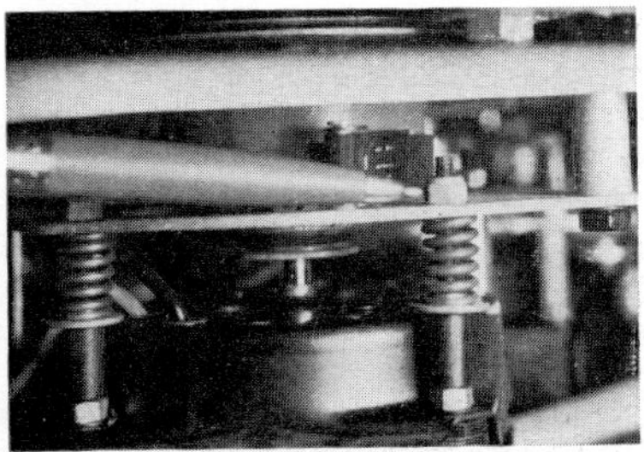

Fig. 11.11 (left): Worn parts should be immediately suspect. This debacle began with a chipped spool carrier, ended with a major repair!

Fig. 11.12 (right): Spool carrier adjustment is not always obvious. In this Magnavox *Studio* example, the motor plate carries a spring-loaded sub-plate, with three locking nuts which determine the verticality of the spindle.

Fig. 11.13 (left): Spool carrier height is adjusted in the *Studio* and similar decks by setting of the brake drum, with fine limitation afforded by the engagement of a central grub screw with the top of the motor spindle. Not to be used for basic height setting; the result, a mass of aluminium swarf within the carrier recess.

Fig. 11.14 (right): Wire-link springs are vulnerable items, especially around the head gate and pressure arm assembly.

spring or the type of bent leaf shown here, the approach to its treatment will depend on how much work it is intended to do. The simple compression spring is not working hard and has to be pretty badly damaged before it seriously affects operation, but the leaf spring is a different problem. Its setting and its springiness can matter a lot.

There will often be a slotted screw hole for its adjustment and the setting should be done through the complete range of travel and at the different tensions the idler or bracket is likely to attain. This is important with all moving part adjustments: make and crosscheck them under all the conditions they are likely to meet, not just at neutral setting.

Springs

Springs of all types can be a tape deck problem. A number of the illustrations accompanying this text have been chosen to show the different uses to which springs may be put, and to point out the type of mechanism where a spring action is vital to correct operation. For example, the hold-

Fig. 11.15: Simplicity is often a feature of better class decks. The spool carrier height setting of the Revox 36 series depends on a screw, which clamps the flatted spindle and which is beneath the brake drum fabric ring. The carrier top is held on with three screws.

Fig. 11.16: Spool carrier adjustment is not always so straightforward. This underside view of a carrier spindle shows three spring-loaded screws on a rocker plate: almost impossible to adjust by eye.

on spring of a motor pulley or drive idler has to give enough pull to ensure good contact and transmission of torque, but must not be so fierce as to initiate 'scuffing'.

The springs that help sliding members need to be fairly long and their tension has to be exact between the full extent of the lever's travel. Quite often the compensation for spring ageing is made by alternative anchor points. Before altering the setting, always ensure that levers, their brackets, stirrups and pivot points are clean and correctly lubricated.

These springs, because of their length and sometimes because of their proximity to the deck and and other parts can rattle and buzz. The cause

Fig. 11.17: The pressure roller 'hold-on' spring of the Collaudio deck used by Van der Molen for their VR7 is bent brass with a securing and adjustment screw. The spring *must* apply an even top and bottom pressure.

of the noise is not always easy to trace. If a long spring is suspected, this can be proved by a reduction of the noise or an alteration of its note when the spring is lightly touched.

A remedy is to insert a small sliver of expanded polystyrene or foam rubber in the spring and, if nearness to the metal deck is a problem, to cover the slide area beneath the spring to beyond the extent of movement with a strip of PVC tape. Beyond the extent . . . because a partial cure here can cause trouble when the spring turns catch on edges and eventually loosen the protective strip.

Return Action

Hook springs and spring clips are fairly obvious in their action. Usually, they are meant to impart a return action to some lever. But occasionally their purpose is deceptive. They can be used to impel a bracket away from an area at a swift rate after the bracket has travelled part of the way slowly, or perhaps to retard action until there is sufficient force to overcome the spring.

Head gate springs are often used this way and trying to reset these to achieve the correct throw independent of the main pressure arm movement can be very tricky because a compromise between inward pressure and the outward 'flick' is needed. Several of our illustrations pinpoint danger areas around the head gates of popular machines and show the importance of spring action.

Head pressure arm adjustment will depend on the maker, but in the absence of instructions it should be possible to determine (*a*) tape travel setting, (*b*) verticality of engaged members, (*c*) direction of excess pressure and (*d*) tape pull. If the head gate and sound channel assembly is properly adjusted the (*a*) and most of (*b*) queries are answered. Setting up the head gate should be an early part of servicing. Observing the tape as it passes

Fig. 11.18: Adjustments around the pressure arm assembly are made easy when access is free, as with this Tandberg example. Note the use of a *Safeblock* power connector for an isolated bench supply. (See Chapter 12.)

through, aided by a brilliant spotlight—even a torch with a focussed bulb will do—soon reveals any tendency of the tape to 'ride' and as long as it is remembered that the tape will ride toward the point of highest pressure, the job can be tackled.

Nearly always, the trouble is wear of the pressure roller or offsetting of the spindle. Look for deformed plastics washers in bearings, and, as with spool carrier drums and other plastics mounted parts which have to have metal insert bearings, for the bearing barrel that has slipped below its surrounding area of metal to present a new, and often uneven surface.

Cassette Recorders

Dealing with the smaller machines can be a finicky business and not a job to be attempted without a good idea of what has to be done. Parts are smaller, of course, and settings more precise. But the trouble that besets the inexperienced owner is in knowing where the necessary pressures must be applied.

Cassette machines have some awkward double-clutched pulleys. The spindles must be clean and even; they are so short that any discrepancy is hard to see. The seatings for pulleys and hubs must be clean and any small plastics washers that are fitted must be in good order. Quite often they get 'dished' after a period of neglect.

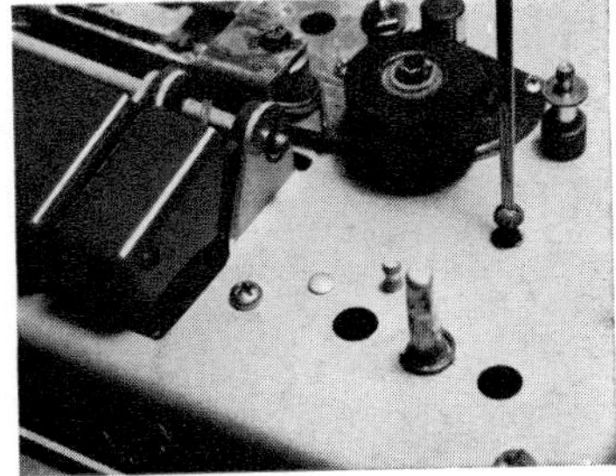

Fig. 11.19 (left): Head slide engagement can be affected by refusal of ejectors and other safety devices to return to neutral when not in use. Example: Loewe-Opta portable using d.c. system cassette.

Fig. 11.20 (right): Beware the innocent screw! Tightening this one down will inevitably jam the flywheel. Many decks use locked screws as limiters, their function not always obvious at first sight.

Fig. 11.21 (left): Brakes can have a double action, as with this Sony example, where both the main and the auxiliary brake (for back tensioning) are peripheral pad types. Adjustment needs patience.

Fig. 11.22 (right): Cork pads are used on this Philips machine for reel braking. They can acquire a polish by dust and heat action. Resurfacing is simple.

Fig. 11.23 (left): Differential brakes on models like the Uher 4000 can be easily overlooked. They consist of rubber rollers on angled brackets (indicated).

Fig. 11.24 (right): Another example from that very fine Uher machine. Reversal of transmission direction is achieved by pulleys on a common spindle with a seesaw action, dependent on bracket setting and accuracy of the rocker indicated.

Rubber tyres and pulley wheels are particularly vulnerable in these small mechanisms because torques are low and diameters are small. In addition, the action of the sliding head plate must complicate matters, giving yet another variable for the operator to worry about. On many of the earlier types there was a tendency for fine-threaded screws to work loose, for pins in the slide plate to become distorted and for the head mountings to swivel.

All this and the cassettes too! Many a good machine has been condemned because a cassette has been neglected until its inner lining of polythene sheeting warped and crinkled to catch the edge of the coiled tape and impose just enough friction to impede the delicate action of the tape recorder. The small pad at the centre of the cassette, on its weak spring blade, is another vulnerable item. Once this spring has become distorted, it is difficult to regain the former efficiency and still rest it neatly in the intended slots.

Brake Troubles

Brakes are another sore point. The timing of their application is what matters. With most mechanisms, the feed spool is given a little priority so that stopping the tape after forward motion does not lead to spillage. Refinements of this idea can lead to 'rocker' brakes where the emphasis is on the supply spool, whichever way the tape is moving. The development of this is the differential brake which applies a tension depending on tape movement and, in the more involved types, amount of tape spooled.

Quite apart from these types, yet achieving similar results, is the servo brake, whose action has been fully described. We shall not waste space repeating the functional descriptions of these different types of brakes but would urge any budding engineers to go back and read Chapter 4 again. Unless some understanding of brake operation has been gained,

Fig. 11.25 (left): Belts, even this simple, direct drive type by Sony, easily accessible, can give trouble when they relax and slip.

Fig. 11.26 (right): Flat fabric belts are subject to impregnation by metal swarf and dirt particles and any erratic setting of pulleys will result in uneven wear, especially frayed edges.

Fig. 11.27: Flat rubber belts such as used in this Sony video tape recorder, are not so common, but they, too, can suffer from impregnation, and need regular cleaning.

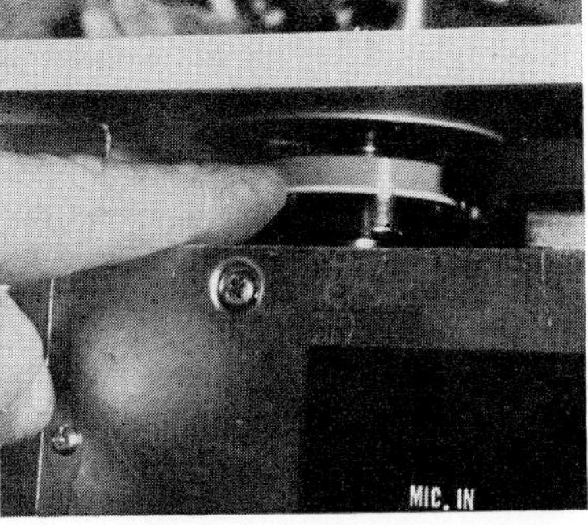

Fig. 11.28: Impregnation is not limited to belts. The highly polished look of a drum such as this clutch section engaged by a wide rubber idler, may indicate a 'polish' achieved by a film of dust, oil and rubber particles. Lack of the necessary friction and a poor drive results.

attempts to adjust them will be useless. The difference between the crude pads of a differential servo brake action is the difference between sticking out your foot to stop the car and and applying regulated disc brakes.

But whatever the type of brake employed, its efficiency will depend as much on being clean and free from impregnation as on the setting. This is part of the deck repair operation too often neglected. So long as everything is running the brakes are forgotten—but you can make an awful mess of your tape if things do not stop when they should!

So long as things are running . . . well yes, but there is another brake which needs special attention, and this is the auxiliary brake. More often employed as a form of back tension device, the pad or blade of a second-

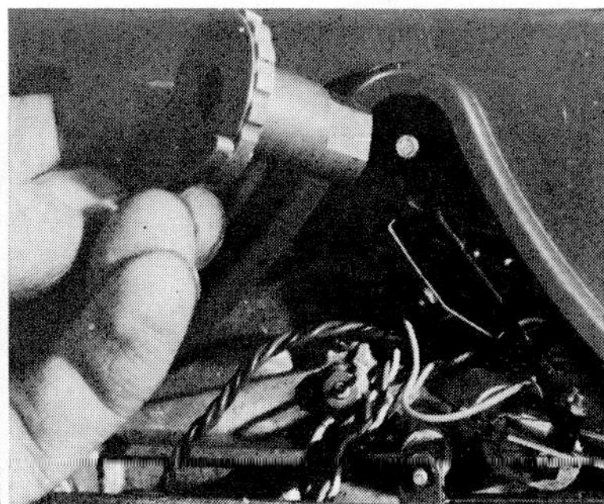

Fig. 11.29: The autostop switch connections of the Revox 36 deck depend on a snap spring action and *(right)* the tensioning device for odd spool sizes also depends on switch setting.

ary brake may be sprung into place, may depend on a long lever and may very easily become dislodged. Too much back tension may lead to flutter. Too little, especially with those machines that operate vertically and depend on a sprung rider jockey, or have spring-actuated autostops at the feed side of the head gate, can even cause the machine to stop unexpectedly as the spillage grows.

Belts and Drive Pulleys

Belts and drive pulleys should be so obvious as to merit only a passing mention. Their action has been fully explained in Chapter 4 and some of the faults that can cause poor pulley action have been discussed earlier in this chapter. But we must have a word or two on the business of belt slackness. Rubber belts age like the rest of us, and (dare I say it?) like the rest of us they grow soft and flabby. There is no remedy but replacement for belts that have thus outlived their usefulness.

I have seen pulley drive systems augmented with sticky paper, belts cut and reformed with glued joints, grooves in drums meticulously filled with resinous substance to increase their diameter and other such horrifying subterfuges to avoid the necessity of replacing a belt. Nowadays, with one or two companies producing a very wide range of pre-packed belts, there should be a solution to the difficulty short of personally redesigning the deck!

The other problem, of a 'formed' belt, usually due to the machine having been left standing unused, and probably in the cold, can be overcome by gentle heating, slow running and patience. More than one severe case of wow has been saved by immersing such a 'belt with a bump in it' in hot water for a while, drying it, dusting with french chalk, refitting and allowing the deck to run for several hours. Like all other mechanisms, the tape deck benefits from regular use. Nothing is saved by shoving it under the bed.

Fig. 11.30: Two examples from an elderly Philips. *Left*—the main record/play switch linkage system needs locknut adjustment. *Right*—track switch, dependent on the clamp screws for accuracy.

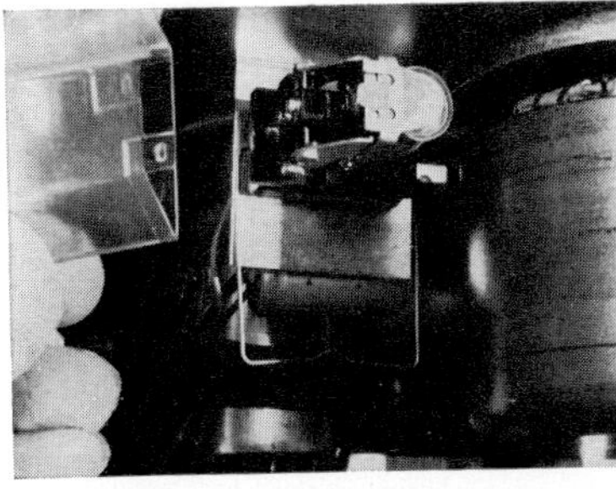
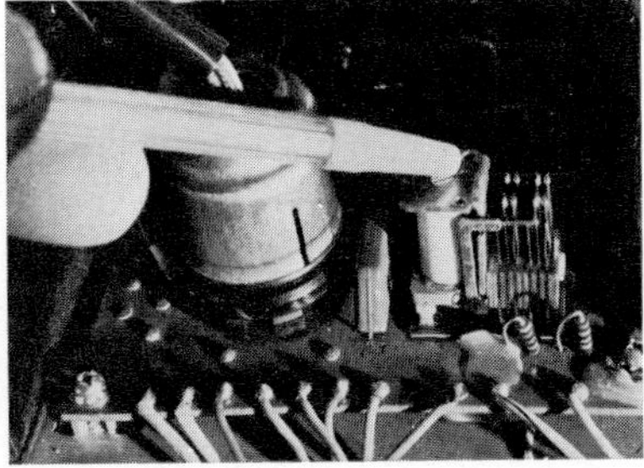

Fig. 11.31: Two views of relays, which may be used as a purely electrical switch for a motor function *(left)* or as a signal circuit routing device *(right)*. The latter type need very accurate make and break setting, and poor contacts can lead to noisy reproduction.

Flat fabric belts have their own problems, not least of which is a propensity to fraying. As they often run over dished pulleys or in guide slots, any discrepancy of pulley plane is more markedly obvious than with round belts. Flat rubber belts are subject to impregnation and very often the tensioning system needs careful attention to maintain a smooth and even run of the mechanism. Slipping belt systems, used for clutches, require that pulleys shall be kept scrupulously clean. Free running pulleys are often employed and the spindles of these need their own modicum of attention.

Electro-mechanical Faults

Electro-mechanical problems can be very tricky and some of the vital points have been illustrated. Among these, the autostop devices consisting of bent wires that ride in slots of guides and actuate microswitches are easily distorted. Leaf spring switches that are acted upon by cams or levers can cause some trouble, especially when the mechanical action is dependent on the physical switch setting and this is determined by screws in slotted holes.

If there are no shakeproof washers fitted, put this omission right. The switches themselves are seldom serviceable except for some contact cleaning. Older types allowed small adjustment of the leaves, and of course, all types of relays have to be checked for correct throw, armature angle, contact closure and, sometimes, for sequential closing.

As we stated at the outset, it is not possible to be precise, to say 'bend this, twist that . . .' with so many different mechanisms to make our lives interesting. Perhaps the foregoing notes and illustrations may have aided those with problems and shown more than one reader that 'using' a tape recorder consists as much of keeping it in working order as in pressing the right button at the right time.

CHAPTER TWELVE

TESTS & MEASUREMENTS

THIS IS ESSENTIALLY a practical book. It has been pointed out before, and cannot be repeated often enough, that repairs to tape recorders, tests of their performance and measurement of their specifications must depend on the tools and instruments with which such work is carried out. Many of the tools are common workshop equipment. Some are special and have been perfunctorily described in earlier chapters.

We are not so much concerned in this final chapter with tools as with instruments and their use. But a brief mention may be needed of some 'service aids' which can shorten working time; for the amateur, time is not so important as for the busy professional, so the counter-attraction is the easing of many tricky tasks around the tape recorder mechanism and its amplifiers which these aids can offer.

Gripping Aids

The bench vice is the most common of tools, yet not always the most convenient. Unless there is adequate bench space, the darn thing always seems to be getting in the way. Portability is a virtue that seems foreign to a vice, yet can be its greatest asset in tape recorder work. Often it is necessary to prop a deck in an awkward position to take measurements as it operates. There is a limit to the number of electrical tests one can make to amplifiers: ultimately, one has to check the specification with the tape running.

It is then that the unconventional use of a common tool, such as the invaluable *Guygrip* of Fig. 12.1, can be condoned. But seriously, the adjustable hand-vice, of which the mole-wrench is a good example, is an important tool to the tape recorder service engineer. There are many 'hold, twist or pull' jobs on mechanisms that are made much easier with the help of a third hand.

As a further aid, especially helpful in the delicate business of holding connectors for soldering, there are universally adjustable bench vices on the market, some with extension bars and curiously shaped jaws. With a heavy, rubber-footed bottom, spring-loaded jaws and milled adjusters, these odd-looking clamps can be most effective.

The author has one which was originally purchased as a camera stand

Fig. 12.1: Bench vices are not always convenient, and seldom as easily adjustable as this *Guygrip* wrench, called into service to support a tape recorder deck for some delicate soldering.

for close-up work. It now acts more often as a convenient holder for DIN plugs, where the soldering of several close connections with cable whose insulation melts as soon as a soldering iron comes within breathing distance can be a nerve-testing matter!

Now and again, these adjustable grips are employed as they were first intended—as spanners. But this engineer's opinion *vide* spanners is that they should be an exact fit for the nut or bolthead, and that the small extra expense entailed in purchasing a suitable kit is more than justified by the ease with which one eventually extracts the one recalcitrant screw that is holding up operations. It is necessary nowadays to lay in a kit of British Standard Whitworth, British Association and Metric box and flat spanners to be sure of coping with all the tape decks that might come our way.

The most effective aids are always those that are so simple that they inspire one to say: 'Now why didn't I think of that?' Among these, the Philips bench mat (See Fig. 12.4) is an obvious choice. Lying flat on the

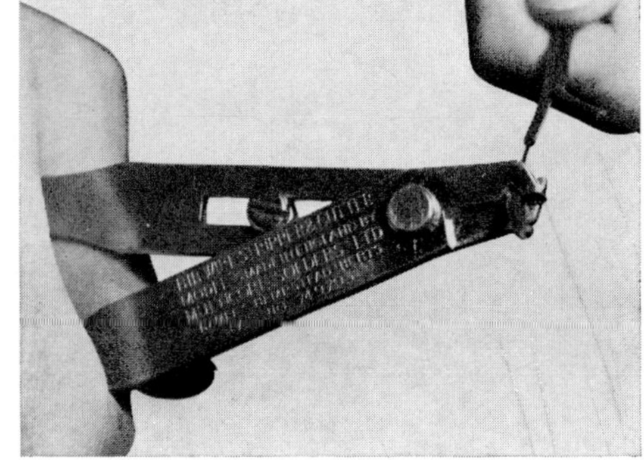

Fig. 12.2: Bib cable strippers in their various versions are well known. This one—Model 3—has the cutting aperture set by a sliding screw, but carries the advantage of two cutting positions, the outer for delicate corners, and for separating extruded cables.

bench, forming small compartments with sloping sides that permit 'fishing' for even tiny screws it offers a resilient bed for the most delicate equipment that has to be inverted, will not harbour solder blobs to scratch cabinets—as will the most carefully nursed fabric mat—and is easily removed for cleaning. The rubber is fairly hard, virtually impervious to normal knocks or solder burns and covers a fairly large area of the bench with its cross-hatch.

Soldering Tools

Soldering irons are so proliferous that it seems invidious to mention one's own favourites. Yet I must say that the best long-term service I have ever enjoyed has been with the Solon range, whose several parts are easily obtained and as easily replaced.

The one snag—common to other types—is the tendency of the bit to wear rapidly when the iron is left on for long periods, as it may be. Permalloy bits reduce this tendency, but the best answer to the problem is a regular release and movement of the bit. This is much easier in screw-type irons, such as the Marksman or the push-fit types such as the Litesold design, than with the split-pin fastening of the Solon.

But everyone to his tastes: for work in the field, I have long favoured the solder gun, which heats up rapidly at the touch of its trigger, which

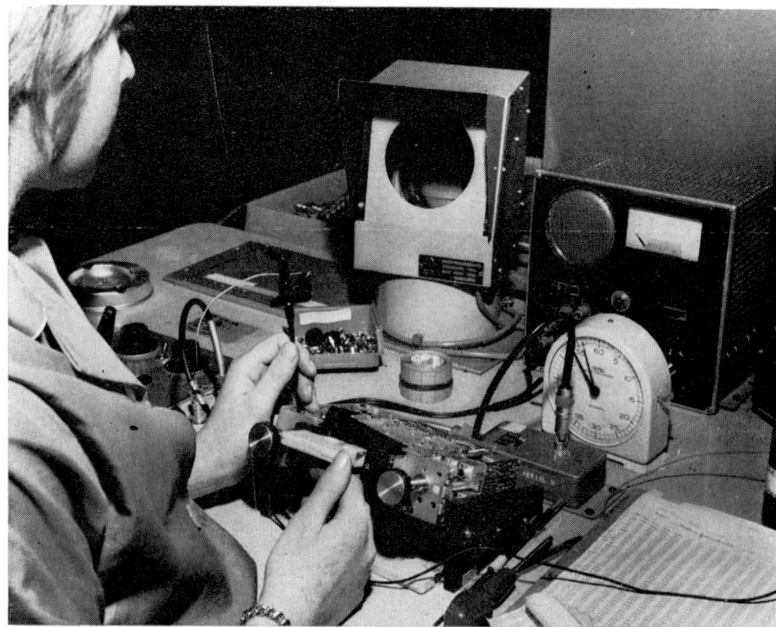

Fig. 12.3: Car radios with inbuilt cassette players are becoming increasingly popular. Sensitivity tests are here being carried out on a Philips model.

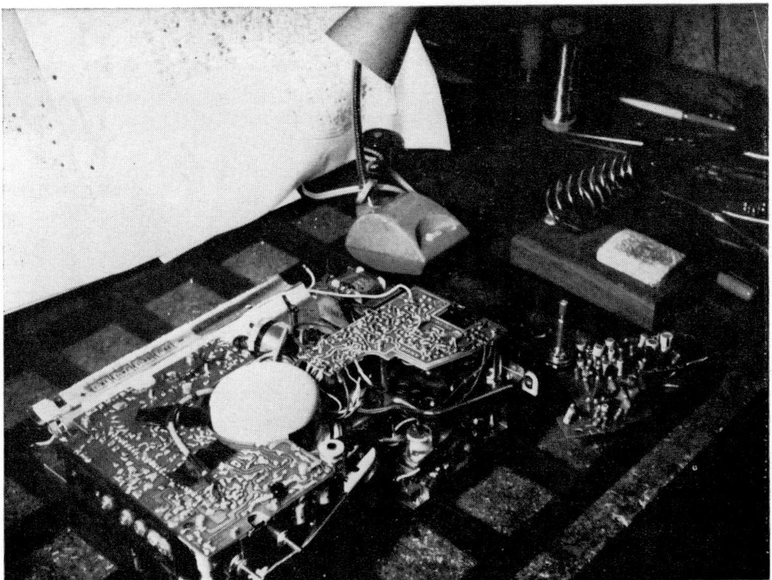

Fig. 12.4: Casual shot of a corner of the author's workshop reveals several useful 'aids'. The Sony 222 tape deck rests on a Philips bench mat, preventing damage and the loss of odd parts; a small bench lamp with swan neck and opaque hood stands nearby and the soldering iron is mounted in a spring safety guard, in whose base is a moistened sponge 'wiper' for cleaning of the iron bit.

has an easily replaceable copper-wire bit and projects a small beam of light on the working area. My Weller gun has proved invaluable in confined spaces behind large furniture, and its weight is not noticed because its function, used properly, is to aid service for short periods. Continued use might become tiresome.

Continued use in the professional capacity might mean eight or ten hours a day, six days a week, when the iron is left switched on and in readiness. To conserve its life, it should be mounted so that its heat is not wasted (thermostatic types, though a little more expensive and sometimes more troublesome, can be saving in the long run). It should be ready to hand and yet its dangerous 'black heat' should be clear of dangling cables, plastics cabinets and other of the vulnerable items that clutter our benches.

I have fallen for the wooden base with moistened sponge for bit cleaning with strong spring holder, such as can be seen in Fig. 12.4 as a most convenient iron rest. You may favour a Harpic tin screwed to the leg of the bench: there's no accounting for tastes, but certainly no excuse for their not being indulged when these aids are so cheap to purchase and, for the keen buff with more time than cash, so easy to make.

Light on the Subject

Plenty of light on the subject is imperative. Attractive bench lamps, some of them quite ingenious in their angled designs, with double beam switching, dimmers and even spotlight hoods, can be purchased in most large stores.

For tape recorder servicing, their illumination can be augmented by a spatula probe or a flexible hand lamp, such as is sold to the motoring fraternity. Magnifying glass lamps are a useful asset for printed circuit board inspection and can usually be obtained in the photographic departments.

Test Meters

Of the instruments which the engineer—amateur or professional—requires the most, a good test meter must inevitably take pride of place. In this field, as in many others, the Japanese industrial expansion has made itself felt. Cheap, and quite respectable, a.c.–d.c. meters can be obtained, but before spending any money on these instruments it would be wise to check the full specification.

Appearances mean nothing, and the number of ranges may not be a very good indication of value unless taken in conjunction with other factors. The principal factor is the rating of the basic meter movement. From this will stem the fundamental specifications.

Fig. 12.5: Colleague John Earl suggests this method of providing a resistive load for output power measurements—a length of electric fire element cut carefully to length and measured for correct matching.

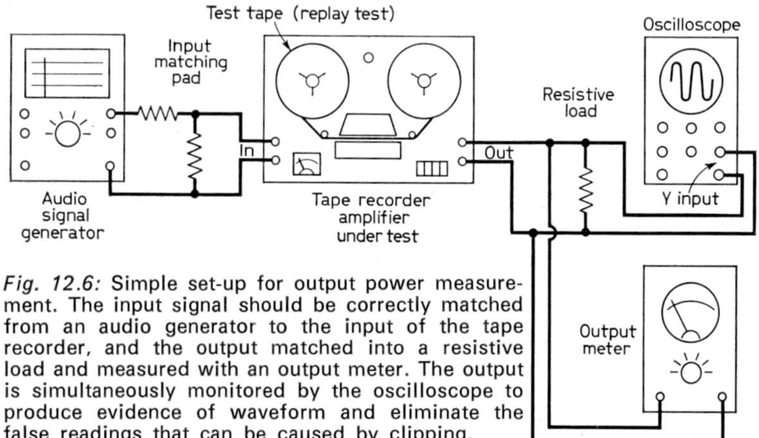

Fig. 12.6: Simple set-up for output power measurement. The input signal should be correctly matched from an audio generator to the input of the tape recorder, and the output matched into a resistive load and measured with an output meter. The output is simultaneously monitored by the oscilloscope to produce evidence of waveform and eliminate the false readings that can be caused by clipping.

The most important that we need to know is the 'ohms/volt rating' of the meter, which determines the load it will put on the circuit. Anything less than 10,000Ω/volt is not likely to be of much use. The d.c. ranges need to cover from 1 volt or thereabouts, full scale deflection, to more than 300 volts. The low volts range is needed for measurements in transistor circuits, where differences of 0·1 volts are not unusual—and are significant—and where these must be read in the most sensitive, mid-scale region.

The sensitivity of the meter depends on the current taken by the basic movement. If the movement required 2-amps for a full-scale deflection, the sensitivity would be no better than 500Ω per volt. A 10,000Ω/V meter has a 100 microampere movement, while a 100,000Ω/V sensitivity indicates a 10 microampere full-scale deflection.

Current ranges again depend on the basic movement, but this time it is the low resistance of the meter that matters, to prevent the circuits being upset by a voltage drop across the meter. The lowest current that can usefully be measured depends on the basic movement, but higher currents

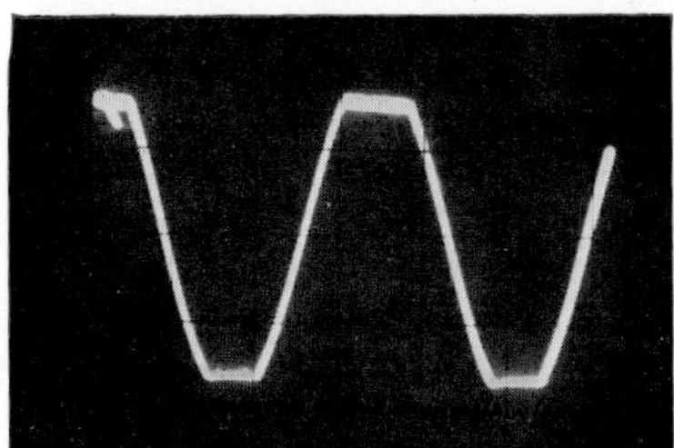

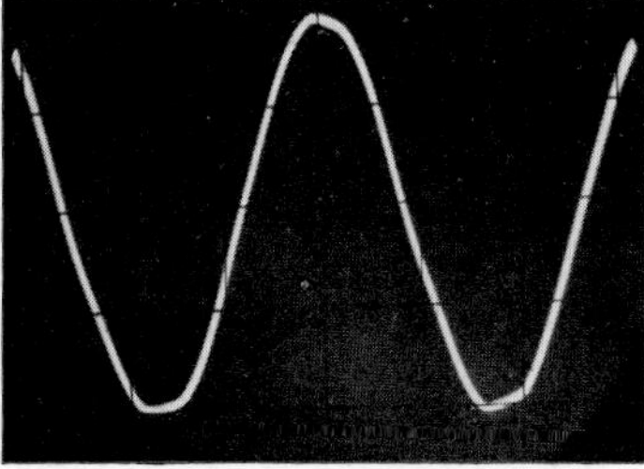

Fig. 12.7 (left): severe waveform clipping caused by overloading of the input (see Fig. 12.6) and *(right)* slight clipping that can easily be overlooked. Take care when setting up; if the maker's data is available, follow this.

will be accommodated by shunts across the meter. These voltage and current ranges may be extended by external resistances in series or shunt.

Resistance (ohms) ranges should be capable of distinction of low resistances, between 1 and 5Ω, and should also provide a means of distinguishing fairly high resistances, even though these come in the cramped upper reaches of the non-linear scale. The higher resistance reading depends on the sensitivity of the instrument as well as the value of the internal battery.

Resistance ranges can be extended by the addition of external voltage, but the low resistance range will depend on the design of the meter, and as there are several types of ohmmeter circuit, care is needed when choosing.

The a.c. ranges are not so important for the average multimeter. The meter works on a simple rectified a.c. principle, and is measuring resultant d.c., so is accurate only over a limited frequency range and has a sensitivity that will be restricted by the characteristics of the rectifier. There are two sorts of a.c. measurement that will be needed: the first is a check of mains voltages and the power unit inputs prior to rectification, which can include transformer secondary voltages of 300 or more.

In addition, motor voltages need checking, and this requires that the meter used by the tape recorder engineer shall handle a.c. voltages at mains frequency of 350 volts or more, full scale deflection. But the second requirement is more stringent: a.c. signal voltages and oscillator voltages

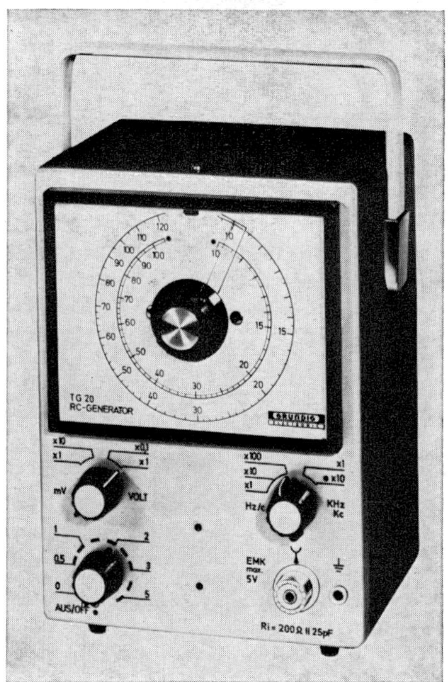

Fig. 12.8: A transistor RC generator covering 10Hz to 1MHz in five ranges with a frequency accuracy better than 3.5%. Four-position output voltage control, with fine adjustment, output impedance 200Ω/25pF, and a signal-to-noise ratio better than 80dB make this a useful source of signal. Distortion factor is better than 2% (in a restricted mid-range, better than 0.1%—see text). Model TG20, by Grundig.

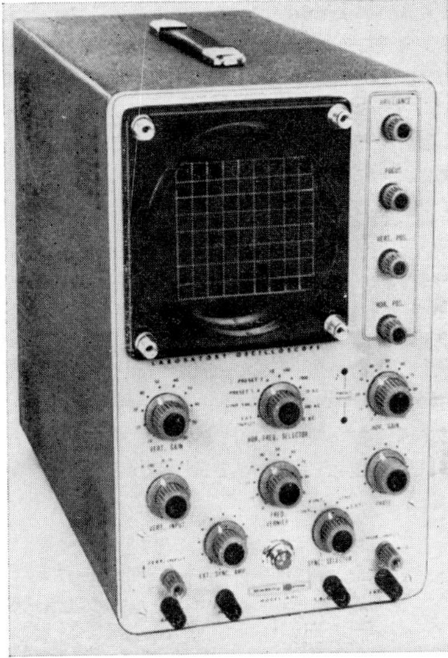

Fig. 12.9(a): A good oscilloscope is a vital tool. The author has just finished constructing the Heathkit IO-18U oscilloscope (see text) to add to his workshop facilities. Test gear of this nature, well up to professional standards, is within the purse and the constructional capabilities of the amateur.

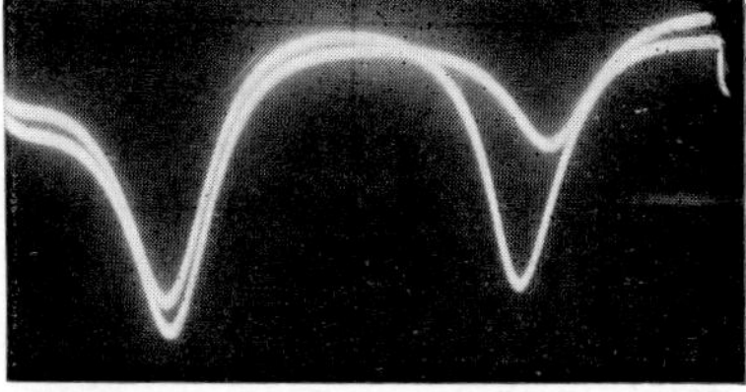

(c)

Fig. 12.9(b): a double-beam oscilloscope is handy, but can be expensive. A less costly expedient is the addition of a beam-switching unit, such as the Heathkit S-3U, which can produce adjacent traces, as in Fig. 12. 9 (c) for immediate comparison.

cannot be measured effectively by the ordinary type of multimeter, although some indication may be gained.

Electronic Voltmeter

For these readings at frequencies in the audio range, the valve voltmeter, or electronic voltmeter has to be called into play. The high impedance of this instrument prevents it from loading the circuits so as to alter their characteristics, and the frequency range covers the audio band, and considerably more, so that the readings are either a peak or root-mean-square measurement of the applied waveform.

Most electronic voltmeters have additional scales in decibels, which can speed up audio testing considerably. Using these instruments to check output power is a straightforward matter of connecting them across the output load of tape recorder or amplifier. To some extent, the good quality a.c. voltmeter can be employed in a similar way, provided a constant sine wave is the source of signal. Then, as shown in Fig. 12.6, the waveform can also be monitored by an oscilloscope to show evidence of clipping, which would indicate overload, and other forms of distortion, which would prevent misinterpretation of readings.

When using a voltmeter to indicate output, the load resistance is matched to the requirements of the amplifier, and the power output will then be the square of the indicated voltage divided by the loading resistance. If there is any difficulty in obtaining a true loading resistance for test purposes, a section of the resistive element of an electric fire can be called into use. A good ohmmeter is needed for making this measurement (see Fig. 12.5).

Signal Generators

When testing tape recorders or any other amplifiers, the results one expects to get will be determined by the quality of the instruments supplying the signal source. Audio generators come in many guises, and can cost a few pounds or a few hundred. For the amateur, who wants quality at a price he can afford, home construction is the only economical answer.

Quite apart from the numerous projected circuits that appear in audio and radio magazines there are one or two kit-makers who are to be trusted. Much of the author's test gear has been built in what odd moments he could find, and a good deal of it is Heathkit. Sine-square wave generators with a low distortion figure are available, having all the necessary test features, including, in the latest I have built, the IG–18U, the means of feeding sine and square wave signals simultaneously.

The utmost care is taken by firms as responsible as Messrs. Daystrom, from whom the Heathkit gear is available. Each and every move in the construction is meticulously detailed, and help for the inexperienced is ready at the ring of a telephone. This may be no place to advertise, but my own experience has proved the worth of this range of equipment.

Remembering that the noise and distortion performance of the test equipment must be better than the equipment under test, we can say that for high fidelity work instruments are likely to be fairly expensive. An example of a good general-purpose generator with suitable ranges for all audio work and the advantage of a very low distortion factor is shown in Fig. 12.8.

Grundig instruments are of high quality, specialist application, and the prices reflect their specifications. Nevertheless, for the professional engineer, skimping on test gear is a short-sighted policy, and it is well worth investigating the possibilities of some of the superior instruments for high fidelity testing.

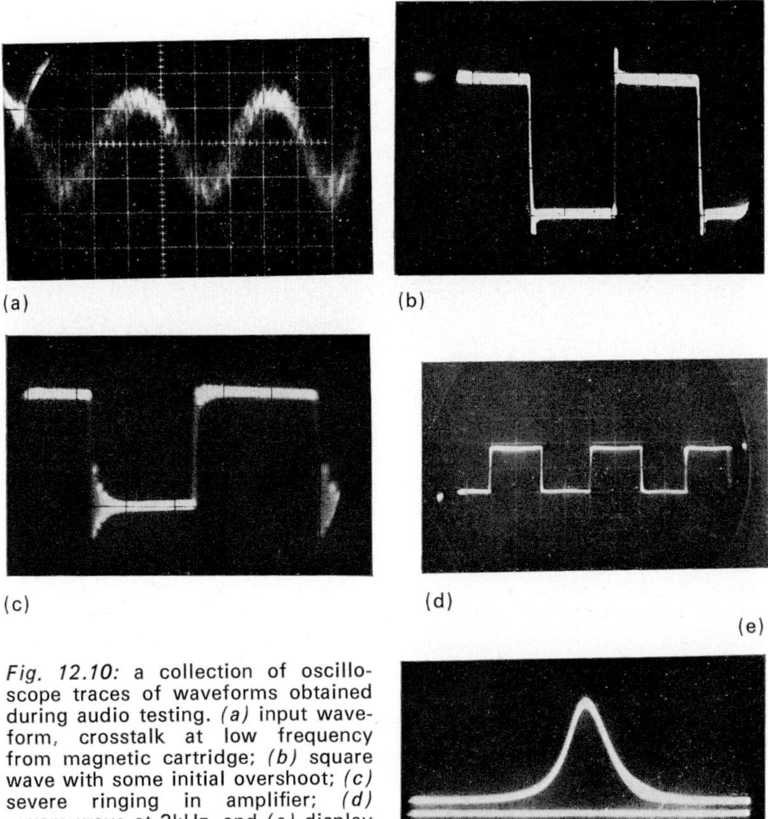

Fig. 12.10: a collection of oscilloscope traces of waveforms obtained during audio testing. *(a)* input waveform, crosstalk at low frequency from magnetic cartridge; *(b)* square wave with some initial overshoot; *(c)* severe ringing in amplifier; *(d)* square wave at 3kHz, and *(e)* display obtained while testing f.m. tuner.

The Oscilloscope

One of the most useful instruments that the engineer will use is the oscilloscope. Using a poor 'scope is an utter waste of time, but as with generators, a good one is worth its weight in gold. Having latterly rushed through the construction of a Heathkit IO–18U to augment my workshop facilities, I am aware both of the ease with which a quite complex design can be built with the kind of detailed guidance that Daystrom Ltd. give and of the results that can be obtained with this class of equipment.

With a vertical sensitivity of 30mV, peak-to-peak per cm. at 1kHz, a frequency response of 3Hz to 4·5MHz ± 3dB, referred to 1kHz, a rise time of 0·08 microseconds, a high input impedance, a timebase range between 10Hz and 500kHz in 5 steps with a vernier for continual change, plus two preset sweep frequencies, with automatic synchronisation and even an intensity-modulation input, this oscilloscope represents the best value for money I have seen.

In conjunction with an electronic switch such as the S–3U, for presenting a dual trace on the single beam oscilloscope, making much audio testing simpler, the oscilloscope is the instrument that the author would least like to be without. See Fig. 12.9.

Some idea of the traces that are obtained during typical tests are shown in Fig. 12.10, and in addition to these the traces most important to the tape recorder user are those depicting comparative input and output waveforms, before and after recording, and elliptical waveforms (feeding the source signal to the horizontal input of the oscilloscope and the output from the tape recorder to the vertical input of the oscilloscope) which can show both distortion and irregular speed.

Measuring Wow and Flutter

For the last application, a more exact method would be the use of a wow and flutter meter or a pen-recorder. Fig. 12.11 shows the block circuitry of a commercial wow and flutter meter which has to deal with pitch fluctuations by converting frequency variations into voltage changes.

The test frequency is first determined, and this would normally fall in the 'sensitive' region between 1 and 5kHz. The (typically) 3kHz recording

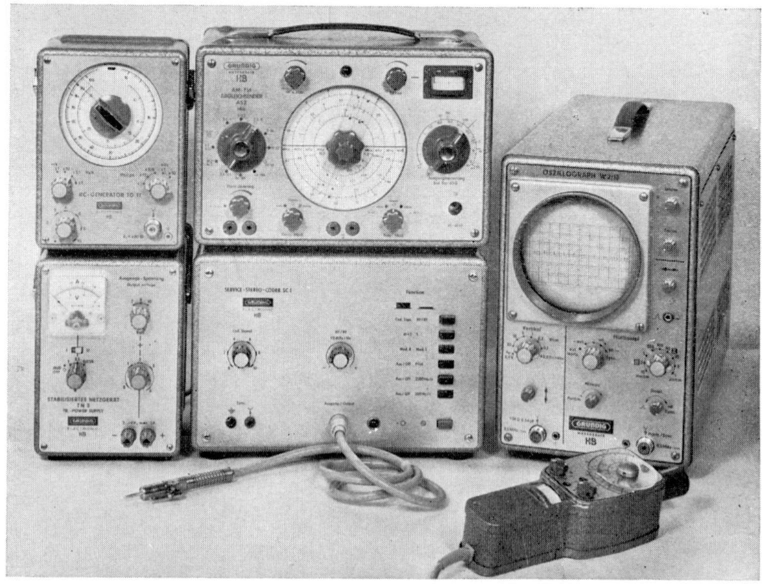

Fig. 12.11: A collection of bench instruments by Grundig, including r.f. and a.f. signal generators, a stereo coding instrument for f.m. tuner testing, a wide-range oscilloscope and, in the foreground, the less frequently encountered grid dip oscillator.

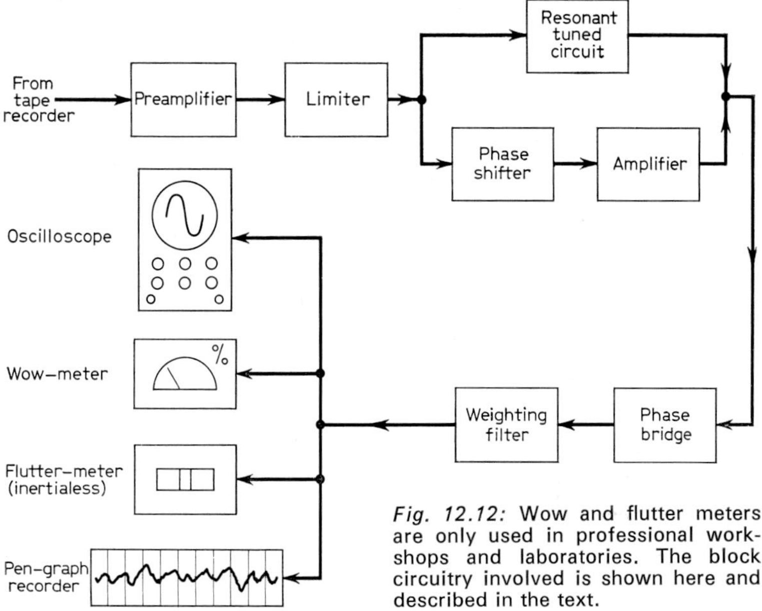

Fig. 12.12: Wow and flutter meters are only used in professional workshops and laboratories. The block circuitry involved is shown here and described in the text.

is made on the tape recorder to be tested and replayed. The replay voltage is fed to the meter input and amplitude variations are eliminated by feeding the signal through limiter stages, after which it is split to take two paths. The upper circuit is tuned to resonance and the lower consists of a phase shifter.

After recombination and further amplification the two voltages pass to a kind of discriminator. The output from this circuit is dependent on frequency deviation. This voltage is taken to a peak voltage indicator calibrated in percentages. An output for an oscilloscope is desirable so that the trace can be monitored visually. Weighting filters are used to attenuate the upper frequencies by a regular rate, to simulate normal hearing conditions.

Studying the foregoing should help us to understand why so much care is needed in studying the specifications of a tape recorder when we choose. The wow and flutter specification is an important one. It depends on the speed at which the machine is running, and is always better at the higher speeds. If the quotation says 'weighted' then the reading will be apparently better, and if r.m.s. values are quoted rather than peak values, the readings will have been divided by 1·414.

A more convincing record may be found by taking a pen recording, such as depicted in Fig. 12.12. We want to know not only the percentage of the variations but also the frequency at which these variations occur. This can give valuable clues to the source of the discrepancy.

There are some drawbacks to aural testing, even when constant tones

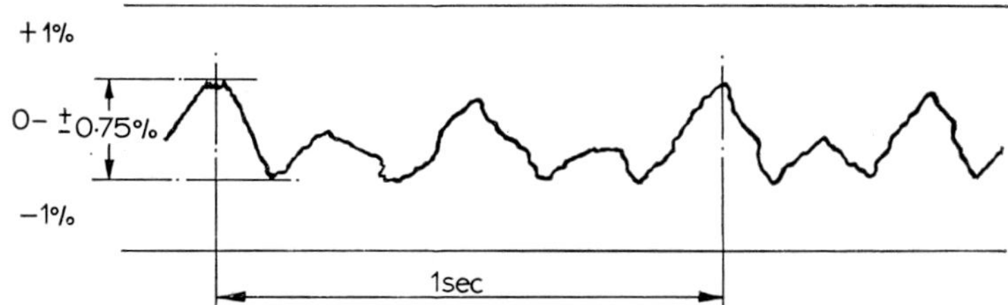

Fig. 12.13: A sample pen recording of wow and flutter, showing how the frequency of the wow and its percentage can both be assessed.

of 3 to 5kHz are used. One's ears become inured to the tone, and accept minor discrepancies, especially if they are regular. The eye is not so easily deceived, and pen-recorders give results that can be studied at leisure.

Distortion Tests

It should always be remembered that the tape recorder is part of a chain of equipment, contributing its own special problems for the engineer. This must be taken into account when tests are made, as shown in Fig. 12.13. Distortion testing is shown here, and the first point we note is the need for an audio generator with a low distortion factor.

Next, matching of this source signal to the amplifier (or the tape recorder amplifier) must be correct or the tests are invalid. Similarly, the output load has to match, as stated before. Across this load resistor there are several instruments.

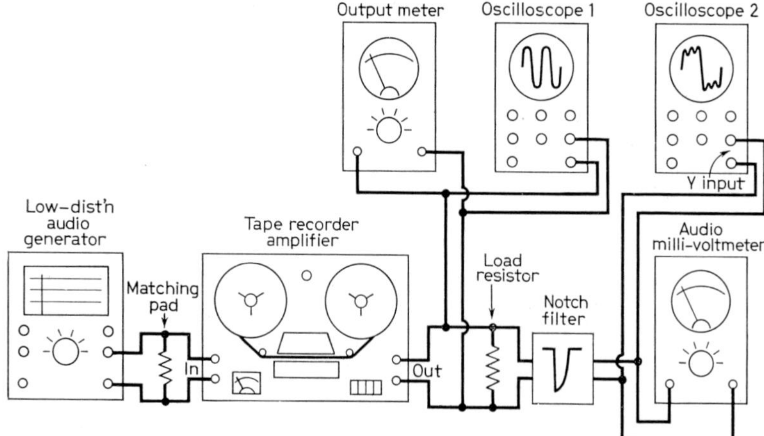

Fig. 12.14: Distortion testing of high-fidelity equipment, of which the tape recorder is part of a carefully balanced chain, requires a complicated hook-up and instruments of even better quality than the equipment under test. See text for details.

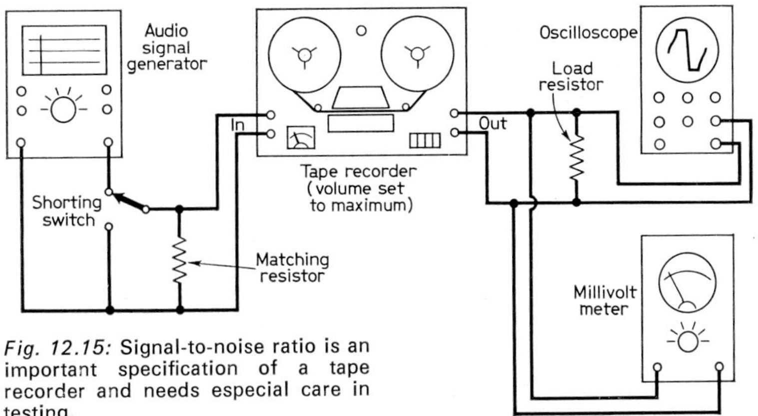

Fig. 12.15: Signal-to-noise ratio is an important specification of a tape recorder and needs especial care in testing.

The upper leg is the 'normal' test rig of output meter and oscilloscope, the latter to show any clipping of the waveform (see Fig. 12.7). The lower leg includes a notch filter which deletes the fundamental frequency and leaves the distortion components. These can be measured, either in the distortion meter or by an external audio millivoltmeter, and the trace again monitored. A switched oscilloscope rather than the double-beam device is an aid here.

It is convenient to rig these switched test assemblies in a semi-permanent form and for this purpose I have found the MAC Development Units invaluable. Interconnections of all sorts are safely and permanently made, loading resistors can be incorporated and switching can be adapted in a wide variety of ways. Added to which, the units are an attractive embellishment to workshop or den.

Signal-to-Noise Ratio

Testing signal-to-noise ratio is very necessary when tape recorder measurements are being carried out. Of the hi-fi chain, the tape recorder is perhaps most vulnerable. Tape hiss is one source of noise that becomes difficult to eradicate, and recording can contribute some noise and distortion because of incorrect bias, as we have noted in earlier chapters.

S/N ratio, in decibels, indicates how far below the full power of the amplifier the mixture of noise and hum may be. A 60dB ratio, good for a tape recorder, means that the noise is one million times below the full-power of the amplifier. Because small power ratios are difficult to measure, voltage ratios are used instead. If we establish the full power voltage across the output load which is caused by a sinewave signal and compare this with the voltage due to hum and noise, we can again arrive at a result.

This full-power voltage is used as the datum and the gain controls are turned up full and tone controls are 'flat'. The input signal must be correctly matched and the generator must itself contribute less noise than the specification of the machine under test. After initial measurement of the full-power voltage, the gain control is turned down (to avoid possible damage due to breakthrough noise and transients) and the signal removed. In place of the signal a screened loading resistor, or even a total short circuit, is applied to the input terminals and the gain is again advanced.

The resultant reading is the residual noise. If a millivoltmeter is used at the output, it will need to be turned to a lower range to obtain an adequate reading. If a decibel range is used, some calculation is saved, but care must be taken in interpretation as the range selector or attenuator is altered.

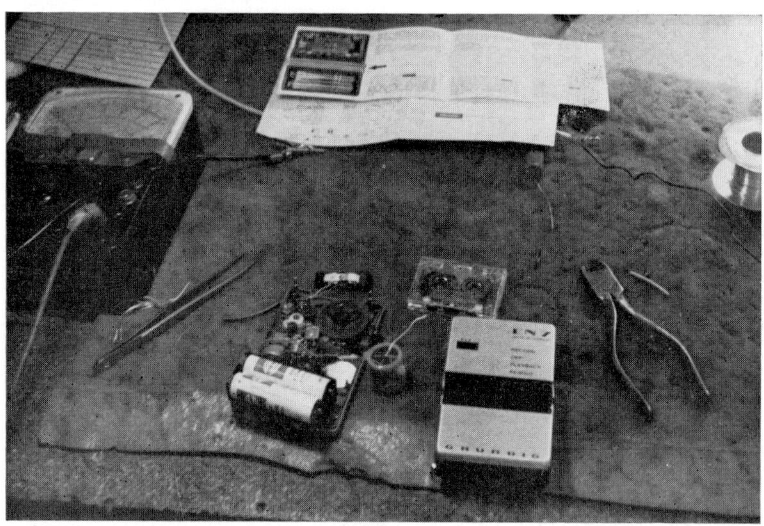

Fig. 12.16: It is not unusual to find that tools and test equipment are bigger than the tape recorder under test. Note the use of a resilient foam rubber mat, to protect the delicate gear and absorb screws, springs, etc. that could otherwise roll from the bench and be lost.

Bias Adjustment

Some of the tests we shall need to carry out are peculiar to tape recorders. Measurement and adjustment of recording bias, for example, which occupied us sufficiently in preceding chapters to be left with only a brief mention here. Some of the specific tests we need to make are checks of head currents and perhaps of the heads themselves. Head current measurements require the checking of voltages dropped across series resistors rather than across the heads themselves. Fig. 12.16a illustrates one method.

If high frequency bias is being measured in this way the meter being employed must be accurate at the bias frequency, which may be anything

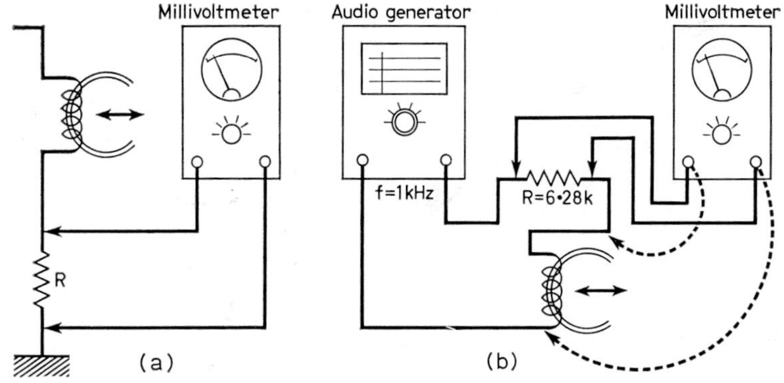

Fig. 12.17: Head measurements. *(a)* head current, and *(b)* a method of determining head inductance.

between 50 and 100kHz. More precise, and less often needed, is a measurement of the inductance of the head itself. Current and voltage tests under controlled conditions, plus a little calculation, can help us here.

Fig. 12.16b shows the simple circuit, with an audio generator in series with a resistor, applied across the head winding, with the voltage across the head monitored for a cross-check. The current in the head circuit is

$$\frac{V_1}{R} = \frac{V_2}{\omega L}$$

We know what omega is by setting our generator first, so that at 1kHz we get a constant of 6·28 × 1,000 or 6·28k. We can now say that

$$L = \frac{V_1}{V_2} \cdot \frac{R}{6{\cdot}28k}$$

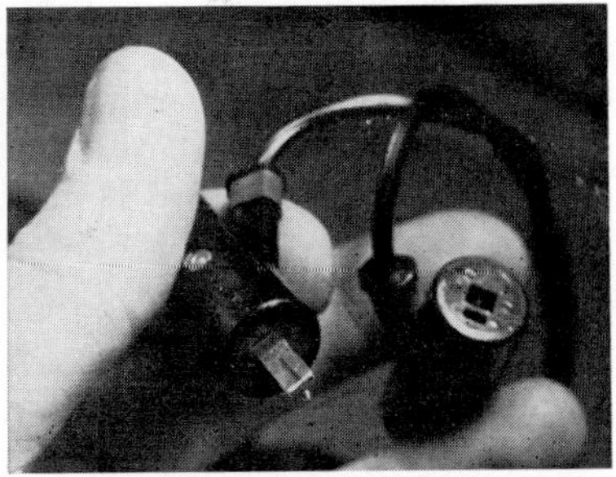

Fig. 12.18: Most useful tool is one's hearing, augmented by a high quality pair of headphones such as the Grundig 220, which the author has used extensively in his workshop. One advantage of their design *(right)* is the straight-through J21 loudspeaker plug, which allows parallel connection of additional equipment. With the aid of a home-made jumper lead connecting these two plugs to a stereo jack, most tape decks can be tested directly. The 400 ohms impedance of the phones makes them a safe choice for any type of output.

Fig. 12.19: Tape recording contests attract a large number of enthusiasts. Here, the entries for the 1969 3M Wildlife Tape Recording Contest are being judged by the experts.

Test Tapes

For most general test work on tape recorders, test tapes are a necessity. There are many available, some to British and some to Continental standards. Typical test tapes would have bands of constant tone, with perhaps sections unrecorded and other sections with white noise, or filtered (pink) noise. The test tapes will have standard flux figures, and this can be important for setting up.

The standard tape magnetisation is useful for setting up of the playback head, and the constant tone as well as white noise signals will prove invaluable for rapid adjustment of azimuth. The sequence of tones enables a quick frequency response test to be made of the playback amplifier and it is not until this is in order that recording amplifier tests can be carried out properly.

Many of these tests and assessments will never concern the average tape recorder user. They are the province of the engineer. But the author is of the opinion that a good understanding of such an essentially 'technical' device as a tape recorder is necessary before one can make a wise choice or use it with any degree of success.

Being a practical man himself, he has attempted to present his case throughout this book in purely down-to-earth ways for the benefit of keen recordists, budding audio buffs and the absolute novice as well. There is a great deal of pleasure to be derived from tape recording, and such pleasures are always enhanced by a modicum of deeper understanding.

INDEX